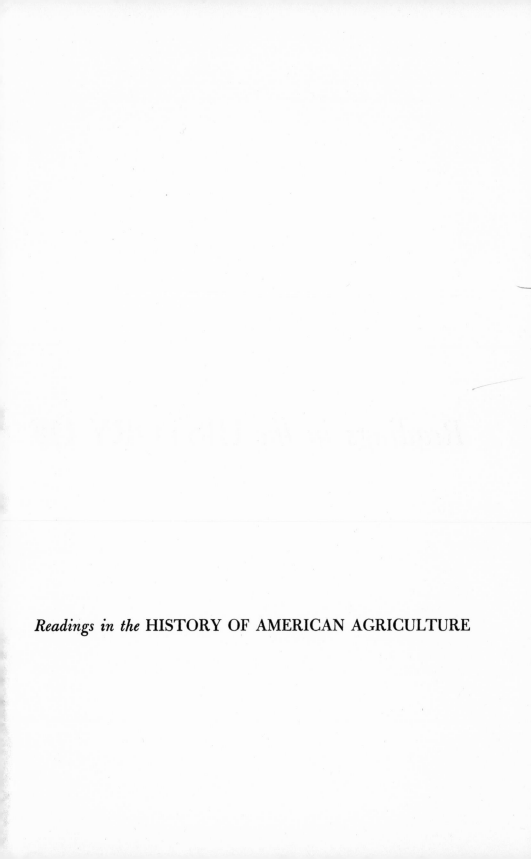

Readings in the HISTORY OF AMERICAN AGRICULTURE

Readings in the HISTORY OF

AMERICAN AGRICULTURE

edited by WAYNE D. RASMUSSEN

University of Illinois Press, Urbana, 1960

*A grant from the Ford Foundation has helped
to defray the cost of publishing this work.*

Preface

Today, Americans have forgotten the spectre of famine faced by their ancestors and, instead, worry over farm surpluses. When the Constitution was adopted, nine out of every ten working persons were employed on farms, and agriculture was at a near-subsistence level. By 1960, one farmer was growing food and fiber for himself and 22 other persons. The freeing of America from the fear of famine and the freeing of America's energies from the necessity of its population spending most of its efforts in feeding itself has been accomplished by the American farmer, with the help of groups established for that purpose. The story of this great achievement is the history of American agriculture.

Certain landmarks indicate the course of this history. For example, a few Indians taught the European immigrants to grow corn, practical men developed types particularly suited to the American corn belt, and scientists developed the techniques for hybrid corn. Each of these helped make corn America's most important crop. The Indians cleared land and planted corn by manpower (or womanpower). The European settlers used oxen to draw the wooden plows of colonial America. Farmers of the Civil War era turned to horses for power to operate the new machinery that characterized the first American agricultural revolution. Operators of large-scale farms in the last decades of the nineteenth century used steam engines as a power source. Farmers of the twentieth century turned to the gasoline tractor, and, by 1950, tractors outnumbered horses on American farms.

This volume includes the first public announcements of a number of the specific events that led to important changes in American agriculture. Some of the readings represent far-reaching changes and numerous events. The discovery or invention of a particular useful thing, however, did not mean its immediate adoption by farmers. Technological change proceeded slowly, at least until World War II.

The colonial period was characterized by the transfer of the agricultural practices common to seventeenth-century Europe to the New World and the modification of these practices by the new environment. The settlers learned much from the American Indians, but were isolated from the changes taking place in English agriculture in the eighteenth century.

The average farmer, at the time of the American Revolution, used most of the same tools and followed many of the same practices in use in Biblical times. The Revolution, however, with its political, social, and economic changes, marked the beginning of a period of gradual improvement in farming methods. New machines, new techniques, and new forces dedicated to improved agriculture led to the first American agricultural revolution at the time of the Civil War. Farmers found that the demand for farm products was so great and the labor shortage so pronounced that it seemed both possible and profitable to adopt the new machines and techniques developed in the preceding decades.

After the Civil War, the increasing industrialization of America and an increased foreign demand for American farm products led to an ever increasing commercialization of American agriculture. The farmer found himself more and more dependent upon the market place for the cash needed to make payments on machinery and on land. The self-sufficient, independent farmer of fiction was disappearing.

About 1900, the farmer reached a comparative state of balance between production and demand and between costs and returns. World War I, with its new impetus for increased production, its high prices, and its labor shortages, led to increased commitments for capital expenditures and increased production. Unfortunately, this increased production did not come into the market until after the war was over and foreign demand had declined. The period from 1920 to 1933 was one of intermittent farm depression.

The Federal Farm Board of 1929 marked the assumption by the Federal government of responsibility for improving economic conditions for farmers. The New Deal inaugurated programs between 1933 and 1939 aimed at giving farmers economic parity with other groups in the population. The outbreak of war in Europe in 1939 led to a short-lived farm depression, but almost at once demand for most farm products increased.

The Japanese attack upon Pearl Harbor on December 7, 1941, forced the United States into full participation in the war. The resulting demands for farm products at favorable prices enabled and encouraged farmers to take advantage of a great many technological advances which had been developing for two decades. The resulting surge in production enabled the United States and, to some degree, her allies, to pursue the war to a successful conclusion without famine and with no serious shortages of farm products.

World War II marked the beginning of the second American agricultural revolution. There is no way of determining the eventual extent of change which will result from this explosion of technology. However, it is evident that the greatly increased productive capacity of the American farmer means that the problem is not of increasing production to meet needs, but of marketing and distribution to dispose of production. It is a problem to which all students of agricultural problems should give serious attention.

This volume is the result of the encouragement and assistance of a number of people. I wish particularly to acknowledge the aid of Vernon Carstensen of the University of Wisconsin, Robert G. Dunbar of Montana State College, Clayton S. Ellsworth of the College of Wooster, Donald Jackson of the University of Illinois Press, C. Clyde Jones of the University of Illinois, Lucille Kellar of the State Historical Society of Wisconsin, Edward C. Kendall of the Smithsonian Institution, John T. Schlebecker of Iowa State University, James H. Shideler of the University of California at Davis, and Virginia Walton of the Montana State Historical Society. Marion F. Rasmussen was of assistance in every stage of the work. Many of my colleagues in the Department of Agriculture lent their knowledge and skills, particularly James P. Cavin, Helen H. Edwards, C. Kyle Randall, Charles Rogers, Mae Smith, Vivian Bedon, and Vivian Wiser. The Yale University Library kindly granted permission to quote from a manuscript letter of Eli Whitney. Finally, I owe a special debt of gratitude to Emerson Brooks for his assistance in selecting illustrations and to Gladys L. Baker for her comments and suggestions throughout the preparation of the volume.

Contents

PART I

*The Beginnings of American
Agriculture, 1607-1775*

1

English Agriculture Sets the Pattern

England, at the time the Jamestown settlers and the Pilgrims left it, was comparatively undeveloped agriculturally. Probably not more than a quarter of its land was under cultivation. Farming practices were but a step removed from the Middle Ages, and differed little from those of two thousand years earlier. These customs and tools brought to America by the first colonists were used with little change, except as modified by the adoption of Indian crops and methods, for two hundred years.

The population of England at the time of the first American settlement was composed of four classes: gentlemen, who owned estates usually known as manors; citizens, who were merchants and city dwellers; yeomen, who owned small farms; and laborers, who worked for the landowners. The manor dominated agriculture and social life.

Most manors were farmed under the three-field system. The arable land was divided into three great fields which in turn were divided into the strips assigned to each man. Every year one of the fields lay fallow; one was planted to wheat or rye and the other was planted to barley, oats, vetches, beans, or peas. After harvest, the livestock, which had been grazing on the commons or waste land, was turned into the fields.

The tools used on the farm were crude. The wooden plows, large and cumbersome, were usually drawn by oxen. After the soil was broken, iron- or wooden-toothed harrows were pulled over the land. All corps were seeded by hand. Grain crops were cut with scythes or reaping hooks and threshed with flails. Hoes, mattocks, spades, and forks completed the list of implements.

The task that a farm worker might accomplish during a day using these implements has been outlined by Gervase Markham in *Farewell to Husbandry*, first published in 1623. Markham (1568-1637) wrote many volumes on farming and other matters, and was one of the most widely read agricultural writers of his day.

What a Farm Worker Should Accomplish during a Day and a Month

Gervase Markham, *Farewell to Husbandry*, edition 2, pp. 143-149, 154-160 (London, Printed by M. F. for Roger Jackson, 1625).

To speake generally of all husbandly workes where the countrey is tolerable without any extraordinarie difficultie, you shal under-

3

stand that a man may well in stiffe ground, plow an acre, or an acre and an halfe, and in light sand grounds two or three acres with one teame in a day, and he may plow and sow in stiffe ground two acres and a halfe each day, and in light ground foure at least with one Teame, and alwayes what he soweth, that he may harrow the same day also.

A man may well mowe of good and deepe loggy meadow, or of rough uneuen meadow, every day one acre, mowing cleane and making a smooth board: of well standing and good smooth meadow an acre and a halfe each day: and of very thinne and short grasse, or upland meadow two acres at the least every day.

Also, he may mowe of Corne, as Barley and Oates, if it be thicke, loggy and beaten downe to the earth, making faire worke, and not cutting of the heads of the eares, and leaving the straw still growing, one acre and an halfe in a day: but if it be good, thicke and faire standing corne, than hee may two acres, or two acres and a halfe in a day: but if the corn be short and thin, then he may mowe three, and sometimes foure acres in a day, and not bee overlaboured: Also of Beanes he may mowe as much, and of Pease mixt with Beanes, having a hooke to follow him, no lesse; for they are workes in this nature most easie and least troublesome.

One man with a binder may well reape an acre of Wheat, or Rye in a day, if it be principall good and well standing, but if laid or beaten downe with weather, then three roode is fully sufficient for a dayes labour; but if it be thin and upright standing, then he may reape and bind five roods in a day: of small Pease, Fetches, and such like, a man may well reape two acres every day.

Now forasmuch as it is a custome in divers countreys (and truely is exceeding profitable and worthy imitation) to sheafe and bind up both Barly and Oates, as well as Wheat or Rye, and that it both saveth much Corne, and also makes it take a great deale lesse roome, and that this labour is to be done after the mowers, as the other was after the reapers by gathering the Barley or Oats up with a sickle or hooke, as it lyes in the swath, and so binding it in sheaves, you shall understand that one man in a day will binde as much as one mower can mowe; and if the men be any thing skilful in the labour, two binders will binde as much as three mowers can mowe.

For the gathering or inning of graine, no man can proportion the number of loads, or quantitie of ground shall dayly be brought home, sith the journeys are uncertaine, some going a quarter of a mile, some halfe a mile, & some a mile: therefore it is the Husbandmans best way, the first day to goe with his Teame himselfe, and both to observe the labour and distance of place, and by that to compute what may be done after without hurt to his cattle, and where he failes of any hope, there to take a strict account of the errour; for it is either ignorance or carelesnesse, which brings forth mischances, speaking of husbandry, as overthrowing the Teame, over-loading the Teame, breaking necessary instruments, or not respecting the wayes and passage, any of which may in a day hinder more then halfe the dayes labour.

Againe, a man may in a day ditch and quick-set of a reasonable ditch foure foot broad, and three foot deep, a rod or a poll a day, allowing sixteene foot to the rod, and so of larger measure lesse ground, and of lesse ground larger measure, according to the sufficiency of the fence which you purpose to make.

A man also may hedge in a day, if the hedge bee good and sustantiall, that is to say, five foot high, well bound, thicke stackt, and close layed, two rod in a day, and if the worke bee lower or thinner then double so much, according to the former proportion.

For this plashing of hedges, or making a quicke fence if he do it workmanly, & that the quick growth be high and well growne; and then he lay it thicke, close, and strongly bound on the top, turning the quicke downward and inward, to plash a rod a day is as much as any man can well doe, but if yee plash it after the West countrey fashion, that is, onely cutting it downe, and laying it along close to the ground, seeking onely thicknesse, and not much guard or comelinesse, then hee may well plash a rod and a halfe in a day without trouble, and sure in this worke is great care and art to be used as well for the preservation of the quicke, as the goodnesse of the fence, being a thing of worth and validitie to every husbandman.

Again, a man may delve or digge, as for garden mould, hempeyard, Flaxeyard, or for the setting of Corne, or levelling of uneven places, one rood in a day, and the ground so digged and delved, hee may rake dresse and levell in the same day also, but if hee digge it deepe, and trench it, and meanure it, as is meet; either for garden, orchard, or corne setting, then to delve halfe a rood in a day, is a very great proportion, because ordinarily to delve, as to receive or-

dinarie seeds, requires but one spade graft in depth, but extraordi-
narily to delve, as for inriching and bettering of the ground, and to
cleanse it from stones, weeds and other annoyances, will require
two spade graft at the least.

Lastly, a man may thrash if the corne be good & cleane, without
some extraordinary abuse or poverty in the graine, in one day foure
bushels of Wheat or Rye, sixe bushels of Barly or Oats, and five
bushels of Beanes or Pease, but the Pulse must then bee imagined
to bee exceeding good, otherwise a man shall thrash lesse of it, then
of any other kinde of graine, for as when it is well loade, it yeeldeth
plentifully, so when it is poore and lightly loden, it yeeldeth little
or nothing, and yet hath not one stroke lesse of the flaile, nor any
labour saved more then belongs to the best Pulse whatsoever being
ever at least three times turned, and foure times beaten over.

Having thus generally runne over (in short computation) the
labours of the husbandman, I will now as briefly as I can, goe over
the Particular dayes labours of a Farmer or Plowman, shewing the
particular expence of every houre in the day, from his first rising,
till his going to bed, as thus for example: wee will suppose it to bee
after Christmas, and about plow day (which is the first letting out
of the plow) & at what time men either begin to fallow, or to break
up Pease earth which is to lye to bait, according to the custome of
the countrey; at this time the Plowman shall rise before foure of
the clocke in the morning, and after thankes given to God for his
rest, and the successe of his labours, he shall goe into his stable, or
beast house, and first he shall fodder his cattle, then cleanse the
house, and make the boothes cleane; rubbe downe the cattle, and
cleanse their skinnes from all filth, then hee shall curry his horses,
rubbe them with cloathes and wispes, and make both them and the
stable as cleane as may be, then hee shall water both his oxen and
horses, and housing them againe, give them more fodder, and to his
horse by all means provender, as chaffe and dry Pease or Beanes,
or Oat-huls, Pease or Beanes, or cleane Oates, or cleane garbadge
(which is the hinder ends of any kinde of graine but Rye with the
straw chopt small amongst it) according as the abilitie of the Husbandman is.

And whilst they are eating their meat, he shal make readie his
collars, hames, treates, halters, mullens, and plowgeares, seeing
everything fit, and in his due place, and to these labours I will also
allow full two houres, that is, from foure of the clocke, till sixe,

then shall he come in to breakfast, and to that I allow him halfe an houre, and then another halfe houre to the gearing and yoaking of his cattle, so that at seven of the clocke he may set forward to his labour, and then hee shall plow from seven of the clocke in the morning, till betwixt two and three in the afternoone, then he shall unyoake and bring home his cattell, and having rub'd them, drest them, & cleansed away all durt and filth, hee shall fodder them, and give them meat, then shall the servants goe in to their dinner, which allowed halfe an houre, it will then bee towards foure of the clocke, at which time hee shall goe to his cattle againe, and rubbing them downe, and cleansing their stalles, give them more fodder; which done, hee shall goe into the barnes, and provide and make ready fodder of all kinds for the next day, whether it be hay, straw, or blend fodder, according to the abilitie of the Husbandman: this being done and caried into the stable, oxe house, or other con- venient place, he shall then goe water his cattle, and give them more meat, and to his horse provender as before shewed: and by this time it will draw past sixe of the clocke, at what time he shall come in to supper, and after supper hee shall either by the fire side, mend shooes both for himselfe and their family, or beat and knocke hempe, or flaxe, or picke and stampe apples, or crabs for cider or verdjuice, or else grinde malt on the quernes, picke candle-rushes, or doe some husbandly office within doores till it be full eight a clocke: Then shall he take his Lanthorne and candle, and goe to his cattle; and having cleansed the stalles and plankes, litter them downe, looke that they be safely tyed, and then fodder and give them meat for all night, then giving God thankes for benefits re- ceived that day, let him and the whole household goe to their rest till the next morning.

Now it is to bee intended, that there may bee in the household more servants then one; and so you will demand of me what the rest of the Servants shall be imployed in before and after the time of plowing: To this I answer, that they may either goe into the barne and thrash, fill or empty the malt fat, load or unload the kilne, or any other good and necessarie worke that is about the yard, and after they come from plowing, some may goe into the barne and thrash, some hedge, ditch, stop gaps in broken fences, dig in the Orchard or Garden, or any other out work which is needfull to be done, and which about the husbandman is never wanting, expecially one must have a care every night to look to the mending or sharpning of the Plow-irons, and the repairing of the Plow and Plow geares, if anie bee out of order, for to deferre them till the morrow, were the losse of a dayes worke, and an ill point of husbandry.

Againe, it is the office and dutie of everie good Plowman to know his severall labours for everie severall Moneth though the whole yeare, whereby no day nor houre may bee misspent, but every time and season employed according as his nature requireth: as thus for example.

In the moneth of January, the painfull Plowman, if he live in fertile and good soiles, as among rich, stiffe, simple clayes, hee shall first plow up his pease earth, because it must lie to take baite before it be sowne; but if hee live in fruitfull well mixt soyles, then in this moneth hee shall begin to fallow the field he will lay to rest the yeare following; but if hee live upon hard barren earths (of which chiefly I write) then in this moneth hee shall water his Meadowes and Pasture grounds, and he shall draine and make dry his arable grounds, especially where he intends to sow Pease, Oates, or Barly, the seed-time following. Also he shall stub up all such rough grounds as he intends to sow the yeare following and shall meanure and trim up your Garden moulds, you shall comfort with meanure, sand, or lime, or al three mixt together, the roots of all barren fruit trees: and also cut downe all such timber, onely there will be losse in the barke, for the time is something too early for it to rise. Lastly, you may transplant all sorts of Fruit trees, the weather being open, and the ground easie: you may reare Calves, remove Bees, and for your owne health keepe you bodie warme, let good diet and wholesome be your Physitian, and rather with excercise then sauce, encrease you appetite.

In the Moneth of Februarie, either set or sow all sorts of Beanes, Pease, and other Pulse, and the stiffer your ground is, the sooner begin your worke, prepare your garden mould, and make it easie and tender, prune & trim all sorts of Fruit trees from mosse, cankers, and all superfluous branches; plash your hedges, and lay your quicksets close and intire together; plant Roses, Gooseberries, and any fruit that growes upon little bushes; graft at the latter end of this moneth upon young and tender stockes, but by all meanes overlade not the stockes.

Lastly, for your health, take heed of cold, forbeare meats that are slimy and flegmatique, and if need require, either purge, bathe, or bleed, as Art shall direct you.

In the moneth of March, make an end of sowing of all sorts of small pulse, and beginne to sow Oates, Barly, and Rye, which is called March Rye; graft all sorts of fruit trees, and with young plants and syens replenish your Nurcery, cover the roots of all trees that are bared, and with fat earth lay them close and warme; if any tree doe grow barren, bore holes in the root, and drive hard wedges or pins of oake wood therein, & that will bring fruitfulnes: transplant all sorts of Sommer flowers, and give new comfort of meanure and earth to all early outlandish flowers, especially to the *Crowne Emperiall, Tulippos, Hyacinth,* and *Narcissus,* of all shapes and colours, cut downe under wood for fuell and fencing, and looke well to your Ewes, for then is the principall time of yeaning: And lastly, bathe often, bleede but upon extremitie, purge not without good counsell, and let your dyet bee coole and temperate.

In the moneth of Aprill finish up all your barley seed, and begin to sow your hempe and Flax: sow your garden seeds and plant all sorts of herbes; finish grafting in the stocke, but beginne you principall inauguration, for then the rynd is most plyant and gentle: open your hives, and give Bees free liberty, leave to succour them with food, and let them labour for their living. Now cut downe all great Oake timber, for now the barke will rise, and bee in season for the Tanner. Now scowre your ditches, and gather such meanure as you make in the streets and highwayes, into great heapes together, lay your meadowes, sleght your corne grounds, gather away stones, repaire your high-wayes, set Ozyers and Willowes, and cast up the bankes and munds of all decayed fences.

Lastly, for your health, either purge, bathe or bleed, as you shall have occasion, and use all wholesome recreation, for then moderate exercise in this moneth, there is no better Physicke.

In the moneth of May sow barley upon all light sands & burning grounds, so likewise do your hempe and flaxe, & also al sorts of tender garden seeds as are Cucumbers and Mellons, and al kind of sweet smelling hearbs and flowers; Fallow your stiffe clayes; Sommer stirre your mixt earths, and soyle all light & loose hot sands: prepare all barren earth for Wheat and Rye, Burne bait, Stub gorsse or Furres, and root out Broome and Ferne: begin to fould your sheepe, lead forth meanure, and bring home fuell and fencing, weed your winter corne, follow your common wotkes, and put all sorts of cattle to grasse, either in pasture or teather: put your Mares to the horse, let nothing be wanting to furnish the Dairy: and now put off al your winter-fed fat cattle, for now they are scarcest and dearest, put yong steares and dry kine now to feed at fresh grasse, and away with all Pease fed sheepe for the sweetnesse of grasse mutton will pull downe their prices.

Lastly for your health, use drinkes that will coole and purge the blood, and all other such physicall precepts, as true Art shall prescribe you: But beware of Mountebanks and old wives tales; the latter hath no ground, and the other no truth but apparant cosenage.

In the moneth of June, carie sand, marle, lyme, and meanure of what kine soeuer to your land; bring home your coales and other necessary fuell fetcht farre off, sheare early fat sheepe, sow all sorts of tender hearbs, cut ranke low medowes, make the first returne of your fat cattle, gather early Sommer fruits, distill all sorts of Plants and hearbs whatsoever.

And lastly for your health, use much exercise, thin dyet, and chaste thoughts.

In the moneth of July, apply your hay-harvest, for a day slackt is many pounds lost, chiefly when the weather is unconstant, sheare al manner of field-sheepe, Sommer-stir rich stiffe grounds, soyle all mixt earths and latter soyle all loose hot sands, let hearbs you would preserve now runne to seed, cut off the stalkes of outlandish flowers, and cover the roots with new earth, so well mixt with meanure as may be, sell all such Lambes as you feed for the Butcher, and still leade forth sand, marle, lyme and other meanure; fence up your Copses, graze your elder underwoods, and bring home all your field-timber.

And lastly for your health, abstaine from all Physicke, bleed not, but upon violent occasion, and neither meddle with Wine, Women, nor other wantonnesse.

In the moneth of August apply your Corne-harvest, sheare downe your Wheat and Rye, mowe your Barley and Oats, and make the second returne of your fat sheepe and cattle; gather all your Sommer greater fruit, as plums, apples, and peares, make your sommer or sweet Perry & Cider; set slips and Syens of all sorts of Gilly-flowers, and other flowers, & transplant them that were set the spring before: and at the end of this moneth, begin to winter-

rigge all fruitfull soiles whatsoever; geld your Lambes, cary meanure from your dove-coats, and put your Swine to the early or
first mast. And lastly for your health, shun feasts and banquets, let
physick alone, hate wine, and only take delight in drinkes that are
coole and temperate.

In the moneth of September, reape your Pease, Beanes, and all
other Pulse, making a finall end of your harvest; now bestow upon
your wheat land your principall meanure, and now sow your
Wheat and Rye, both in rich, and in barren climats; now put your
swine to mast of all hands, gather your winter fruit, and make sale
of your wooll, and other sommer commodities; now put off those
stocks of Bees, you meane to sell or take for your owne use; close
thatche and dawbde warme, all the surviving hives, and looke that
no droanes, mice or other vermine be in or about them, now thatche
your stackes and reekes, thrash your seed Rye and Wheat, and
make an end with your cart of all foraine journeys.

Lastly, for your health in this moneth use Physicke, but mod-
erately, forebeare fruits that are too pleasant or rotten, and as death
shun ryot and surfet.

In the moneth of October, finish up your Wheat-seed, scowre
ditches and ponds, plash and lay hedges & quickset, transplant, remove, or set all manner of fruit trees of what nature or qualitie
soever; make your winter cider and perry, spare your private
pastures, and eate up the corne-fields and commons, and now make
an end of winter ridging, draw furrowes to draine and keepe dry
your new sowne Corne, follow hard the making of your malt,
reare all such calves as shall fall, and weane those foales from your
draught mares, which the Spring before were foaled: now sell all
such sheepe as you will not winter, give over folding, and separate
Lambes from the Ewes which you purpose to keepe for your owne
stocke.

Lastly, for your health refuse not any needfull physicke at the
hands of the learned Physician, use all moderate sports, for any
thing now is good which reviveth the spirits.

In the moneth of Nouemb. you may sow either wheat, or Rye in
exceeding hot soyles, you may then remove all sorts of fruit trees,
and plant great trees, either for shelter or shadow: now cut down
all sorts of timber, for plowes, carts, axeltrees, naves, harrows, &
other husbandly offices, make now the last returne of your grasse
fed cattle; bring your swine from the maste, and feed them for

slaughter, reare what calves so ever fall, & breake up all such Hemp and Flaxe as you intend to spin in the winter season.

Lastly, for your health, eate wholesome and strong meats, well spiced and drest, free from rawnesse, drinke sweet wines, and for disgestion ever before cheese prefer good and moderate exercise.

In the moneth of December, put your sheepe and swine to the Pease reekes, and fat them for the slaughter and market; now kill your small Porks and large Bacons, lop hedges and trees, saw out your timber for building, and lay it to season, and if your land bee exceeding stiffe, and rise up in an extraordinarie furrow, then in this moneth begin to plow up that ground whereon you meane to sow cleane Beanes only, now cover your dainty fruit trees all over with canvase, and hide all your best flowers from frosts and stormes with rotten old horse litter; now draine all your corne-fields, and as occasion shall serve, so water and keepe moist your meadowes; now become the Fowler with piece, nets and all manner of engin, for in this moneth no foule is out of season: Now fish, for the Carpe, the Breame, Pyke, Tench, Barbel, Peale and Salmon. And lastly, for your health, eate meats that are hot and nourishing: drinke good wine that is neat, sprighty and lusty, keep thy body well clad, and thy house warme, forsake whatsoever is flegmatick, and banish all care from thy heart, for nothing is now more unwholesome, then a troubled spirit.

2

American Indian Crops Adopted by European Settlers

The American Indians had been practicing agriculture for several centuries before the first European settlers arrived in the New World. It was not until the English settlers adopted the Indians' agricultural plants, cultivation and harvesting methods, and processes of food preparation that they were assured of adequate food supplies. At the present time, over one-half of the total crop production of the United States, measured in farm values, consists of plants first domesticated by the Indians.

The major centers in which New World cultivated plants originated were the mountains and plateaus of Peru and Bolivia and the highlands of Mexico and Guatemala. The Indians of what is now the United States domesticated only a few minor crops, acquiring the rest from the Indians of Mexico.

The major crops developed by the Indians include corn or maize, the white potato, tobacco, and peanuts. The most widely grown variety of cotton, *Gossypium hirsutum L.*, was cultivated by the Indians of Mexico. Other food plants grown by the Indians and now cultivated commercially in the United States include avocados, kidney and lima beans, chili peppers, pumpkins, squashes, sweetpotatoes, and tomatoes. Many nuts and berries, including pecans, black walnuts, blackberries, blueberries, cranberries, huckleberries, raspberries, and strawberries, were gathered but not domesticated by the Indians. Sugar cane was unknown, but the North American Indians in some areas collected and boiled maple sap for syrup and sugar.

The Indians lacked domesticated animals and fowls, having only the dog and turkey. Agriculture was carried on entirely by hand. The Indians had not learned to use metals, so their tools were of wood, stone, bone, or shell. They cleared fields by burning or girdling the trees. As the trees died, the ground was exposed to sunlight and was planted.

Many clearings resulting from this activity were of large size, were on fertile ground, and were well located. As the fields declined in fertility, the Indians moved to new fields or returned to old fields that had not been cultivated for some years. The Indians found, as did the European settlers later, that it required less effort to clear new fields than to restore fertility to old. There were exceptions. In New England, the Indians planted fish with their corn, which, as they decomposed, released nitrogen.

Nearly all the crops grown by the Indians and adopted by the Europeans, such as corn, tobacco, and beans, required intertillage. This method of cultivation was a contribution by the Indians; nearly all crops grown in Europe before the discovery of America were seeded broadcast and neither permitted nor required intertillage.

Thus, the American Indian developed a number of plants which are among our most important staples; he left clearings which were used by the first European settlers; he taught the settlers how to clear land; he developed methods of planting corn which are used, in greatly modified form, to the present; he taught the New Englanders the value of fish as fertilizer; he practiced land rotation instead of crop rotation; and he used intertillage, a practice that was adopted by the new settlers.

The first substantial account of Indian agriculture in the region of English settlement was written by Thomas Hariot. Hariot was one of the settlers on the island of Roanoke in 1585. He returned to England in 1586 when the colony was abandoned, and published *Briefe and True Report of New Found Land of Virginia* in 1588. The volume was reprinted with illustrations in 1590, and several times thereafter.

Food and Farming in Aboriginal Virginia

Thomas Hariot, *Narrative of the First English Plantation of Virginia*, pp. 21-32 (London, Bernard Quaritch, 1893).

OF SUCH COMMODITIES AS VIRGINIA IS knowne to yeelde for victuall and sustenace of mans life, usually fed upon by the naturall inhabitants; as also by us during the time of our aboad. And that of such as are sowed and husbanded.

PAGATOWR, a kinde of graine so called by the inhabitants; the same in the West Indies is called MAYZE: English men call it Guinney wheate or Turkie wheate, according to the names of the countreys from whence the like hath beene brought. The graine is about the bignesse of our ordinary English peaze and not much different in forme and shape: but of divers colours: some white, some red, some yellow, and some blew. All of them yeelde a very white and sweete flowre: beeing used according to his kinde it maketh a very good bread. Wee made of the same in the countrey some mault, whereof was brued as good ale as was to be desired. So likewise by the help of hops thereof may bee made as good Beere. It is a graine of marveilous great increase; of a thousand, fifteene hundred and some two thousand fold. There are three sortes, of which two are ripe in an eleven and twelve weekes at the most; sometimes in ten, after the time they are set, and are then of height in stalke about sixe or seven foote. The other sort is ripe in fourteene, and is about ten foote high, of the stalkes some beare foure heads, some three, some one, and two: every head containing five, sixe, or seven hundred graines within a fewe more or lesse. Of these graines besides bread, the inhabitants make victuall eyther by parching them; or seething them whole until they be broken; or boyling the floure with water into a pappe.

Okindgier, called by us *Beanes*, because in greatnesse & partly in shape they are like to the Beanes in England; saving that they are flatter, of more divers colours, and some pide. The leafe also of the stemme is much different. In taste they are altogether as good as our English peaze.

Wickonzówr, called by us *Peaze*, in respect of the beanes for distinction sake, because they are much lesse; although in forme they little differ; but in goodnesse of tast much, & are far better then our English peaze. Both the beanes and peaze are ripe in tenne weekes after they are set. They make them victuall either by boyling them all to pieces into a broth, or boiling them whole until they bee soft and beginne to breake as is used in England, eyther by themselves or mixtly together: Sometime they mingle of the wheate with them. Sometime also beeing whole sodden, they bruse or pound them, in a morter, & thereof make loaves or lumps of dowishe bread, which they use to eat for varietie.

Macóqwer, according to their severall formes called by us, *Pompions*, *Mellions*, and *Gourdes*, because they are of the like formes as those kindes in England. In *Virginia* such of severall formes are of one taste and very good, and do also spring from one seed. There are of two sorts; one is ripe in the space of a moneth, and the other in two moneths.

There is an hearbe which in Dutch is called *Melden*. Some of those that I describe it unto, take it to be a kinde of Orage; it groweth about foure or five foote high: of the seede thereof they make a thicke broth, and pottage of a very good taste: of the stalke by burning into ashes they make a kinde of salt earth, wherewithall many use sometimes to season their brothes; other salte they knowe not. Wee our selves, used the leaves also for pothearbes.

There is also another great hearbe in forme of a Marigolde, about sixe foote in height; the head with the floure is a spanne in breadth. Some take it to bee *Planta Solis:* of the seedes heereof they make both a kinde of bread and broth.

All the aforesaide commodities for victuall are set or sowed, sometimes in groundes apart and severally by themselves; but for the most part together in one ground mixtly: the manner thereof with the dressing and preparing of the ground, because I will note unto you the fertilitie of the soile; I thinke good briefly to describe.

The ground they never fatten with mucke, dounge or any other thing; neither plow nor digge it as we in England, but onely prepare it in sort as followeth. A fewe daies before they sowe or set, the men with wooden instruments, made almost in forme of mattockes or hoes with long handles; the women with short peckers or parers, because they use them sitting, of a foote long and about five inches in breadth: doe onely breake the upper part of the ground to rayse up the weedes, grasse, & old stubbes of corne stalkes with their rootes. The which after a day or twoes drying in the Sunne, being scrapte up into many small heapes, to save them labour for carrying them away; they burne into ashes. (And whereas some may thinke that they use the ashes for to better the grounde; I say that then they woulde eyther disperse the ashes abroade; which wee observed they doe not, except the heapes bee too great: or els would take speciall care to set their corne where the ashes lie, which also wee finde they are carelesse of.) And this is all the husbanding of their ground that they use.

Then their setting or sowing is after this maner. First for their corne, beginning in one corner of the plot, with a pecker they make a hole, wherein they put foure graines with that care they touch not one another, (about an inch asunder) and cover them with the moulde againe: and so through out the whole plot, making such holes and using them after such maner: but with this regard that they bee made in rankes, every ranke differing from other halfe a fadome or a yarde, and the holes also in every ranke, as much. By this meanes there is a yarde spare ground betwene every hole: where according to discretion here and there, they set as many Beanes and Peaze: in divers places also among the seedes of *Macocqwer, Melden* and *Planta Solis.*

The ground being thus set according to the rate by us experimented, an English Acre conteining fourtie pearches in length, and foure in breadth, doeth there yeeld in croppe or ofcome of corne, beanes, and peaze, at the least two hundred London bushelles: besides the *Macocqwer, Melden,* and *Planta Solis:* When as in England fourtie bushelles of our wheate yeelded out of such an acre is thought to be much.

I thought also good to note this unto you, if you which shall inhabite and plant there, maie know how specially that countrey corne is there to be preferred before ours: Besides the manifold waies in applying it to victuall, the increase is so much that small labour and paines is needful in respect that must be used for ours. For this I can assure you that according to the rate we have made proofe of, one man may prepare and husbande so much grounde (having once borne corne before) with lesse than foure and twentie houres labour, as shall yeelde him victuall in a large proportion for the twelve moneth if hee have nothing else, but that which the same ground will yeelde, and of that kinde onelie which I have before spoken of: the saide ground being also but of five and twentie yards square. And if neede require, but that there is ground enough, there might be raised out of one and the selfsame ground two harvestes or of-comes; for they sowe or set and may at anie time when they thinke good from the middest of March until the ende of June: so that they also set when they have eaten of their first croppe. In some places of the countrey notwithstanding they have two harvests, as we have heard, out of one and the same ground.

For English corne nevertheles whether to use or not to use it, you that inhabite maie do as you shall have farther cause to thinke best. Of the grouth you need not to doubt; for barlie, oates and peaze, we have seene proof of, not beeing purposely sowen but fallen casually in the worst sort of ground, and yet to be as faire as any we have ever seene here in England. But of wheat because it was musty and hat taken salt water wee could make no triall: and of rye we had none. Thus much have I digressed and I hope not unnecessarily: nowe will I returne againe to my course and intreate of that which yet remaineth appertaining to this Chapter.

There is an herbe which is sowed a part by it selfe & is called by the inhabitants Vppówoc. In the West Indies it hath divers names, according to the severall places & countries where it groweth and is used: The Spaniardes generally call it Tobacco. The leaves thereof being dried and brought into powder: they use to take the fume or smoke thereof by sucking it through pipes made of claie into their stomacke and heade; from whence it purgeth superflouous fleame & other grosse humors, openth all the pores & passages of the body: by which meanes the use thereof not only preserveth the body from obstructions: but also if any be, so that they have not beene of too long continuance, in short time breaketh them: whereby their bodies are notable preserved in health, & know not many greevous diseases wherewithall wee in England are oftentimes afflicted.

This Vppówoc is of so precious estimation amongest them, that they thinke their gods are marvelously delighted therwith: Wherupon sometime they make hallowed fires & cast some of the pouder therein for a sacrifice: being in a storme uppon the waters, to pacifie their gods, they cast some up into the aire and into the water: so a weare for fish being newly set up, they cast some therein and into the aire: also after an escape of danger, they cast some into the aire likewise: but all done with strange gestures, stamping, somtime dauncing, clapping of hands, holding up of hands, & staring up into the heavens, uttering therewithal and chattering strange words & noises.

We our selves during the time we were there used to suck it after their maner, as also since our returne, & have found mainie rare and wonderful experiments of the vertues thereof; of which the relation woulde require a volume by it selfe: the use of it by so manie of late, men & women of great calling as else, and some learned Phisitions also, is sufficient witnes.

And these are all the commodities for sustenance of life that I know and can remember they use to husband: all else that followe are founde growing naturally or wilde.

OF ROOTES.

OPENAVK are a kind of roots of round forme, some of the bignes of walnuts, some far greater, which are found in moist & marish grounds growing many together one by another in ropes, or as thogh they were fastened with a string. Being boiled or sodden they are very good meate.

OKEEPENAVK are also of round shape, found in dry grounds: some are of the bignes of a mans head. They are to be eaten as they are taken out of the ground, for by reason of their drinesse they will neither roste nor seeth. Their tast is not so good as of the former rootes, notwithstanding for want of bread & somtimes for varietie the inhabitants use to eate them with fish or flesh, and in my judgement they doe as well as the houshold bread made of rie heere in England.

Kaishcúpenauk a white kind of roots about the bignes of hen egs & nere of that forme: their tast was not so good to our seeming as of the other, and therfore their place and manner of growing not so much cared for by us: the inhabitants notwithstanding used to boile & eate many.

Tsinaw a kind of roote much like unto the which in England is called the *China root* brought from the East Indies. And we know not anie thing to the cotrary but that it maie be of the same kind. These roots grow manie together in great clusters and doe bring foorth a brier stalke, but the leafe in shape far unlike; which beeing supported by the trees it groweth neerest unto, wil reach or climbe to the top of the highest. From these roots while they be new or fresh beeing chopt into small pieces & stampt, is strained with water a juice that maketh bread, & also being boiled, a very good spoonemeate in maner of a gelly, and is much better in tast if it bee tempered with oyle. This *Tsinaw* is not of that sort which by some was caused to be brought into England or the *China roote,* for it was discovered since, and is in use as is afore saide: but that which was brought hither is not yet knowne neither by us nor by the inhabitants to serve for any use or purpose; although the rootes in shape are very like.

Coscúshaw, some of our company tooke to bee that kinde of roote which the Spaniards in the West Indies called *Cassavy*, whereupon also many called it by that name: it groweth in very muddie pooles and moist groundes. Being dressed according to the countrey maner, it maketh a good bread, and also a good sponemeate, and is used very much by the inhabitants: The juice of this root is poison, and therefore heede must be taken before any thing be made therewithal: Either the rootes must bee first sliced and dried in the Sunne, or by the fire, and then being pounded into floure wil make good bread: or els while they are green they are to bee pared, cut into pieces and stampt; loves of the same to be laid neere or over the fire until it be floure, and then being well pounded againe, bread, or spone meate very good in taste, and holsome may be made thereof.

Habascon is a roote of hoat taste almost of the forme and bignesse of a Parseneepe, of it selfe it is no victuall, but onely a helpe beeing boiled together with other meates.

There are also *Leekes* differing little from ours in England that grow in many places of the countrey, of which, when we came in places where, wee gathered and eate many, but the naturall inhabitants never.

OF FRUITES.

CHESTNUTS, there are in divers places great store: some they use to eate rawe, some they stampe and boile to make spoonemeate, and with some being sodden they make such a manner of dowe bread as they use of their beanes before mentioned.

WALNUTS: There are two kindes of Walnuts, and of then infinit store: In many places where very great woods for many miles together the third part of trees are walnuttrees. The one kind is of the same taste and forme or litle differing from ours of England, but that they are harder and thicker shelled: the other is greater and hath a verie ragged and harde shell: but the kernell great, verie oylie and sweete. Besides their eating of them after our ordinarie maner, they breake them with stones and pound them in morters with water to make a milk which they use to put into some sorts of their spoonmeate; also among their sodde wheat, peaze, beanes and pompions which maketh them have a farre more pleasant taste.

MEDLARS a kind of verie good fruit, so called by us chieflie for these respectes: first in that they are not good until they be rotten: then in that they open at the head as our medlars, and are about the same bignesse: otherwise in taste and colour they are farre different: for they are as red as cheries and very sweet: but whereas the cherie is sharpe sweet, they are lushious sweet.

METAQUESUNNAUK, a kinde of pleasaunt fruite almost of the shape & bignes of English peares, but that they are of a perfect red colour as well within as without. They grow on a plant whose leaves are verie thicke and full of prickles as sharpe as needles. Some that have bin in the Indies, where they have seen that kind of red die of great price which is called Cochinile to grow, doe describe his plant right like unto this of Metaquesunnauk but whether it be the true Cochinile or a bastard or wilde kind, it cannot yet be certified; seeing that also as I heard, Cochinile is not of the fruite but founde on the leaves of the plant; which leaves for such matter we have not so specially observed.

GRAPES, there are of two sorts which I mentioned in the merchantable cōmmodities.

STRABERIES there are as good & as great as those which we have in our English gardens.

MULBERIES, Applecrabs, Hurts or Hurtleberies, such as wee have in England.

SACQVENVMMENER a kinde of berries almost like unto capres but somewhat greater which grow together in clusters upon a plant or herb that is found in shalow waters: being boiled eight or nine hours according to their kind are very good meate and holesome, otherwise if they be eaten they will make a man for the time franticke or extremely sicke.

There is a kind of reed which beareth a seed almost like unto our rie or wheat, & being boiled is good meate.

In our travailes in some places wee founde *wilde peaze* like unto ours in England but that they were lesse, which are also good meate.

OF a kinde of fruite or berrie in forme of Acornes.

There is a kind of berrie or acorne, of which there are five sorts that grow on severall kinds of trees; the one is called *Sagetémener,* the second *Osámener,* the third *Pummuckóner.* These kind of

acorns they use to drie upon hurdles made of reeds with fire under-
neath almost after the maner as we dry malt in England. When
they are to be used they first water them until they be soft & then
being sod they make a good victuall, either to eate so simply, or
els being also pounded, to make loaves or lumpes of bread. These
be also the three kinds of which, I said before, the inhabitants
used to make sweet oyle.

An other sort is called *Sapúmmener* which being boiled or parched
doth eate and taste like unto chestnuts. They sometime also make
bread of this sort.

The fifth sort is called *Mangúmmenauk,* and is the acorne of
their kind of oake, the which beeing dried after the maner of the
first sortes, and afterward watered they boile them, & their
servants or sometime the chiefe themselves, either for variety
or for want of bread, doe eate them with their fish or flesh.

Of Beastes.

Deare, in some places there are great store: neere unto the sea
coast they are of the ordinarie bignes as ours in England, & some
lesse: but further up into the countrey where there is better seed
they are greater: they differ from ours onely in this, their tailes are
longer and the snags of their hornes looke backward.

Conies, Those that we have seen & al that we can heare of are
of a grey colour like unto hares: in some places there are such
plentie that all the people of some townes make them mantles of
the furre or flue of the skinnes of those they usually take.

Saquenúckot & Maquówoc; two kindes of small beastes greater
then conies which are very good meat. We never tooke any of
them our selves, but sometime eate of such as the inhabitants had
taken & brought unto us.

Squirels which are of a grey colour, we have taken & eaten.

Beares which are all of black colour. The beares of this countrey
are good meat; the inhabitants in time of winter do use to take &
eate manie, so also somtime did wee. They are taken commonlie
in this sort. In some Ilands or places where they are, being hunted
for, as soone as they have spiall of a man they presently run
awaie, & then being chased they clime and get up the next tree
they can, from whence with arrowes they are shot downe starke
dead, or with those wounds that they may after easily be killed;
we sometime shotte them downe with our caleevers.

I have the names of eight & twenty severall sortes of beasts which I have heard of to be here and there dispersed in the countrie, especially in the maine: of which there are only twelve kinds that we have yet discovered, & of these that be good meat we know only them before mentioned. The inhabitānts somtime kil the *Lyon* & eat him: & we somtime as they came to our hands of their *Wolves* or *wolvish Dogges*, which I have not set downe for good meat, least that some woulde understand my judgement therin to be more simple than needeth, although I could alleage the difference in taste of those kindes from ours, which by some of our company have beene experimented in both.

Of Foule.

Turkie cockes and *Turkie hennes*: *Stockdoves*: *Partridges*: *Cranes*: *Hernes*: & in winter great store of *Swannes* & *Geese*. Of al sortes of foule I have the names in the countrie language of fourescore and sixe of which number besides those that be named, we have taken, eaten & have the pictures as they were there drawne with the names of the inhabitaunts of severall strange sortes of water foule eight, and seventeene kinds more of land foul, although wee have seen and eaten of many more, which for want of leasure there for the purpose coulde not bee pictured: and after wee are better furnished and stored upon further discovery, with their strange beastes, fishe, trees, plants, and hearbes, they shall bee also published.

There are also *Parats, Faulcons, & Marlin haukes*, which although with us they bee not used for meate, yet for other causes I thought good to mention.

Of Fishe.

For foure monethes of the yeere, February, March, Aprill and May, there are plentie of *Sturgeons*: And also in the same monethes of *Herrings*, some of the ordinary bignesse as ours in England, but the most part farre greater, of eighteene, twentie inches, and some two foote in length and better; both these kindes of fishe in those monethes are most plentifull, and in best season which wee founde to be most delicate and pleasant meate.

There are also *Troutes, Porpoises, Rayes, Oldwives, Mullets, Plaice*, and very many other sortes of excellent good fish, which we have taken & eaten, whose names I know not but in the countrey language; wee have of twelve sorts more the pictures as they were drawn in the countrey with their names.

The inhabitants use to take then two maner of wayes, the one is by a kind of wear made of reedes which in that countrey are very strong. The other way which is more strange, is with poles made sharpe at one ende, by shooting them into the fish after the maner as Irishmen cast dartes; either as they are rowing in their boates or els as they are wading in the shallowes for the purpose.

There are also in many places plentie of these kindes which follow.

Sea crabbes, such as we have in England.

Oystres, some very great, and some small; some rounde and some of a long shape: They are founde both in salt water and brackish, and those that we had out of salt water are far better than the other as in our owne countrey.

Also *Muscles, Scalopes, Periwinkles*, and *Creuises*.

Seekanauk, a kinde of crustie shell fishe which is good meate, about a foote in breadth, having a crustie tayle, many legges like a crab; and her eyes in her backe. They are founde in shallowes of salt waters; and sometime on the shoare.

There are many *Tortoyses* both of lande and sea kinde, their backes & bellies are shelled very thicke; their head, feete, and taile, which are in appearance, seeme ougly as though they were membres of a serpent or venemous: but notwithstanding they are very good meate, as also their egges. Some have bene founde of a yard in bredth and better.

And thus have I made relation of all sortes of victuall that we fed upon for the time we were in *Virginia*, as also the inhabitants themselves, as farre foorth as I knowe and can remember or that are specially worthy to bee remembred.

3

Settlers at Jamestown and Plymouth
Learn to Plant Corn

The adoption of maize or corn cultivation from the Indians marked a turning point in the success of the Jamestown and Plymouth colonies, and the beginnings of the cultivation by European settlers of what was to become the most important American farm product.

The efforts of the Jamestown colonists to grow European crops in 1607 and 1608 failed. In 1609, with two Indian captives instructing them, the settlers planted 30 or 40 acres of corn. While the crop succeeded, it was not sufficient to feed all the settlers, and "the starving time" of 1609-1610 resulted. Much greater emphasis was given corn cultivation in 1610, and thereafter the colonists had sufficient food.

Shortly after the Pilgrims landed in New England in the winter of 1620, they found a supply of maize and beans which had been stored for the winter by the Indians. This fortunate event supplied the settlers with food until the spring of 1621, when farming began under the guidance of a friendly Indian named Squanto or Tisquantum. Squanto taught the Pilgrims how to plant corn, using the Indian method of fertilizing each hill with fish. The English grain that was planted failed but the corn succeeded, and the Pilgrims celebrated the harvest with the first Thanksgiving.

William Bradford's Account, 1621

William Bradford, *History of Plymouth Plantation*, pp. 100, 105 (Boston, Little, Brown, and Company, 1856).

Afterwards they (as many as were able) began to plant ther corne, in which servise Squanto stood them in great stead, showing them both the maner how to set it, and after how to dress & tend it. Also he tould them, excepte they gott fish & set with it (in these old grounds) it would come to nothing, and he showed them that in the midle of Aprill they should have store enough come up the brooke, by which they begane to build, and taught them how to take it, and wher to get other provisions necessary for them; all which they found true by traill & experience. Some English seed they sew, as wheat & pease, but it came not to good, eather by the badness of the seed, or lateness of the season or both, or some other defecte . . . .

They begane now to gather in the small harvest they had, and to fitte up their houses and dwellings against winter, being all well recovered in health & strength, and had all things in good plenty; for as some were thus imployed in affairs abroad, others were excersised in fishing, aboute codd & bass & other fish, of which they tooke good store, of which every family had their portion. All the somer ther was no wante. And now begane to come in store of foule, as winter aproached, of which this place did abound when they came first (but afterward decreased by degrees). And besids water foule ther was great store of wild turkies, of which they tooke many, besids vension, etc. Besids they had aboute a peck a meale a weeke to a person, or now since harvest, Indean corn to that proportion. Which made many afterwards write so largly of their plenty hear to their friends in England, which were not fained but true reports.

4

English Agricultural Revolution Brings
Changes in American Agriculture

English agriculture underwent a transformation during the eighteenth century. Many of the practices and tools carried to the New World by the first English colonists were modified beyond recognition, although another century would pass before these changes greatly influenced American agriculture.

The key to the English agricultural revolution was the enclosure of former open-field farms and the conversion of arable land into pasture. Common rights, that is, the right to use certain meadow, wood, and other lands in common with fellow villagers, were extinguished, by force if not by mutual consent. The small landholders and laborers could not support themselves without common rights and were forced to leave farming.

At the same time, many improvements in farming could be made. These included the adoption of improved methods of cultivation, the introduction of new crops and more productive varieties, the development of scientific stock breeding, the betterment of transportation facilities, and a closer attention of both landlords and tenants to agricultural production.

These changes, according to Lord Ernle, were identified with a number of leading agricultural reformers, the most noted of whom were Jethro Tull, Charles Townshend, Robert Bakewell, Arthur Young, and Thomas Coke. Tull was identified with his invention of a grain drill and his advocacy of more intensive cultivation and the use of animal power. Townshend set an example of better farming through improvements in crop rotations and in emphasizing the field cultivation of turnips and clover. Bakewell devoted himself to developing better breeds of livestock. Arthur Young was an influential agricultural writer and publicist. Thomas Coke developed a model agricultural estate, working particularly with wheat and sheep.

Although there has been controversy regarding Tull's contributions to the agricultural revolution, Lord Ernle has said of him: "In the progress of scientific farming Tull is one of the most remarkable of pioneers." Tull's work may at least be considered as representative of that which went to make up the English agricultural revolution.

Jethro Tull (1674-1740) was educated as a lawyer but became a gentleman farmer in 1699. Dissatisfied with the results of his undertaking following the agricultural methods of his day, Tull set out, through observation and experimentation, to improve upon those methods. He invented a seed drill and reintroduced the horse hoe or cultivator into English agriculture. These implements were used to achieve the major points of Tull's agricultural system: pulverizing the soil, planting in drills, and thorough cultivating with plow and hoe during the growing season.

Tull Discusses Improvements in Farming

Jethro Tull, *The Horse Hoeing Husbandry*, pp. 21, 24-25, 122-125, 130-131 (London, For the Author, 1733).

Tillage is breaking and dividing the Ground by Spade, Plow, Hoe, or other Instruments, which divide by a sort of Attrition (or Contusion) as Dung does by Fermentation.

By Dung we are limited to the Quantity of it we can procure, which in most Places is too scanty.

But by Tillage, we can enlarge our Field of Subterranean Pasture without Limitation, tho' the external Surface of it be confin'd within narrow Bounds.

Tillage may extend the Earth's internal Superficies, proportion to the Division of its Parts, and as Division is Infinite, so may that Superficies be.

Every time the Earth is broken by any sort of Tillage, or Division, there must arise some new Superficies of the broken Parts, which never has been open before: For when the Parts of Earth are once united, and incorporated together, 'tis morally Impossible that they, or any of them, should be broken again, only in the same Places; for to do that, such Parts must have again the same Numerical Figures, and Dimensions, they had before such breaking, which even by an infinite Division could never be likely to happen. As the Letters of a Distichon, cut out and mixt, if they should be thrown up never so often, would never be likely to fall into the same Order and Position with one another, so as to recompose the same Distich.

Altho' the internal Superficies may have been drain'd by a preceding Crop, and the next Plowing may move many of the before divided Parts, without new breaking them, yet such as are new broken, have at such places where they are so broken, a new Superficies, which never was, or did exist before; because we cannot reasonably suppose, that any of those Parts can have in all Places (if in any Places) the same Figure and Dimensions Twice. . . .

Farmers, just when they have brought their Land into a Condition, fit to be further Till'd, to much greater Advantage, leave off, supposing the Soil to be Fine enough, when, with the help of Harrows, they can cover the Seed; and afterwards with a Roller they break the Clods; to the end, that if a Crop succeed, they may be able to mow it, without being hinder'd by those Clods. By what I could ever find, this Instrument, call'd a Roller, is seldom Beneficial to good Husbands: It rather Untills the Land, and Anticipates the subsiding of the Ground, which in strong Land happens too soon of it self.

But more to blame are they, who neglect to give their Land due Plowing, trusting to the Harrow to make it fine; and when they have thrown in their Seed, go over it Twenty Times with the Harrows, 'till the Horses have trodden it almost as hard as a Highway, which in moist weather spoils the Crop: But on the Contrary, the very Horses, when the Earth is moist, ought all to tread in the Furrows only, as in Plowing with a Hoe-Plow they always do, when they use it instead of a common Plow . . . .

In order to make a Comparison between the *Hoing Husbandry*, and the *Old Way*, there are four Things; whereof the Differences ought to be very well considered.

I. *The Expence* ⎫
II. *The Goodness* ⎬ of a Crop
III. *The Certainty* ⎭
IV. *The Condition in which the Land is left after a Crop.*

The Profit or Loss arising from Land, is not to be computed, only, from the Value of the Crop it produces; but from its Value, after all Expences of Seed, Tillage, etc. are deducted.

Thus when an Acre brings a Crop worth *four Pounds,* and the Expences thereof amount to *five Pounds,* the Owner's Loss is *one Pound*; and when an Acre brings a Crop which yields *thirty Shillings,* and the Expence amounts to no more than *ten Shillings,* the Owner received *one Pound* clear Profit from this Acre's very small Crop, as the other loses *one Pound* by his greater Crop.

The usual Expences of an Acre of Wheat, sown in the Old Husbandry, in the Country where I live, is, in some Places, for two Bushels and a half of Seed; in other Places four Bushels and a half, the lease of these Quantities at three Shillings *per Bushel, being the present Price, is* seven Shillings *and* Six-pence. *For three Plowings, Harrowing, and Sowing,* sixteen Shillings; *but if plow'd four times, which is better,* one Pound. *For thirty Load of Dung, to a Statute Acre, is* two Pounds five Shillings. *For Carriage of the Dung, according to the Distance, from* two Shillings to Six-pence *the Load;* one Shilling *being the Price most common, is* one Pound ten Shillings. *The Price for Weeding is very uncertain, it has sometimes cost* twelve Shillings, *sometimes* two Shillings per *Acre.*

	l.	s.	d.
In Seed and Tillage, nothing can be abated of............	01	03	06
For the Weeding, one Year with another, is more than....	00	02	00
For the Rent of the Year's Fallow......................	00	10	00
For the Dung; 'tis in some Places a little cheaper, neither do they always lay on quite so much; therefore abating 15 s. in that Article, we may well set Dung and Carriage at	02	10	00
Reaping commonly 5 s. sometimes less...................	00	04	06
Total	04	10	00

Folding of Land with Sheep is reckoned abundantly cheaper than Cart-Dung; but this is to be questioned, because much Land must lie still for keeping a Flock (unless there be Downs) and for their whole Year's Keeping, with both Grass and Hay, there are but three Months of the twelve wherein the Fold is of any considerable Value; this makes the Price of their Manure quadruple to what it would be, if equally good all the Year, like Cart-Dung: And Folding Sheep yield little Profit, besides their Dung; because the Wool of a Flock, except it be a large one, will scarce pay the Shepherd and the Shearers. But there is another Thing yet, which more inhances the Price of Sheep Dung, and that is the dunging the Land with their Bodies, when they all die of Rot, which happens too frequently in many Places; and then the whole Crop of Corn must go to purchase another Flock, which may have the same Fate the ensuing Year, if the Summer prove wet: And so may the Farmer be served for several more successive Years, unless he should break, and another take his Place, or that dry Summers come in Time to prevent it. To avoid this Misfortune he would be glad to purchase Cart-Dung at the highest Price, for supplying the Place of his Fold; but 'tis only near Cities, and great Towns, that a sufficient Quantity can be procured.

But, supposing the Price of Dunging to be only two Pounds ten Shillings, and the general Expence of an Acre of Wheat, when sown, at three Shillings per Bushel, to be four Pounds ten Shillings, with the Year's Rent of the Fallow.

The Expences of Planting an Acre of Wheat in the *Hoing Husbandry*, is three Pecks of Seed, at *three Shillings per* Bushel, is *two Shillings* and Three pence. The whole Tillage, if done by Horses, would be *eight Shillings;* because our two Plowing and six Hoings, are equal to two Stirrings, the common Price whereof is *four Shillings* each; but this we diminish half, when done by Oxen kept on *St. Foin*, in this manner, *viz.* Land, worth *thirty Shillings* Rent, drill'd with *St. Foin*, will well maintain an Ox a Year, and sometimes Hay will be left to pay for the Making; we cannot therefore allow more than *one Shilling* a Week for his Work, because his Keeping comes but to Seven-pence a Week round the Year.

In plain Plowing, six Foot contains eight Furrows: but we plow a Six-Foot Ridge at four Furrows, because in this there are two Furrows cover'd in the Middle of it, and one on each Side of it lies open. Now, what we call one Hoing, is only two Furrows of this Ridge, which is equal to a fourth Part of one plain Plowing; so that the Hoing of four Acres requires an equal Number of Furrows with one Acre, that is Plow'd plain, and equal time to do it in (except that the Land that is kept in Hoing, works much easier than that which is not).

All the *Tillage* we ever bestow upon a Crop of Wheat that follows a Ho'd Crop, is equal to eight Hoings, two of which may require four Oxen each, one of them three Oxen, and the other five Hoings two Oxen each. However allow three Oxen to each single Hoing, taking them all one with another, which is three Oxen more than it comes to in the whole.

Begin at five in the Morning; and in about six Hours you may Hoe three Acres, being equal in Furrows to three Rood, *i.e.* three Quarters of an Acre. Then turn the Oxen to Grass, and after resting, eating, and drinking two Hours and a half, with another Set of Oxen begin Hoing again; and by, or before half an Hour after Seven at Night, another like Quantity may be Ho'd. These are the Hours the Statute has appointed all Labourers to work, during the Summer Half-year.

To Hoe these six Acres a Day, each Set of Oxen draw the Plow only eight Miles and a Quarter, which they may very well do in five Hours; and then the Holder and Driver will be at their Work of Plowing ten Hours, and will have four Hours and a half to rest, etc.

The Expence then of Hoing six Acres in a Day, in this manner, may be accounted; at *one Shilling* the Man that holds the Plow, *Six-pence* the Boy that drives the Plow, *one Shilling* for the six Oxen, and *Six-pence* for keeping the Tackle in Repair. The whole Sum for Hoing these six Acres is *three Shillings*, being *Six-pence per* Acre.

They who follow the *Old Husbandry* cannot keep Oxen so cheap, because they can do nothing without the Fold, and Store-Sheep will spoil the *St. Foin*. They may almost as well keep Foxes and Geese together, as Store-Sheep and good *St. Foin*. Besides, the sowed *St. Foin* cost ten times as much the Planting as drill'd *St. Foin* does, and must be frequently manured, or else it will soon decay; especially upon all Sorts of Land, whereon 'tis most commonly sown.

The Expence of Drilling cannot be much, for as we can Hoe six Acres a Day, at two Furrows on each Six-Foot Ridge, so may we drill twenty-four Acres a Day, with a Drill that plants two of those Ridges at once; and this we may reckon a *Penny Half-penny* an Acre. But because we find it less trouble to drill single Ridges, we will set the Drilling, at most, *Six-pence per* Acre.

As every successive Crop (if well managed) is more free from Weeds than the preceding Crop; I will set it all together at *Sixpence* an Acre for Weeding.

For a Boy or a Woman to follow the *Ho-Plow*, to uncover the young Wheat, when any Clods or Earth happen to fall on it, for which Trouble there is seldom necessary above once to a Crop, Two-pence an Acre. *One Penny* is too much for Brine and Lime for an Acre.

Reaping this Wheat is not worth above half as much as the Reaping of a sown Crop of equal Value; because the Drill'd standing upon about a sixth Part of the Ground, a Reaper may cut almost as much of the Row at one Stroke, as he could at six, if the same stood dispersed all over the Ground, as the Sowed does. And because he who reaps sowed Wheat, must reap the Weeds along with the Wheat; but the Drilled has no Weeds; and besides, there goes a greater Quantity of Straw, and more Sheaves, to a Bushel of the sowed, than of the drilled. And Since some hundred Acres of drilled Wheat has been reaped at *two Shillings* and *Six-pence per* Acre, I will count that to be the Price.

The whole Expence of an Acre of Drilled Wheat.	l.	s.	d.
For Seed 00		02	03
For Tillage 00		04	00
For Drilling 00		00	06
For Weeding 00		00	06
For Uncovering 00		00	02
For Brine and Lime 00		00	01
For Reaping 00		02	06
Total	00	10	00
The Expence of an Acre of Sowed Wheat is 04		00	00
To which must be added, for the Year's Rent of the Fallow 00		10	00
Total	04	10	00

If I have reckon'd the Expence of the Drilled at the lowest Price, to bring it to an even Sum, I have also abated in the other more than the whole Expence of the Drilled Amounts unto.

And thus the Expence of a drilled Crop of Wheat is but the ninth Part of the Expence of a Crop sown in the common Manner.

'Tis also some Advantage, that less Stock is required where no Store-Sheep are used. . . .

They object against us, saying, That sometimes the Hoing makes

Wheat too strong and gross, whereby it becomes the more liable to the Blacks (or Blight of Insects); but this is the Fault of the Hoer, for he may chuse whether he will make it too strong, because he may apply his Hoings at proper times only, and apportion the Nourishment to the Number and Bulk of his Plants. However, by this Objection they allow, that the Hoe can give Nourishment enough, and therefore they cannot maintain that there is a Necessity of Dung in the *Hoing Husbandry;* and that, if our Crops of Wheat should happen to suffer, by being too strong, our Loss will be less than theirs, when that is too strong, since it will cost them nine times our Expence to make it so.

A second Objection is, that as Hoing makes poor Land become rich enough to bear good Crops of Wheat for several Years successively, the same must needs make very good Land become too rich for Wheat. I answer, That if possible it should so happen, there are two Remedies to be used in such a Case; the one is to plant it with Beans, or some other *Vegetables,* which cannot be over-nourished, as Turneps, Carots, Cabbages, and such like, which are excellent Food for fatting of Cattle; or else they may make Use of the other infallible Remedy, when that rich Land, by producing Crops every Year in the *Hoing-Husbandry,* is grown too vigorous and resty, they may soon take down its Mettle, by Sowing it a few Years in their *Old Husbandry,* which will fill it again with a new Stock of Weeds, that will suck it out of Heart, and exhaust more of its Vigour, than the Dung, that helps to produce them, can restore.

There is a third Objection, and that is, that the Benefit of some Ground is lost where the *Ho-Plow* turns at each End of the Lands; but this cannot be much, if any, Damage; because about four square Perch to a Statute Acre, is sufficient for this Purpose, and that, at the Rate of *ten Shillings* Rent, comes to but *Three-pence,* tho' this varies, according as the Piece is longer or shorter; and supposing the most to be eight Perch, that is but *Six-pence per* Acre; and that is not lost neither, for whether it be of natural or artificial Grass, the *Ho-Plow* in turning on it, will scratch it, and leave some Earth on it, which will enrich it so much, that it may be worth its Rent for Baiting of Horses or Oxen upon it. And besides, these Ends are commonly near Quick-Hedges or Trees, which do so exhaust it, that when no Cattle come there to manure it 'tis not worth the Labour of Plowing it.

PART II

Agriculture During the
Confederation, 1776-1789

5

The Sale and Government of Western Lands

The United States became a nation in 1781 with the ratification of the Articles of Confederation. The ratification was preceded by differences over land policy. At the beginning of the American Revolution, seven states laid claim to western lands while six states had no such claims. The states without claims asserted that the unsettled western land should be the property of the new nation; those with claims argued for the retention of their rights to the land. Speculators were active on both sides.

In 1780, New York ceded its claims to the central government. The Continental Congress then declared as its policy that such land should be disposed of for the common benefit of the United States, and settled and formed into states equal in every respect to the original states. Eventually, the other states ceded all or parts of their claims to the central government.

A committee headed by Thomas Jefferson drew up a plan for establishing ten states in the Old Northwest, that is, the area now made up of the states of Ohio, Indiana, Illinois, Michigan, and Wisconsin. The plan was passed by the Continental Congress as the Ordinance of 1784. It never became effective.

Jefferson was also on a committee appointed to draft a plan for surveying and selling the western lands. The plan eventually adopted as the Ordinance of 1785 provided for surveying the west into townships, each containing 36 sections of one square mile. One section in each township was to be reserved for schools. The lands were to be sold for cash at auction at a minimum price of one dollar per acre. The system of surveys permitted the exact fixing of boundaries and led to straight-line roads and fences.

Various influences led to a demand for the replacement of the Ordinance of 1784. The new law, known as the Ordinance of 1787, was one of the most important pieces of legislation ever passed in the United States.

Briefly, the Ordinance of 1787 provided: the Northwest would eventually become at least three but not more than five territories; the territories were to receive more powers of self-government as their populations increased; when a territory numbered 60,000 inhabitants it might frame a constitution and apply for admission into the Union on equal terms with the original thirteen states; a bill of rights guaranteed settlers certain basic freedoms; slavery was prohibited; and laws permitting the perpetuation of great landed estates were forbidden.

The genius of the Ordinance lay in its provision for the admission of new states on equal terms with the original states. No longer were there to be colonials without political privileges; settlers could move into the new areas secure in their personal privileges and in the eventual exercise of their political rights. The West was now bound to the nation by the strongest of all possible ties—that of equal rights.

Land Policy is Established

"Resolution of October 10, 1780," U.S. Continental Congress, *Journals of the Continental Congress, 1774-1789*, 18: 915 (Washington, Government Printing Office, 1910); "Land Ordinance of 1785," Clarence E. Carter, ed., *The Territorial Papers of the United States*, 2: 12-15 (Washington, Government Printing Office, 1934); and "Ordinance of 1787," *ibid.*, 2: 39, 46-49.

Resolved, That the unappropriated lands that may be ceded or relinquished to the United States, by any particular states, pursuant to the recommendation of Congress of the 6 day of September last, shall be disposed of for the common benefit of the United States and be settled and formed into distinct republican states, which shall become members of the federal union, and have the same rights of sovereignty, freedom and independence, as the other states: that each state which shall be so formed shall contain a suitable extent of territory, not less than one hundred nor more than one hundred and fifty miles square, or as near thereto as circumstances will admit:

That the necessary and reasonable expences which any particular state shall have incurred since the commencement of the present war, in subduing any of the British posts, or in maintaining forts or garrisons within and for the defence, or in acquiring any part of the territory that may be ceded or relinquished to the United States, shall be reimbursed;

That the said lands shall be granted and settled at such times and under such regulations as shall hereafter be agreed on by the United States in Congress assembled, or any nine or more of them.

LAND ORDINANCE OF 1785

An Ordinance for ascertaining the mode of disposing of lands in the Western territory

Be it ordained by the United States in Congress assembled That the territory ceded by individual States to the United States which has been purchased of the Indian inhabitants shall be disposed of in the following manner. . . .

The Surveyors as they are respectively qualified shall proceed to divide the said territory into townships of six miles square, by lines running due north and south and others crossing these at right angles as near as may be, unless where the boundaries of the late Indian purchases may render the same impracticable, and then they shall depart from this rule no farther than such particular circumstances may require. . . .

The plats of the townships respectively shall be marked by subdivisions into lots of one mile square or 640 acres, in the same direction as the external lines and numbered from 1 to 36, always beginning the succeeding range of the lots with the number next to that with which the preceding one concluded. And where, from the causes before mentioned, only a fractional part of a township shall be surveyed, the lots protracted thereon shall bear the same numbers as if the township had been entire. And the surveyors in running the external lines of the townships shall at the interval of every mile mark corners for the lots which are adjacent, always designating the same in a different manner from those of the townships. . . .

The board of treasury shall transmit a copy of the original plats previously noting thereon the townships & fractional parts of townships, which shall have fallen to the several states by the distribution aforesaid to the Commissioners of the loan office of the several states, who after giving notice of not less than two nor more than six months by causing advertisements to be posted up at the court houses or other noted places in every county and to be inserted in one newspaper published in the states of their residence respectively shall proceed to sell the townships or fractional parts of townships at public vendue, in the following manner, viz. The township or fractional part of a township N 1. in the first range shall be sold entire, and N. 2 in the same range by lots, and thus in alternate order through the whole of the first range. The township or fractional part of a township N 1. in the second range shall be sold by lots, and N. 2 in the same range entire, and so in alternate order through the whole of the second range; and the third range shall be sold in the same manner as the first and the fourth in the same manner as the second and thus alternately throughout all the ranges; provided that none of the lands within the said territory be sold under the price of one dollar the acre to be paid in specie or loan

office certificates reduced to specie value by the scale of depreci-
ation or certificates of liquidated debts of the United States including interest, besides the expence of the survey and other charges
thereon, which are hereby rated at thirty six dollars the township
in specie or certificates as aforesaid, and so in the same proportion
for a fractional part of a township or of a lot, to be paid at the
time of sales, on failure of which payment the said lands shall again
be offered for sale.

There shall be reserved for the United States out of every township the four lots being numbered, 8. 11. 26. 29 and out of every
fractional part of a township so many lots of the same numbers as
shall be found thereon for future sale: There shall be reserved the
lot N 16 of every township for the maintenance of public schools
within the said township; also one third part of all gold, silver, lead
and copper mines, to be sold or otherwise disposed of as Congress
shall hereafter direct.

ORDINANCE OF 1787

*An Ordinance for the government of the territory of the United
States North west of the river Ohio.*

Be it ordained by the United States in Congress Assembled that
the said territory for the purposes of temporary government be one
district, subject however to be divided into two districts as future
circumstances may in the opinion of Congress make it expedient. . . .

It is hereby Ordained and declared by the authority aforesaid,
That the following Articles shall be considered as Articles of compact between the Original States and the People and States in the
said territory, and forever remain unalterable, unless by common
consent, to wit,

ARTICLE THE FIRST. No person demeaning himself in a
peaceable and orderly manner shall ever be molested on account of
his mode of worship or religious sentiments in the said territory—

ARTICLE THE SECOND. The Inhabitants of the said territory
shall always be entitled to the benefits of the writ of habeas corpus,
and of the trial by Jury; of a proportionate representation of the
people in the legislature, and of judicial proceedings according to
the course of the common law; all Persons shall be bailable unless
for capital offences, where the proof shall be evident, or the pre-
sumption great; all fines shall be moderate, and no cruel or unusual

punishments shall be inflicted; no man shall be deprived of his liberty or property but by the judgment of his Peers, or the law of the land; and should the public exigencies make it necessary for the common preservation to take any persons property, or to demand his particular services, full compensation shall be made for the same;—and in the just preservation of rights and property it is understood and declared, that no law ought ever to be made, or have force in the said territory, that shall in any manner whatever interfere with, or affect private contracts or engagements, bona fide and without fraud previously formed

ARTICLE THE THIRD. Religion, Morality and knowledge being necessary to good government and the happiness of mankind, Schools and the means of education shall forever be encouraged The utmost good faith shall always be observed towards the Indians; their lands and property shall never be taken from them without their consent; and in their property, rights and liberty, they never shall be invaded or disturbed, unless in just and lawful wars authorised by Congress; but laws founded in justice and humanity shall from time to time be made, for preventing wrongs being done to them, and for preserving peace and friendship with them—

ARTICLE THE FOURTH. The said territory, and the States which may be formed therein, shall forever remain a part of this Confederacy of the United States of America, subject to the Articles of Confederation, and to such alterations therein as shall be constitutionally made; and to all the Acts and Ordinances of the United States in Congress Assembled, conformable thereto. The Inhabitants and Settlers in the said territory, shall be subject to pay a part of the federal debts contracted or to be contracted, and a proportional part of the expences of Government, to be apportioned on them by Congress, according to the same common rule and measure by which apportionments thereof shall be made on the other States; and the taxes for paying their proportion, shall be laid and levied by the authority and direction of the legislatures of the district or districts or new States, as in the original States, within the time agreed upon by the United States in Congress Assembled. The Legislatures of those districts, or new States, shall never interfere with the primary disposal of the Soil by the United States in Congress Assembled, nor with any regulations Congress may find necessary for securing the title in such soil to the bona fide purchasers. No tax shall be imposed on lands the property of the United States; and in no case shall non Resident proprietors be taxed higher than Residents. The navigable Waters leading into the Missisippi and St. Lawrence, and the carrying places between the same shall be common highways, and forever free, as well to the Inhabitants of the said territory, as to the Citizens of the United States, and those of any other States that may be admitted into the Confederacy, without any tax, impost or duty therefor—

ARTICLE THE FIFTH. There shall be formed in the said territory, not less than three or more than five States; and the boundaries of the states, as soon as Virginia shall alter her act of Cession and consent to the same, shall become fixed and established as follows, to wit: The Western State in the said territory, shall be bounded by the Missisippi, the Ohio and Wabash Rivers; a direct line drawn from the Wabash and post Vincents due North to the territorial line between the United States and Canada, and by the said territorial line to the lake of the Woods and Missisippi. The middle State shall be bounded by the said direct line, the Wabash from post Vincents to the Ohio; by the Ohio, by a direct line drawn due North from the mouth of the great Miami to the said territorial line, and by the said territorial line.—The eastern State shall be bounded by the last mentioned direct line, the Ohio, Pennsylvania, and the said territorial line; provided however, and it is further understood and declared, that the boundaries of these three States, shall be subject so far to be altered, that if Congress shall hereafter find it expedient, they shall have authority to form one or two States in that part of the said territory which lies north of an east and west line drawn through the southerly bend or extreme of lake Michigan: and whenever any of the said States shall have sixty thousand free Inhabitants therein, such State shall be admitted by its Delegates into the Congress of the United States, on an equal footing with the original States, in all respects whatever; and shall be at liberty to form a permanent Constitution and State Government; provided the Constitution and Government so to be formed, shall be Republican, and in conformity to the principles contained in these Articles; and so far as it can be consistent with the general interest of the Confederacy, such admission shall be allowed at an earlier period, and when there may be a less number of free Inhabitants in the State than sixty thousand.

ARTICLE THE SIXTH—There shall be neither Slavery nor involuntary Servitude in the said territory otherwise than in the punishment of crimes, whereof the Party shall have been duly convicted: Provided always that any Person escaping into the same, from whom labor or service is lawfully claimed in any one of the original States, such fugitive may be lawfully reclaimed and conveyed to the person claiming his or her labor or service as aforesaid.—

6

Agricultural Societies Encourage Improved Farming

Improvements taking place in European agriculture during the eighteenth century gradually became known in the United States. Scientific societies, such as the American Philosophical Society, founded in 1743, and the American Academy of Arts and Sciences, founded in 1780, encouraged the investigation of European ideas and experiences and agricultural experimentation. Societies devoted entirely to agriculture were soon organized. The first of record was established in New Jersey in 1781. The Philadelphia Society for Promoting Agriculture, organized in 1785, was, however, the first such society to publish the results of its work. It was followed closely by the South Carolina Society for Promoting and Improving Agriculture in the same year, by the Society of Maryland for the Encouragement and Improvement of Agriculture, in 1786, and by others within a few years.

The early agricultural societies were made up of groups of men of all professions who could afford experimentation and who would seek out and adapt to American conditions the progress made in other countries. The twenty-three charter members of the Philadelphia Society for Promoting Agriculture included a number of distinguished men. Four had signed the Declaration of Independence, two were members of the convention which drew up the Constitution of the United States, one had served as Secretary of the Continental Congress during the Revolution, seven had served as officers in the Revolutionary army, seven had served in the Continental Congress, four were physicians, and one taught at the University of Pennsylvania. None were farmers dependent solely upon the produce of their farms for a living.

The societies such as the Philadelphia Society and similar groups awarded premiums, not for definite itemized products that could be raised by the ordinary farmer, but rather for the best solutions of problems of general significance. They were pioneers in agricultural education and experimentation, even though they had little direct influence upon the ordinary farmers of the time.

A First Prospectus of the Philadelphia Society

Timothy Pickering, *An Address from the Philadelphia Society for Promoting Agriculture, with a Summary of Its Laws;* and *Premiums Offered,* pp. A2-5, 8-13 (Philadelphia, 1785).

The very imperfect state of AMERICAN Husbandry, in general, compared with that of some countries in Europe, is too well known to be controverted.

It was a conviction of our great inferiority, in this respect, which gave rise to the present Society, formed after the example of institutions in Europe, whose laudable endeavours to promote the Agriculture of their several countries, have been rewarded with the happiest effects. And here it may be observed that, the difficulties those societies had originally to overcome, were much greater than what we shall have to contend with: they found Husbandry, generally, in a rude and unprofitable state, and had to recommend improvements from single instances of more skilful and fortunate management, until the whole, from the force of imitation, gradually became more perfect.—But we instead of solitary examples of extraordinary and successful conduct amongst ourselves, may have the established practice of entire nations to hold up, as an encouragement, which we purpose to lay before the public, from time to time.

The Husbandry of this country, and of England, were fifty years ago both imperfect, and perhaps nearly alike;—here it has ever since remained nearly stationary, there it has been continually advancing: —A short parallel, drawn between them in their present state, will shew how far they are now apart.

American Method:—Unproductive fallows precede crops; after crops, the land is generally given up for a number of years to weeds and poor natural grasses, until it shall come into heart again; the husbandman, in the mean while, employing his labours upon his other fields in succession.

English Method, with variations arising from soils and circumstances:—A field, when broken up, is manured with all the husbandman's force, and what is called a fallow crop taken off, that is such a crop as requires the frequent use of the plough or the hoe, as in turnips, potatoes, beans, &c. the land is then laid down in some kind of grain and clover, the last continuing sometimes two or three years, which is succeeded by wheat upon a single ploughing. —This course, or rotation of crops, is then renewed in the same order, the land never being idle or resting, as it is called. . . .

Societies abroad have proceeded by occasional communications of improved methods, and by honorary premiums given for experiments made. It is the design of this Society to tread in their steps; and they hope, they address themselves to a people sufficiently liberal to reject no practice they shall recommend, merely because it is new, or runs counter to former habits and prejudices;—they freely invite communications, upon all subjects comprehended within their extensive plan, and hope from their example to promote lesser institutions, of a similar nature, in different parts of the country amongst neighbours, each one exciting a spirit of improvement within its proper sphere.

A Summary of the Society's Constitution is subjoined; together with Premiums offered upon proposed subjects.—Some of the particulars contending for premiums, require a length of time, a series of years, to ascertain them by experiment; others are already experienced by individuals, or may be within the year.

SUMMARY of the CONSTITUTION.

THE Society's attentions shall be confined to *Agriculture and rural Affairs;* especially for promoting a greater increase of the products of land within the American states. The members are distinguished into *Residing Members,* or *Members,* and *Honorary Members,* (that is, *Corresponding Members.*) Members to be hereafter added, are to be elected out of such persons only as reside within a ready distance to attend the meetings at Philadelphia with convenience; and those are defined to be only such as shall reside within ten miles of the said city, on either side of the Delaware: All Members of Agricultural Societies in other states or countries, with whom the Society shall correspond, and all persons of this and other states or countries, who shall be elected for the purpose by the Society, are to be *Honorary* (or *corresponding*) *Members,* and will be invited to assist the Society, whenever they come to Philadelphia: Besides they will have a right to be present at the meetings, without being invited.—*Strangers*, who have a propensity to Agriculture, and wish to attend, as Auditors, may be introduced by a Resident Member.—The Society will publish select collections of memoirs and observations on subjects communicated to them. They will annually propose prizes, upon interesting subjects relative to actual experiments and improvements, and for the best pieces written on proposed subjects.—All claims for prizes are to be in writing; and when read, the Society will determine, upon every prize, which of the claims are most worthy to be selected for the definitive judgment on a future comparison of them: This judgment is to be given on the first Monday in February:—In the same meeting is to be determined the subjects to be proposed for prizes the next year; which will be announced in the public Newspapers. The Society will promote the establishment of other Agricultural Societies in the principal places in the country; the Members of those Societies will be requested to attend the meetings as often as they come to Philadelphia; and the friends of Agriculture are invited to assist the Society with information of experiments and incidents in Husbandry. Premiums and prizes are equally due to persons residing in any of these states, according to the merit of their respective exhibitions. Honorary Members may be of any nation in the world.

PREMIUMS *proposed by the* SOCIETY.

1. For the best experiment made of a course of crops, either large or small, or not less than four acres, agreeable to the principles of the English mode of farming, mentioned in the aforegoing Address,—a piece of plate of the value of two hundred dollars, inscribed with the name and the occasion: and, for the experiment made of a course of crops next in merit,—a piece of plate, likewise inscribed, of the value of one hundred dollars. Certificates to be produced by the 20th of December, 1790.

2. The importance of complete farm or fold-yards, for sheltering and folding cattle,—and of a preferable method of conducting the same, for procuring great quantities of compost or mixed dung and manure, within the husbandman's own farm, induces the Society to give, for the best design of such a yard and method of conducting it, suitable to this climate and circumstances of common farmers,—a gold medal:—and, for the second best, a silver medal. The design to be presented to the Society by the 20th of December next.

3. For the best method of counteracting the injurious effects of frost, in heaving or spewing up ground, and exposing roots of wheat to the drying winds of the Spring,—founded in experience, a gold medal: and, for the second best, a silver medal. The account to be presented to the Society by the 20th of December next.

4. The best method of raising hogs, from the pig, in pens or sties, from experience, their sometimes running in a lot or field not totally excluded, if preferred,—a gold medal: and, for the second best, a silver medal. To be produced by the 20th of December next.

5. The best method of recovering worn-out fields to a more hearty state, within the power of common farmers, without dear or far-fetched manures; but, by judicious culture, and the application of materials common to the generality of farmers; founded in experience;—a gold medal: and, for the second best, a silver medal. To be produced by the 20th of December, 1786. . . .

PART III

Gradual Improvements in American
Agriculture, 1789-1861

7

Whitney Invents the Cotton Gin

In 1793, Eli Whitney, a young graduate of Yale University who had accepted a teaching job in South Carolina, invented a practical machine for separating the seeds from the lint of short-staple cotton. The device revolutionized southern agriculture. Production of cotton increased from an estimated 10,500 bales in 1793 to 4,486,000 bales in 1861.

The machine consisted of a cylinder fitted with wire teeth which drew the lint through a wire screen, leaving the seeds behind. The lint was removed from the wire teeth by a revolving brush. Whitney received a patent on his invention early in 1794. He and his partner, Phineas Miller, planned to erect gins and do custom ginning for southern planters. However, they had difficulties in building enough gins to satisfy the need and many planters resented the high tolls charged. Since the machine was simple, any local mechanic could build one. The partners brought a number of law suits for patent infringement, with varying success, then decided to license the manufacture and use of the gins. The most important license was sold for $50,000 to the state of South Carolina. Whitney did not realize his ambition of making a fortune.

Extensive commercial production of cotton, made possible by the cotton gin, led to the expansion of the plantation system, with its use of slave labor. The South depended upon one staple crop and consequently neglected more diversified agriculture. Dependence upon cotton led to further economic and political differences with the North. At the same time, cotton cultivation brought about the rapid settlement of the region and returned large sums to the planters.

It was some years after its invention before the cotton gin was discussed in the press. The following letter, however, describes the circumstances under which Whitney made his invention.

Whitney Discusses His Invention

Letter, Eli Whitney to his father, September 11, 1793, in Whitney Papers, Yale University Library. Reproduced by permission of Yale University Library.

New Haven Sept. 11th, 1793

Dear Parent,

. . . I will give you a summary account of my southern expedition.

I went from N. York with the family of the late Major General Greene to Georgia. I went immediately with the family to their Plantation about twelve miles from Savannah with an expectation of spending four or five days and then proceed into Carolina to take the school as I have mention in former letters. During this time I heard much said of the extreme difficulty of ginning Cotton, that is, separating it from its seeds. There were a number of very respectable Gentlemen at Mrs. Green's who all agreed that if a machine could be invented which would clean the Cotton with expedition, it would be a great thing both to the Country and to the inventor. I involuntarily happened to be thinking on the subject and struck out a plan of a Machine in my mind, which I communicated to Miller, (who is agent to the Executors of Genl. Greene and resides in the family, a man of respectability and property) he was pleased with the Plan and said if I would pursue it and try an experiment to see if it would answer, he would be at the whole expence. I should loose nothing but my time, and if I succeeded we would share the profits. Previous to this I found I was like to be disappointed in my school, that is, in stead of a hundred, I found I could get only fifty Guineas a year. I however held the refusal of the school until I tried some experiments. In about ten Days I made a little model, for which I was offered, if I would give up all right and title to it, a Hundred Guineas—I concluded to relinquish my school and turn my attention to perfecting the machine—I made one before I came away which required the labour of one man to turn it and with which one man will clean ten times as much cotton as he can in any other way before known and also cleanse it much better than in the usual mode. This machine may be turned by water or with a horse, with the greatest ease, and one man and a horse will do more than fifty men with the old machines—It makes the labour fifty times less, without throwing any class of People out of business.

I returned to the Northward for the purposes of having a machine made on a large scale and obtaining a Patent for the invention. I went to Philadelphia soon after I arrived, made myself acquainted with the steps necessary to obtain a Patent, took several of the steps and the Secretary of State Mr. Jefferson agreed to send the Patent to me, as soon as it could be made out—so that I apprehend no difficulty in obtaining the Patent—Since I have been here I have employed several workmen in making machines and as soon as my business is so that I can leave it a few days, I shall come to Westboro'—I think it is probable I shall go to Philadelphia again before I come to Westboro', and when I do come I shall be able to stay but few days—I am certain I can obtain a patent in England—As soon as I have got a Patent in America, I shall go with the machine which I am now making to Georgia, where I shall stay a few weeks to see it at work, from thence I expect to go to England where I shall probably continue two or three years—How advantageous this business will eventually prove to me, I cannot say—It is generally said by those who know any thing about it, that I shall make a Fortune by it. I have no expectation that I shall make an independent fortune by it, but think I had better purchase it than any other business into which I can enter. Something which cannot be foreseen may frustrate my expectations and defeat my Plan: but I am now so sure of success that ten thousand dollars, if I saw the money counted out to me, would not tempt me to give up my right and relinquish the object—

I wish you, Sir, not to show this letter nor communicate any thing of its content to any body except My Brothers and Sister, *enjoining* it on them to keep the whole a *profound Secret.*

8

First American Agricultural Journal

The movement to improve agriculture and raise its professional standing that began after the Revolutionary War and became particularly notable in the first decades of the nineteenth century was marked by the establishment of agricultural societies, fairs, and journals. Until well after the Civil War, the movement was spearheaded by the editors of agricultural journals. Usually the journals publicized agricultural fairs and served as official organs of one or more agricultural societies.

The first journal devoted exclusively to agriculture was *The Agricultural Museum*, which made its first appearance at Georgetown, D.C., on July 4, 1810. The editor and publisher, David Wiley, was a Presbyterian minister, principal of the Columbian Academy of Georgetown, postmaster, mayor of Georgetown, and secretary of the Columbian Agricultural Society. This versatile and public-spirited man published his farm paper for nearly two years. The first year it appeared semimonthly; the second, monthly. *The Agricultural Museum* served as an organ for the Columbian Agricultural Society, and also published proceedings of others, such as the Richmond, Virginia, society. Nearly all aspects of agriculture received some mention, although Wiley gave particular attention to sheep raising.

The American Farmer, established by John Stuart Skinner in Baltimore on April 2, 1819, became the first farm periodical to achieve prominence and relative permanence. For this reason, Skinner is sometimes regarded as the founder of agricultural journalism in the United States.

Skinner's successful periodical was followed on June 15, 1819, by *The Plough Boy* in Albany, New York, and by many others. By mid-century the agricultural press had made its influence felt throughout the United States.

The First Farm Periodical is Introduced

David Wiley, "Introduction," *Agricultural Museum*, 1: 1-3. July 4, 1810.

In presenting the public with the first number of the AGRICULTURAL MUSEUM, without having previously solicited or obtained a single subscriber, it may be supposed that the Editor has calculated too largely on the liberality of his friends and fellow citizens. It may be so. Still, however, he would not be discouraged. This has not been the principal source on which he has relied for support. His dependence is rather on the advantages which such a Publication promises to the community than on their liberality.

For some time past considerable exertion has been made throughout the UNITED STATES, to promote the improvement of AGRICULTURE, and to encourage and extend DOMESTIC MANUFACTURES. Nor has the exertion been without effect.—In many parts of the country the success has equalled the most sanguine expectation. By the adoption of proper modes of culture the produce of whole districts has been more than doubled—thousands of acres of waste and worn out lands have been clothed with a rich abundance—the desert has been literally changed into a fruitful field—large and profitable Manufactories of various kinds have been established, and families have found it by no means impracticable, not only, to feed, but to clothe themselves from the produce of their own farms. Such a state of things may well be considered as a happy presage of lasting greatness and prosperity to our Country, and as laying a solid basis of real INDEPENDENCE. Yet much still remains to be done. The mass of the common Farmers are slow in changing their mode of agriculture—To dissipate their prejudices, they want information, as well as the successful example of their more enlightened neighbours. The institution of Agricultural Societies, and the distribution of Premiums for proper objects may be highly useful. When under suitable regulations and restrictions they may be expected to produce, ultimately, the most important results. But, without a free communication of ideas—without the means of diffusing correct principles—their operation must necessarily be retarded, and their influence on the community be circumscribed within narrow limits. The man of Science may have access to the books of other countries—he may be able to derive important instruction from them, by proper selection of such articles as are applicable to the soil and climate of his own country. But such books are not within the reach of every one; and if they were, a judicious and profitable use of them could not be expected —The common Newspapers are so engrossed by politics, and so devoted to party purposes as, in a great measure, to preclude their utility in this respect. The Magazines, Museums and other periodical Works, which have heretofore been published in this country, have embraced so wide a range, and been so appropriated to other sciences and pursuits, as to render them of little service to the Agriculturalist.

Similar observations might be made in regard to Manufactures. It has therefore been supposed that a Periodical Paper, devoted, almost exclusively, to the interest of Agriculture and Domestic Manufactures, must be useful, and can scarcely fail of support. The design of the Editor is to make the AGRICULTURAL MUSEUM, a repository of valuable information to the Farmer and Manufacturer, and the mean of a free communication of sentiment, and general interchange of ideas on the important subjects of their occupations. In this view, it will be a convenient appendage to the *Columbian Agricultural Society*. The Constitution and proceedings of that Institution, and especially the Premiums proposed and awarded at its general meetings, will be prominent articles. The proceedings of other similar Societies in the United States, and elsewhere, will be noticed. Pains will be taken to make the best selections from the most approved Authors, Journalists and Periodical Works. Original Essays and other communications on Agriculture, on Domestic Manufactures, on the Arts, and on the productions and resources of our country in general, will be received with gratitude and attention. And whilst the interests, growth and improvement of this District, and of the adjacent States, shall not be neglected, the objects and mode of Culture, the Manufactures, the Growth, the Improvements, the Roads, the Rivers, and Canals of every state and district in the Union, will be occasionally brought into view, as far as correct information can be obtained.

Nor are the benefits to be derived from such a publication, confined to the Farmer and Manufacturer alone. They will extend to every class of the community—In a country such as ours, Commerce must draw her resources and wealth from Agriculture. The great body of the population of all flourishing Towns and Cities are Manufacturers and Artisans.

9

Local Agricultural Societies Organized to Sponsor Annual Fairs

While the agricultural fair is sometimes traced to the sheep shearings sponsored by George Washington Parke Custis on his Arlington, Virginia, farm from 1803 on, or to the fairs sponsored in Washington, D.C., by the Columbian Agricultural Society beginning in 1809, the major impetus to purely agricultural fairs came from Elkanah Watson and his Berkshire Agricultural Society.

Watson, a retired banker and businessman, purchased an estate near

Pittsfield, Massachusetts. Shortly after moving there in 1807, he brought the first Merino sheep into the area and exhibited them in the town square. This attracted so much attention that in 1811 Watson organized the Berkshire Agricultural Society, made up of neighborhood farmers, which had for its purpose the sponsoring of an annual cattle show or fair.

The idea spread rapidly, and by 1820 agricultural societies had been formed in all New England counties except those of Rhode Island. One reason for this rapid expansion was that the states made grants to the societies. These grants were used mainly for paying premiums for products exhibited at fairs. The emphasis was upon growing greater and better looking crops and fatter animals without regard to production costs or market demands. The exaggerated hopes of many farmers for benefits to be found in organization were soon disappointed. Little effort was made to preserve the societies when most states discontinued aid after the depression of 1825, and most of them collapsed. Beginning about 1840, the states again made subsidies available, and societies and fairs revived with the establishment of new state and county groups.

Watson Discusses the Origin of the Society

Elkanah Watson, *History of the Rise, Progress, and Existing Condition of the Western Canals in the State of New York . . . Together with the Rise, Progress, and Existing State of Modern Agricultural Societies . . .* , pp. 116-120, 123-126 (Albany, D. Steele, 1820).

In the fall of 1807, I procured the first pair of Merino sheep, that had appeared in Berkshire, if not in the state. They were the first I had ever seen: although defective in the grade I was led to expect, yet, as all who examined their wool, were delighted with its texture and fineness, I was induced to notify an exhibition under the great elm tree in the public square, in Pittsfield, of these two sheep, on a certain day. Many farmers, and even women, were excited by curiosity to attend this first novel, and humble exhibition. It was by this lucky accident, I reasoned thus,—If two animals are capable of exciting so much attention, what would be the effect on a larger scale, with larger animals? The farmers present responded to my remarks with approbation.—We became acquainted, by this little incident; and from that moment, to the present, agricultural societies, cattle shows, and all in connexion therewith, have predominated in my mind, greatly to the injury of my private affairs.

The winter following, I addressed, (under the signature of Projector,) the farmers of Berkshire, with a view to the spread of the Merino sheep; which I considered as invaluable; especially in the hilly countries of New-England. In these first essays, the following extracts were an introduction to the subject of establishing an Agricultural society.

"The most certain and direct road to effect this great object, appears to me, will be the organization of an Agricultural society, which will ultimately embrace all the respectable farmers of the county, who will bring to this common fund, like bees to the hive, their stock of experience, for the good of the whole; whereas, for the want of such a central point of communication, how much useful information is necessarily swallowed up in the grave; which, of right, should be the common property of mankind," &c.

The public mind was gradually maturing to embrace the prize in full view.

The breed of swine in Berkshire, was of the most unprofitable kind;—long legs,—tall,—lank sides,—large bones, requiring more to fat them than their value.

In 1808, I procured from Dutchess county, in the state of New-York, a pair of small boned,—short legged, grass fed pigs, so called. The old breed gradually disappeared, and the community have gained largely by the exchange. In the same year, I purchased a young bull at Cherry-Valley, of the celebrated English stock, with a view of ameliorating the breed of cattle. The winter of 1809, I introduced into my pond, in connexion with a few friends, the first pickerel which had been seen in Berkshire, with the exception of a commencement at Stockbridge two years previous. Their prolific increase in all the ponds, and streams, now affords an essential item of delicious, and increasing food for the inhabitants, which cost them nothing but the trouble of catching, and eating them.

I stood alone, the butt of ridicule, till the 1st of August, 1810, when I wrote an appeal to the public, thus:

"BERKSHIRE CATTLE SHOW.

'The multiplication of useful animals is a common blessing to mankind.' Washington.

TO FARMERS.

The subscribers take the liberty to address you on a momentous subject, which, in all probability, will materially affect the agricultural interest of this county."

After several other remarks, it concludes:

"In a hope of being instrumental in commencing a plan so useful in its consequences, we propose to exhibit in the square in the village of Pittsfield, on the 1st October next, from 9 to 3 o'clock, bulls, &c. &c. It is hoped this essay will not be confined to the present year, but will lead to permanent annual cattle shows, and that an incorporated agricultural society will emanate from these meetings, which will hereafter be possessed of funds sufficient to award premiums, &c."

Signed, 1st August, 1810, Samuel H. Wheeler, and twenty-six farmers, among whom I include myself.

In consequence of this first step, on the 1st October, 1810, I find the following notice in the Pittsfield Sun.

"The first Berkshire cattle show was exhibited with considerable eclat on Monday last. This laudable measure cannot fail to be highly beneficial, considering its novelty in this part of the world, and that many had their doubts, and even a dread of being held up for the finger of scorn to point at. The display of fine animals, and the number exhibited, exceeded the most sanguine hopes of its promoters, and a large collection of people participated in the display: the weather was delightful. The ice is now broke,—all squeamish feelings buried,—and a general satisfaction evinced. It will now be impossible to arrest its course; we have every thing to hope, and to expect, the year ensuing."

A committee of fourteen respectable farmers, from different parts of the county, was appointed to take preparatory measures for a real exhibition in October, 1811. As I had thus far taken the lead in every thing, by common consent, I was placed at the head of a procession of farmers, marching round the square, without motive, or object; having returned from whence we started, and to separate with some eclat, I stepped in front, gave three cheers, in which they all united,—we then parted, well pleased with the day, and with each other.

The following winter we were incorporated into an Agricultural Society, with ample powers to do good,—but no funds. The persons named in the law, met to organize. I was chosen president, and devoted myself in preparation for a splendid exhibition, the following 24th of September; in pursuance of which, on the 1st August of the same year, in a public notice, in my official capacity, I stated:

"We take the liberty to recommend to farmers, to select and prepare prime animals for the exhibition, also for manufacturers to exhibit their best cloth, &c. for inspection or sale. All members of the society are requested to appear in American manufactures. Innocent recreations will be permitted, but every thing tending to immorality, will be discountenanced," &c. &c.

On the 24th September, 1811, we were blessed with another fine day; and the village of Pittsfield was literally crowded with people, at an early hour, by estimation, three or four thousand. Domestic animals were also seen coming from every quarter. . . .

The procession was immediately formed,—it was splendid, novel, and imposing, beyond any thing of the kind, ever exhibited in America. It cost me an infinity of trouble, and some cash, but it resulted in exciting general attention in the Northern States; and placing our society on elevated ground. In this procession were sixty yoke of prime oxen, connected by chains, drawing a plough, held by two of the oldest men in the county,—a band of music,— the society carrying appropriate ensigns, and each member carrying a badge of wheat in his hat, a stage drawn by oxen, having a broad-cloth loom and a spinning jenny, both in operation by English artists, as it moved on,—mechanics, with an appropriate flag, and another stage filled with American manufactures. Four marshals on grey horses, headed by sheriff Larned, conducted the procession, which extended about half a mile. The pens were handsomely filled with many excellent animals. Twelve premiums, amounting only to seventy dollars, were awarded to the most meritorious. Nothing was yet offered for agriculture,—the best farmer,—or domestic manufactures.

The grand difficulty of procuring funds to enable the society to give a powerful impulse on the public mind, was the most serious obstacle we had to combat. From the farmers we could only calculate upon the annual dollar, and as the members did not exceed one hundred and fifty, and as five hundred dollars was indispensable to produce the effect in contemplation, it was evident the difference must be supplied by private donations; or, the society must sink into contempt, and be abandoned. Under this deep apprehension, and encouraged by some gentlemen from Boston, who were present at the recent exhibition; I determined to proceed there, at my own expense, as the society had no funds. I spent one month soliciting charity; although our efforts were highly applauded, and I was greatly honoured in the legislature by personal attentions, yet all my exertions were unavailing. I found myself pursuing an *ignis fatuus*,—and although flattered by some with encouragement, yet I had to abandon the pursuit, much mortified and humbled with this abortive, begging expedition; and returned to Pittsfield, after expending about one hundred and fifty dollars.

The exhibition of 1812, was distinguished by a great increase of premiums, amounting to two hundred and eight dollars, of which fifty dollars was awarded to me, for the best piece of superfine broadcloth, made of the down of my wool, which I gave up to the artists; the residue was awarded on animals. This cloth made a great noise in America. The president of the United States, and several distinguished characters were clothed with it.

Satisfied of the propriety of solemnizing these occasions in the church, by intermixing religious excersises, with appropriate addresses; and the delivery of premiums, and as peculiarly proper in devout acknowledgement for the blessings of the year; being also impressed with a belief that this measure would tend to give popularity to the society, among the graver class of the community; we suggested our wishes to several of the clergy, who were present, soliciting their co-operation in our views. They were also shy; probably considering our measures the bubble of a moment, and that they would make themselves ridiculous. In explaining our views to the Rev. Mr. Porter, of Roxbury, he ascended the pulpit preparatory to the address, and the delivery of our premiums, and favoured us with an animated, pastoral prayer, which was, probably, the first that was ever made on a similar occasion.

The preceding section furnishes an historical review of the successful establishment of the Berkshire agricultural society. The next feature will be to exhibit the means by which the female part of the community were induced, indirectly, to identify themselves with the society.

The grand secret, in all our operations, was to trace the windings of the human heart, and to product effects from every step. It was a great object to excite the females to a spirit of emulation; we were satisfied no measures would lead to that result with so much certainty, as premiums on domestic manufactures, and closing the second "Farmer's Holiday," in "innocent festivity," by an agricultural ball. Also, to unite them in singing pastoral odes at the church. These measures gave us access to hearts naturally warm, and patriotic; we found no difficulty, once in possession of the field, to give their excited minds a direction which will promote their own happiness, and independence; and save millions to our country, as we shall see in the sequel. All this was effected in 1813, as well as the organization of a viewing committee of agriculture. The successful establishment of these two prominent features of the institution, may be considered of primary importance. . . .

10

John Lorain Develops Methods to Breed
Golden Yellow Maize

The golden yellow maize of the corn belt of the United States was developed during the nineteenth century by pioneer farmers and corn breeders. These open-pollinated varieties dominated corn culture from about 1870 to about 1940, when they were largely displaced by hybrid corn.

The corn that the first English settlers in colonial America adopted from the Indians was probably the long, slender-stalked northern flint variety grown in what is now the eastern United States. This corn, usually yellow in color, matured early and kept well because of the hardness of its kernels.

A very different corn, the white southern dent, was grown in parts of what is now known as the south-central United States. The dents, mostly of Mexican origin, were late maturing, heavy stalked, and soft kerneled. Called "gourdseed" corn by the Europeans, the dents gave heavier yields than the flints, but most Indians seemed to prefer the flint varieties as food.

Haphazard mixing of some of the dent and flint varieties probably occurred even before the Europeans arrived in the New World. However, the first definite record of the conscious mixing of the two varieties came in 1812. John Lorain of Phillipsburg, Pennsylvania, saw and demonstrated that certain mixtures of dent and flint varieties would result in a yield much greater than the flint, yet with many of its desirable qualities.

Other farmers and breeders followed Lorain's example, some aware of his pioneer work, others not. One famous variety, Reid's Yellow Dent, originated in 1846 when Robert Reid took a late, rather light reddish colored variety from Ohio to Illinois. Because of a poor stand the next year, a small early yellow variety, probably a flint, was used in replanting the missing hills. The resulting mixture was grown by the family, and the new variety eventually came to dominate the corn belt. By 1850, purposeful blending of different varieties, particularly gourd-seed and flint, was being carried out in many parts of the country. Within 25 years this work was being reflected in varieties that gave high yields and were well suited to growing conditions in the corn belt.

John Lorain Discusses Cross-Breeding of Corn

John Lorain, "Observations on Indian Corn and Potatoes," in Philadelphia Society for Promoting Agriculture, *Memoirs*, 3: 308-311 (1814).

The traces of numerous original corns, are evidently seen in our fields and gardens. Only five of those are in general use for field planting. First, the big yellow and white, in size and form very much alike, the cobs, long and thick, the grains are large, firm, and without indenture; but their size consists principally in their width, which is greatest near the cob, and from this point, the rotundity of their outside surface forms a very considerable vacuity between the rows; and a large circumference, being filled with a few rows of very wide grains, which are short even at their deepest points, covers an extensive surface, without introducing measurement in proportion to the size of the cobs. Secondly, the little yellow and white, resembling each other in size, form and texture, producing still harder grains, more compactly arranged, but not sufficiently so, which, with shorter and slimmer cobs, render them less productive than the two first mentioned; but they ripen early, and are considered safer crops in high latitudes. Thirdly, the gourd-seed. The cob of this is neither so long or thick as the large, solid corns; but the grains are very long, forming a compact round, from the cob to the outside surface of the ear, and gradually taper to a point, where they join into the cob; of course it is vastly more productive than any other known original corn, but ripens late, and the grains are too soft and open for exportation, unless kiln dried. This variety, so far as my observation goes, is invariably white; for although I have frequently heard of a solid yellow gourd-seed corn, yet on investigation, nothing more has appeared than a mixture of the hard yellow corns, with the white gourd-seed. If such an original, firm yellow corn, equally productive with the white gourd-seed, could be procured, it would be invaluable; but by forming a judicious mixture with the gourd-seed and the flinty corn, a variety may be introduced, yielding at least one third more per acre, on equal soil, than any of the solid corns are capable of producing, and equally useful and saleable for exportation. But this mixture should be with the yellow corns; that colour being greatly preferred by shippers, and is most productive, it having the longest and thickest cobs, and would at least compensate for shortening the grain of the original gourd-seed; provided a sufficiency is introduced to lengthen the grain so far as will be consistent with retaining solidity, and that yellow tinge required to make it saleable.

The proportion of the big yellow with the gourd seed, may be determined by the length and thickness of the cob, with wide grains; and of the little yellow, by shorter, slimmer cobs, with narrower grains, of a brighter yellow tinge, and an increased number of rows, in proportion to the width of the grains, and size of the cob; which sometimes amount to upwards of thirty, and seldom less than twenty rows. This sort is firmer and handsomer than that formed with the big yellow, and better calculated for high latitudes, but not so productive. I am induced to believe, that by combining those three, the most valuable properties of each, might be concentered in one variety, in a much greater degree, than at first sight appears, by selecting the ears with the greatest number of rows, compactly formed on the cob, and ripening early. The experiment is easy, and the prospect promising; for in the present unimproved state of that plant, from ninety, to more than one hundred bushels of shelled corn, per acre, have been frequently obtained, and when the seed has been improved, and the arrangement and cultivation of the plant better understood, it does not appear unreasonable to suppose, that one bushel per perch, (160 bushels per acre,) will be obtained with equal facility.

Mr. Stevens's crop of 118 bushels, published in your edition of the Domestic Encyclopedia, is the largest I have noticed; he introduced 26,880 plants per acre. A large ear shells one pint of corn; moderate sized ears will average more than half a pint; if each plant in his field had produced only half a pint of shelled corn, his crop would have yielded at the rate of about 200 bushels per acre, of consequence the number of plants, or their arrangement, or, perhaps, both those causes combined, injured his crop. And the same cause produced similar effects in my crop of 91 bushels, grown in the year 1811, in double rows, on ridges half a perch asunder. The number of plants not exceeding 20,000 per acre, were too much crowded, and leaned out from the ridges into the intervals, to procure the air, until the tops of the plants standing on opposite ridges, intersected, and those which got undermost in the scuffle were entirely barren; and those which predominated, had the shortest ears which had ever been grown before by me; but still the greatest crop of corn. If the same number of plants had been introduced on the same ground, in the single rows, at half the distance, it appears reasonable to suppose, that the crop would have been much more productive, but whether so many can be arranged on an acre, so that they will produce large and perfect ears, is unknown to me. Those crops are merely introduced to show, that large increase does not always determine judicious management of the crop; and that if cultivators would carefully observe the progress of their crops, and publish their errors with the publication of the management and the result; those errors, instead of being copied and perpetuated by others, would be avoided, and the knowledge of agriculture rapidly increase.

11

Introduction of Improved Cattle

The agricultural revolution in England had been marked by the development of improved breeds of livestock which could pass on their desirable characteristics with fair certainty. By the early nineteenth century many farm leaders in the United States were conscious of the need of a similar improvement in American cattle. The need was emphasized by the proponents of a diversified agriculture, featuring the use of lime, clover, and manure. Such an agriculture, argued the reformers, might serve to restore the fertility of the lands along the Atlantic coast that had been exhausted by tobacco and grain.

The first importations of improved cattle from England, of which a record exists, were made in 1783. Longhorns developed by Robert Bakewell, and what were probably early examples of Shorthorns were imported by Matthew Patton of the south branch of the Potomac and H. D. Gough of Maryland. These cattle, with the importations of a Mr. Miller of Augusta County, Virginia, formed the foundation of the famous Patton stock of Kentucky. The effect of this stock in increasing the market weight of Kentucky livestock was remarkable.

English cattle, probably of Bakewell lines, were imported into Connecticut, Maine, and New York before 1800. Some twenty years later, Devons enjoyed a wave of popularity.

Herefords, which eventually became one of the dominant beef breeds in this country, were first imported by Henry Clay in 1817. Clay was in England in 1816, and learned that his friend and fellow Kentuckian, Colonel Lewis Sanders, had purchased Shorthorns and Longhorns for shipment to Kentucky. Clay then decided to purchase some Herefords, which were attracting much attention at the Smithfield Fat Stock Show in London. He sent a cow, two bulls, and a heifer of the Hereford breed on the same ship that carried Sanders' eight Shorthorns and four Longhorns to America in 1817. The Herefords were maintained as a pure breed for only a few years, and were then mixed with the prevalent Shorthorns.

Shorthorns were the most widely known of the improved English breeds before 1850. Many persons imported them during the first quarter of the nineteenth century, but none achieved the distinction of John Hare Powel of Philadelphia County, Pennsylvania. Powel began his importations of improved Shorthorns in 1822 and soon built up a herd. His stock spread widely and rapidly over Pennsylvania and neighboring states. By the time Powel disposed of his herd in 1836, it was evident that even one superior herd kept in a pure state for so short a time as fifteen years could have a profound influence toward improving livestock.

Importations of Herefords and Shorthorns

"English Cattle" and "Improvement of Neat Cattle," *American Farmer*, 4: 223, 271 (Oct. 4, 1822, Nov. 15, 1822).

ASHLAND, 19th August, 1822.

Dear Sir,

Your letter under date the 11th ultimo, reached Lexington, whilst I was absent from home, on a visit to one of our watering places, and on that account there has arisen some delay in my answer. I received the portraits by mail, shortly after I addressed you on the subject of them.

You request some account of my imported English Cattle, which I give with great pleasure. In 1816, I wrote to my friend, Peter Irving at Liverpool, the brother of our distinguished countryman, Washington Irving, and requested him to purchase for me two pair of English Cattle, one of the beef and the other of the milk breed. I gave him a carte blanche, both as to price and races. He took great pains to satisfy himself of the best breeds in the kingdom, by a resort to all the means of information at his command; and he became convinced that the Hereford reds was the best, as combining in themselves the three great qualities, beef, milk and draught, which it is desirable that cattle should possess.—Accordingly he caused to be selected and purchased for me, in January 1817, two pair of that breed of cattle. Two of them were two year-olds, and the other two yearlings; the sum of their cost was £105 sterling. They were shipped at Liverpool, in March 1817, on board the same ship, which imported the English Cattle, for some gentlemen in this neighbourhood, an account of which you have already published, but that was altogether accidental, there having been no concert whatever between those gentlemen and me, in making our respective importations. They were received by Messrs. McDonald and Ridgely, in April or May 1817, and I immediately upon hearing of their landing in the United States, despatched a messenger for them. He brought them about one hundred and fifty miles from Baltimore into the State of Virginia, and owing to the great heat of the season and the wearing away of their hoofs, he was obliged to leave them there to rest, until the weather became cooler; so that it was late in August before they reached Kentucky. One of the bulls died on his way from Baltimore to Virginia, from over feeding on red clover. Estimating the first cost of the cattle, and all incidental charges from the time they were purchased in England, until I received them in Kentucky, and charging the three survivors with what was lost by the death of their companion, those three have come to me at five hundred dollars each. My cattle are very beautiful, fine form, symmetry and color.—They are all without exception, a deep red, white faces, white under the belly, at the tip end of the tail and on one or more of the feet. As I have generally parted with the young, I am not able yet to pronounce, with certainty, whether they will realize the high expectations, which were entertained of them by my friend, Mr. Irving; but I believe he has not been deceived as to their qualities.

We have been for some years breeding in this State, very extensively, from some English Cattle, imported forty or forty-five years ago, by, I believe, Mr. Gough, of Maryland, and Mr. Miller of Virginia. This race of cattle attains a larger size, than any of those of the late importations which we have made. The latter do not, however, want size, and the circumstance of their being smaller than the descendants of the old importation is abundantly compensated by their having less bone, being greatly superior in symmetry, and distributing their flesh on the carcase much better, so as to produce more meat on the good parts. Animals which are ill made, are difficult to keep in good order, because they cannot struggle for subsistence as well as those which are well built. I may, at some future period, inform you how my cattle turn out.

With great respect,

I am your obedient servant,

H. CLAY

. . . .

We have witnessed with peculiar pleasure, the persevering and praiseworthy zeal which Col. Jno. H. Powell, of Philadelphia, continues to manifest for the improvement of our breeds of Neat Cattle; as well by judicious selections from our native stock, as by the importation of chosen animals from England.

In No. 6, of this Vol. page 48, we published a list of animals, which he had collected chiefly from the Eastern States, for the purpose of exhibiting them in Pennsylvania, and distributing them, *at cost*, amongst the Farmers of his native and other states. And in No. 16, pages 122-3, our readers will have noticed an official account of the exhibition, made by the same gentleman, of some of those animals, and of other native and imported stock, before the Philadelphia Agricultural Society, for nearly all of which premiums were awarded to Col. Powell, that were instantly and generously relinquished by him, for the benefit of the Society.

In the same number, the effects of this gentleman's judicious and spirited efforts, to advance the interests of his neighbours, may be traced through the list of premiums obtained by them for superior young Neat Cattle, that partook of the blood of the improved breed, which he had brought to their notice and placed at their service.

We rejoice to learn that Col. Powell has ordered some more

animals from England, and hope that he may realize his loftiest expectations from the enterprize. From Mr. Wetherill, the breeder of Mr. Williams' celebrated Bull "Denton," and from Mr. Champion, the breeder of Colonel Lloyds' beautiful and promising Bull "Champion," he may justly expect to receive some of the most improved cattle of Great Britain. And no where could such Stock be better placed than within the reach of Pennsylvania Farmers; who, like their judicious fellow citizens of Massachusetts, will gladly embrace every opportunity to improve the breeds of their Neat Cattle.

12

Jethro Wood Patents Practical Cast-Iron Plow

The plows of the eighteenth century were heavy and awkward contrivances. The moldboard was constructed of wood according to some rule-of-thumb that might or might not result in a plow that would turn the soil. It was covered with odd scraps of iron to prevent rapid wear, but this plating was rough and uneven, causing much friction. The share was often of iron, with a hardened steel point. It took two men, or a man and a boy, using two or three horses or four to six oxen, an entire day to plow one to two acres.

By the close of the century, Americans were attempting to build better plows. In 1793, Thomas Jefferson developed a moldboard made according to a scientific scheme that would result in its offering the least resistance to the soil as it turned it. Following the pattern, anyone could turn out identical moldboards.

The first patent issued for a plow went to Charles Newbold of New Jersey in 1797. The plow, except for the handles and beam, was to be of solid cast iron. Although Newbold's plow worked well, it was not accepted by the farmers, as they claimed the iron poisoned the land and made the weeds grow.

The next great improvement in the plow was Jethro Wood's cast iron plow, first patented in 1814 but patented in greatly improved form in 1819. Wood, of Scipio, New York, claimed that his moldboard was of particular value. The moldboard, share, and landside were cast in three parts. Although Wood did not emphasize it in his patent application, the interchangeability of the parts was one of Wood's major contributions to the development of the modern plow.

Farmers gradually overcame their fear that iron plows would poison the soil. Part of this change in outlook came with the efforts of agricultural societies and farm journals to induce farmers to use better equipment. The secretary of the Agricultural Society of Maryland, reporting on a meeting held December 15, 1819, stated: "Some of Wood's patent ploughs, made at the foundry of general John Mason, near Georgetown, were exhibited. These ploughs were highly thought of on account of the ease with which the beam might be raised or lowered, and particularly on account of the excellent form of the cast iron mould board."

At the first plowing match at Brighton, Massachusetts, held in 1817, no cast iron implements were used. Ten years later, however, most of the plows were of the improved cast-iron type. Others improved upon it, but Wood's cast-iron plow with interchangeable parts was a major contribution to American agriculture.

Wood Describes His Plow in a Patent Application

Frank Gilbert, *Jethro Wood, Inventor of the Modern Plow*, pp. 22-25, 29-35 (Chicago, Rhodes and McClure, 1882).

In the first place, the said Jethro Wood claims an exclusive privilege for constructing the part of the Plough, heretofore, and to this day, generally called the mould-board, *in the manner hereinafter mentioned.* This mould-board may be termed a plano-curvilinear figure, not defined nor described in any of the elementary books of geometry or mathematics. But an idea may be conceived of it thus:

The land-side of the Plough, measuring from the point of the mould-board, is two feet and two inches long. It is a strait-lined surface, from four to five and one-half inches wide, and half an inch thick. Its more particular description will be hereinafterwards given. It is sufficient to observe here, that of the twenty-six inches of length on the land-side, eighteen inches belong to the part of the Plough strictly called the land-side, and eight inches to the mould-board. The part of the mould-board comprehended by this space of eight inches is very important, affording weight and strength and substance to the Plough; enabling it the better to sustain the cutting-edge for separating and elevating the soil or sward, and likewise the standard for connecting the mould-board with the beam, as will hereinafter be described more at large.

The figure of the mould-board, as observed from the furrow-side, is a sort of irregular pentagon, or five-sided plane, though curved and inclined in a peculiar manner. Its two lower sides touch the ground, or are intended to do so, while the three other sides enter into the composition of the oblique, or slanting mould-board, over-hanging behind, vertical midway, and projecting forward. The angle of the mould-board, as it departs from the foremost point of, or at, the land-side, is about forty-two degrees, and the length of it, or, in other words, of the first side, is eleven inches. The line of the next, or the second side, is nearly, but not exactly parallel with the before mentioned right-lined land-side, for it widens or diverges from the angle at which the first and second sides join towards it posterior or hindermost point, as much as one inch. Hence, the distance from the hindermost point of the mould-board, at the angle of the second and third sides, directly across to the landside, is one inch more than it is from the angle of the first and second sides, directly across. The length of this, the second side is eight inches. The next side, or what is here denominated the third side, leaves the ground or furrow in a slanting direction backward, and with an over-hanging curve, exceeding the perpendicular outwards from three to six inches, according to the size of the Plough. The length of this third side is fourteen inches and one-half. The fourth side of this mould-board is horizontal, or nearly so, extending from the uppermost point of the third side, to the fore part, or pitch, eighteen inches. The fifth, or last side, descends or slopes from the last mentioned mark, spot, or pitch, to the place of beginning at the low and fore point of the mould-board, where it joins the land side. Its length is thirteen inches. . . .

In the second place, the said Jethro Wood claims an exclusive right and privilege in the construction of a standard of cast iron, like the rest of the work already described, for connecting the mould-board with the beam. This standard is broad, stout, strong; and rises from the fore and upper part of the mould-board, being cast with it, and being a projection or continuation of the same from where the fourth and fifth sides meet. Its figure, strength, and arrangement are such as best to secure the connexion, and to enable the standard thus associated with the beam, to bear the pull, tug, and brunt of service. By a screw bolt and nut properly adjusted above the top of the standard and acting along its side, assisted, if need require, by a wedge for tightening and loosening, the beam may be raised and lowered; and the mould-board, with its cutting edge, enabled to make a furrow of greater or smaller depth, as the ploughman may desire, and a latch and key fixed to the beam, and capable of being turned into notches, grooves, or depressions on one edge or narrow side of the standard, serves to keep the beam from settling or descending. By means of these screw bolts, wedges, latches, and keys, with their appropriate notches, teeth, and joggles, the Plough may be deepened or shallowed most exactly.

In the third place, the said Jethro Wood claims an exclusive privilege in the inventions and improvements made by him in the construction of the cutting edge of the mould-board, or what may be called, in plain language, the plough-share. The cutting edge consists of cast iron, as do the mould-board and land-side themselves. It is about twelve inches and one half of one inch long, four inches and one half of one inch broad, and in the thickest part three quarters of an inch thick. It is so fashioned and cast, that it fits snugly and nicely into a corresponding excavation or depression at the low and fore edge of the mould-board, along the side hereinbefore termed the first side. When properly adapted, the cutting edge seems, by its uniformity of surface and evenness of connexion, to be an elongation of the mould-board, or, as it were, an extension or continuation of the same. To give the cutting edge firm coherence and connexion, it is secured to the mould-board by one or more knobs, pins or heads in the inner and higher side, which are received into one or more holes in the fore and lower part of the mould-board. By this mechanism, the edge is lapped on and kept fast and true, without the employment of screws. That the cutting edge may be the more securely and immovably kept in its place, it has a groove, or ship-lap of one inch in length, below, or at its under side, near the angle between the first and second sides, for the purpose of holding it, and for the further accomplishment of the same object, another groove or ship-lap, stouter and stronger than the preceding, is also cast in the iron, at or near the point of the mould-board, so as to cover, encase, and protect it effectually, on the upper and lower sides, but not on the land side.

After the cutting edge is thus adapted and adjusted to the mould-board by means of the indentations, pins, holes, ship-laps, and fastenings, it is fixed to its place and prevented from slipping back, or working off, by wedges or pins of wood, or other material, driven into the holes from the inner and under side, and forced tight home by a hammer.

In the fourth place, the said Jethro Wood claims the exclusive right of securing the handles of his plough to the mould-board and land-side of the plough by means of notches, ears, loops, or holders, cast with the mould-board and land-side respectively, and serving to receive and contain the handles, without the use of nuts and screws. For this purpose one or more ears or loops, or one or more pairs of notches or holders are cast on the inner side of the mould-board and land side, toward their hinder or back parts, or near their after margins, for the reception of the handles of the Plough. And these, when duly entered and fitted, are wedged in, instead of being fastened by screws.

In the fifth place, the said Jethro Wood claims an exclusive right to his invention and improvement in the mode of fitting, adapting and adjusting the cast iron landside to the cast iron mould-board. Their junction is after the manner of tenon and mortice; the tenon being at the fore end of the land-side and the mortice being at the inside of the mould-board and near its point. The tenon and mortice are joggled, or dove-tailed together in the casting operation, so as to make them hold fast. The fore end of the tenon is additionally secured by a cast projection from the inside of the mould-board for its reception; and if any other tightening or bracing should be requisite, a wooden wedge, well driven in, will bind every part effectually, and all this is accomplished without the assistance or instrumentality of screws.

The said inventor and petitioner wishes it to be understood, that the principal metallic material of his Plough is cast iron. He has very little use for wrought iron, and by adapting the former to the extent he has done, and by discontinuing the latter, he is enabled to make the Plough stronger and better, as well as more lasting and cheap.

13

First American Soil Scientist Demonstrates Value of Lime

Agricultural reform, in the sense of better management of soil and the other factors of production, took many forms in the first half of the nineteenth century. Societies, journals, and fairs contributed, as did many individuals. Progress was particularly notable in the South Atlantic states, partly because agriculture had declined greatly in those states and reform seemed absolutely necessary for survival.

Edmund Ruffin was the most influential leader of the reform movement in Southern agriculture. His great contribution was in popularizing the use of marl, essentially clay mixed with carbonate of lime, often in the form of fossil shells. The use of lime in marl and other forms had been advocated by others, and the theory that lime made for better utilization of other fertilizers had been advanced. Ruffin conducted careful experiments in its use and actively publicized the results of his experiments. The scientific attitude with which Ruffin approached the problem is evident in his famous "Essay on Calcareous Manures," published in the *American Farmer* of December 28, 1821, and subsequently expanded into a book first issued in 1832.

The use of marl and the chemical analysis of soil needs was the beginning for an improved agriculture that, according to Ruffin, should be followed by the adoption of other reforms. In his advocacy of the adoption of better agricultural methods Ruffin wrote over fifty agricultural articles, founded the *Farmers' Register* in 1833 and edited it until 1842, aided in the establishment of local agricultural fairs and societies, was elected a member of the newly established Virginia State Board of Agriculture in 1841, and was the first president of the Virginia State Agricultural Society.

Ruffin succeeded as a progressive farmer and he succeeded in persuading others to adopt his methods. Through his influence the fertility of large areas of Virginia soil was restored and barren wastelands were brought back into production.

Ruffin Advocates the Use of Calcareous Manures

Edmund Ruffin, "Essay on Calcareous Manures," *American Farmer*, 3:313-316, 319. December 28, 1821.

The following ESSAY, on SOILS, and the means of rendering them *permanently fertile*, was written by a practical farmer, in the state of Virginia, who some years since determined to examine into the nature or composition of the Soils in his vicinity; and who, at the same time, commenced a course of experiments to ascertain the permanent as well as the immediate effects of several manures. He has now given an account of the modes and results of his examinations of many soils—accompanied by detailed statements of the effects of specified manures upon several crops, cultivated upon soils of known properties.

This Essay presents the first systematic attempt that has fallen under our observation, wherein a plain, practical, unpretending farmer, has undertaken to examine into the real composition of the soils which he possesses, and has to cultivate. . . .

Such are our favorable impressions as to the merits of this essay, that we have determined to extend its circulation by issuing, and gratuitously distributing an extra impression of this number of our Journal.

Editor American Farmer.

ON THE COMPOSITION OF SOILS, AND THEIR IMPROVEMENT BY CALCAREOUS MANURES.

Received from the Agricultural Society of Prince George, by the Delegation of the United Agricultural Societies of Va. Dec. 6, 1821—Read and ordered to be printed in the AMERICAN FARMER.

Three years ago, I ventured to lay before this Society, opinions respecting the nature of soils, and the action of calcareous manures, which had then received no support from my own experience, and but little from that of others. I was fully aware of the risk, in presenting a theory so general and comprehensive in its application, and on that account, so easy to overthrow, if untrue: but I was induced to take that course, from my conviction of its correctness, and the hope of gaining the assistance of others, towards furnishing the proofs, which numerous and varied experiments with calcareous manures, could only afford. It was my intention to resume the subject, whenever I should be able to offer practice, as well as theory, and either to sustain the opinions before advanced, or to acknowledge whatever experience might show to be erroneous.

The propositions formerly submitted, were as follows:

That soils are essentially different in their capacity for improvement, from some general cause which is far more operative, than such particular and auxiliary causes, as being stiff or light, moist or dry, level or hilly.

That soils under similar circumstances, are capable of improvement, by animal and vegetable manures, in proportion to the degree of their natural fertility.

That the fertility or barrenness of soils, is caused by the presence or absence of a proper proportion of carbonate of lime, or calcareous earth; and of course that the quantity which soils contain of this ingredient, measures their capacity for improvement.

That the fertilizing effects of calcareous earth, are principally produced by its power of combining manures with soils, between which there would otherwise be no attraction, and of neutralizing acids, which exist in all soils destitute of calcareous matter.

That for the want of these properties, it is impossible to improve poor soils with profit, by means of animal and vegetable manures, without previously correcting the defect in their constitution.

The different capacities of Soils for improvement.

Of the foregoing propositions, none perhaps will so readily obtain the assent of experienced cultivators, as those which affirm soils of similar texture to possess very unequal capacities for improvement, and that the degree is in proportion to their original productiveness. These facts, however, so important to every rational scheme of improvement, appear to have excited but slight, if indeed any attention, either in Europe or America. To make and apply as much manure as possible, seems to be considered by all writers, as sufficient to insure fertility to the soil, and profit to the cultivator. They do not tell us, that many exceptions to this rule may be found, and that some soils, without any apparent defect, if not incapable of being enriched by animal and vegetable manures, would at least cause more loss than profit by their improvement.

Some persons admit this difference in soils, but consider a deficiency of clay to be the obstacle to permanent improvement. The general excess of sand in our poor lands, would warrant this belief to a superficial observer. But clays, in proportion to their extent, are as frequently found poor, as sands, and the most steril bodies of land in this county, are also the stiffest. A poor clay soil will certainly retain manure longer, and may be rendered more productive than a poor sandy soil: but when the difference of expense in manure and cultivation, is considered, I doubt whether the improvement of the lighter soil would not be attended with more profit, or rather with less actual loss.

If all soils of similar texture, were equally capable of being enriched, we should not see extensive districts altogether rich or altogether poor, and which have maintained their respective characters, from the time they were brought under cultivation. It cannot be supposed that every farmer in one district is an improver, and in the other, every one an exhauster. If soils were equally fit to be improved, we should see their value vary as much, as the industry and intelligence of their owners. Animal and vegetable manures, applied to any amount whatsoever to the clays of Prince George, or the sands of Sussex, would not make them as valuable as the stiff lands of Back river, or the light loam of Nansemond; and even if such means caused the greatest productiveness, not as much would be retained after five years of exhaustion, as the others now shew after a century.

Calcareous earth the cause of fertility.

Soils containing a proper portion of calcareous earth, are invariably rich in their natural state, and those which are steril, either contain an excessive quantity, or are totally destitute of this necessary ingredient.

This opinion was formed entirely on the visible qualities of soils, and the effects of calcareous manures. But it is obvious that the only certain test of its truth, is an accurate and extensive examination of soils of different characters, by chemical analysis, and thus ascertaining the exact proportion of carbonate, or other compounds of lime, contained in each. This did not appear very difficult to perform, according to Professor Davy's directions, even though the operator might possess but slight knowledge of chemistry in general. Under this impression, I did not fail to attempt obtaining proof in this way, though unacquainted with either the theory or practice of chemistry, and without any opportunity of receiving instruction, from communication with others who were better informed. Thus situated, perhaps it would have been better (and certainly more prudent) to leave such investigations to those who are fully competent. I should have chosen that course, had there been any hope of similar operations from chemists; but their almost total neglect of the chemistry of agriculture, leaves no ground to expect a change, until farmers themselves point out the abundant harvest of discovery, which will hereafter reward some successful investigator. . . .

Much the greater part of the lands of lower Virginia are rendered unproductive by acidity, and generation after generation have toiled on them without being remunerated, and without suspecting that their land throughout, was even then as rich, as their few improved lots appeared to be. The cultivator of such soil, who knows not its particular disease, has no other prospect, than a gradual decrease of his present scanty crops; but if the evil is understood, and the means of its removal within his reach, he has reason to rejoice that his soil was so constituted, as to be preserved from the effects of his own improvidence and that of his forefathers. The presence of acid, by restraining the productive power of the soil, has in a great measure, saved it from exhaustion; and after a course of cropping, which would have utterly ruined more productive lands, the powers of our soils remain scarcely impaired, and ready to be called into action at will, by the use of calcareous manures. If an English agriculturist was asked, what would be the effect of 50 years continued and severe cropping & close grazing, without manure, his answer would certainly be, that such a course could not fail to be followed by complete and hopeless sterility. Yet *we* know instances enough, where such has been the practice, on soils never productive, and which however damaged, still continue under cultivation. In other countries, the existence of soils which were incapable of being either improved or exhausted, to any considerable extent, would justly be considered a fact so remarkable, as to merit all the labour of investigation, which it might require. Here, its frequency causes it to be unnoticed; and they who seek improvement, continue to obey rules drawn from English agriculturists, on soils to which England furnishes no parallel. . . .

When I first recommended the use of shell marl, in 1818, no information whatever, of the practice had been given to the public, nor was it known to us in this neighbourhood, that any other experiments had been made in the United States, than the very few of a prior date which I have stated. Since, however, I have learned that the value of this manure, was practically known in the counties of King William and James City; and in the latter, its use is now rapidly extending. I have made several attempts to procure from different farmers of these counties, some account of the effects experienced—but without success, or even the least encouragement to continue such inquiries. It appears from some general notices in the newspapers, that shell marl is used extensively in New Jersey. Two very valuable papers on this subject have since been published. The first of these is Mr. Singleton's letter "On Shell Marl," (in the 4th volume of Memoirs of the Agricultural Society of Philadelphia,) which gives testimony to the worth of this manure, from a very intelligent farmer, who has used it longer, and to greater extent, than any other in the United States. The other is Dr. Black's essay, "On the intrinsic value of land," published in the second volume of the American Farmer. This essay may at first be thought to contradict rather than sustain my opinions, as the author speaks so slightlingly of marl, as no way tends to encourage it use. This seeming contradiction is only a striking example of the necessity of attending to the *properties* of manures, without regarding their *names*. Dr. Black's plan of improvement is founded on the use of *lime* which he considers essential to the object in view. Caustic lime has powers entirely different from mild lime, and of which I have not spoken, as they are not connected with my subject: but that essay informs us, that the author does not look for the benefit from lime in the first crop, and it is certain, that it must become *carbonated*, and its caustic action cease, before the second year. We must therefore attribute nearly, if not quite all the benefits which Dr. Black has thus derived, to carbonated or mild lime, which has precisely the same properties with shell marl; and the whole argument in favour of caustic lime, goes in support of the carbonate.

When opinions are advanced which are either unsupported by, or directly opposed to those most generally received, it is highly necessary to state them as clearly and distinctly as possible. Such has been my object throughout this essay;—every less important requisite of composition has been sacrificed for the sake of perspicuity, and perhaps I may thus have subjected myself to other charges, besides that of being tedious. In no other respect, however, do I offer any apology, nor ask favour or forbearance towards the opinions presented. If my views are well founded, they deserve consideration: if erroneous, it is proper that they should be fully exposed, and none will see their errors corrected, more willingly than myself.

EDMUND RUFFIN.

14

Steel Plows for Prairie Soil

The cast-iron plow, first patented by Charles Newbold and then put on a commercial basis by Jethro Wood, was successful in the New England and Middle Atlantic states. But it would not scour in the heavy, sticky soils of the prairies; the soil would cling to the moldboard instead of sliding by and turning over.

The steel plow was the answer to the problem of the prairie soil. Its high polish and comparative freedom from surface imperfections kept the soil from clinging to the share and moldboard. In 1833, John Lane, a blacksmith at Lockport, Illinois, began fashioning strips of saw steel over wooden moldboards. This is the first recorded use of steel for plows. Lane's plows successfully turned furrows in the Illinois prairie loam, but Lane apparently did not realize the significance of his improved implement. At least he made no attempt at that time to patent his idea or to manufacture his steel-faced plows on an extensive scale.

In 1837, John Deere, a blacksmith at Grand Detour, Illinois, began using saw steel to make the share of a one-piece share and moldboard. The steel share and the moldboard which, according to recent research, was made of wrought iron, were ground smooth so that the plow would scour. By 1846, Deere and his partner, sawmill owner Leonard Andrus, were producing about one thousand plows a year. In 1847 Deere moved to Moline, Illinois, and by 1857 was turning out 10,000 plows annually. Other manufacturers added to the total. By the time of the Civil War, the steel plow had largely displaced the cast-iron plow in the prairies.

Deere Advertises His Plows

Advertisement in *Rock River Register,* March 10, 1843, reproduced in Edward C. Kendall, "John Deere's Steel Plow," *Contributions from the Museum of History and Technology,* United States National Museum Bulletin 218 (Washington, Government Printing Office, 1959).

John Deere respectfully informs his friends and customers, the agricultural community, of this and adjoining counties, and dealers in Ploughs, that he is now prepared to fill orders for the same on presentation.

The Moldboard of this well, and so favorably known PLOUGH, is made of wrought iron, and the share of steel, 5/16th of an inch thick, which carries a fine sharp edge. The whole face of the mold board and share is ground smooth, so that it scours perfectly bright in any soil, and will not choke in the foulest of ground. It will do more work in a day, and do it much better and with less labor, to both team and holder, than the ordinary ploughs that do not scour, and in consequence of the ground being better prepared, the agriculturalist obtains a much heavier crop.

The price of Ploughs, in consequence of hard times, will be reduced from last year's prices. Grand Detour, Feb. 3, 1843.

15

Mechanical Grain Reaper Introduced

The mechanical reaper was probably the most significant single invention introduced into farming between 1830 and 1860. It replaced much human power at the crucial point in grain production when the work must be completed quickly to save a crop from ruin. Its advent marked the transition from the hand to the machine age of farming.

At the time of the American Revolution, the cradle had replaced the sickle and ordinary scythe for harvesting grain. The cradle was a scythe with a light framework which gathered the stems and laid the grain down evenly.

Many inventive minds both in Europe and America turned to the problem of devising a machine for harvesting grain. The first American invention sufficiently practical to find a market was patented by Obed Hussey in 1833. The cutting knife of this machine consisted of a series of triangular plates riveted to a flat iron bar, one end of which was attached to a pitman, or connecting rod, moved by a crank and receiving its motion from the main axle by means of cogs. Hussey began its manufacture in 1834, but sold only about 45 machines by 1840.

In 1834, Cyrus H. McCormick of Virginia patented a reaper. He had completed his first machine in 1831, continuing work along lines begun by his father. The cutting edge of this machine was given a reciprocating motion through a series of cogs. The knife, smooth at first but soon given a serrated form, vibrated between projecting wires which held the grain while it was cut. The wires were later modified until they became spear-shaped iron guards. McCormick sold his first machine in

1840 and in 1844 sold 50. By 1845, both the Hussey and McCormick machines were coming into use in the East.

There was vigorous competition between the two machines for a period of years. At the many field trials held at fairs and elsewhere, sometimes one and then the other machine would seem to perform the best. Both McCormick and Hussey made substantial improvements in their machines in 1847. That same year, McCormick moved his manufacturing operations to Chicago. By 1851 he was making 1,000 machines a year.

The Marsh harvester, patented and successfully operated in 1858 by two young farmers of DeKalb County, Illinois, represented another advance in grain harvesting. The distinctive feature of this machine was that a traveling apron elevated the cut grain into a receiving box, from which it was taken and bound by two men riding on a platform. By 1870, annual production was about 1,000 machines. In 1871 the inventors licensed several other manufacturers to use their patents, Cyrus H. McCormick joining the group in 1875.

The labor required to bind the grain cut by the harvester was so great that it became only a matter of time until an automatic binding device was patented. In 1850, John E. Heath patented an unsuccessful twine binder. It was not until 1878 that John F. Appleby perfected a twine-knotter, which he sold to William Deering. Meanwhile, several people had perfected wire binders and this device came into commercial use in 1873. Wire was a nuisance because it had to be removed before the bundles of grain were fed into a threshing machine. The twine binder rapidly replaced the wire binder after 1880.

McCormick Describes His Invention

C. H. McCormick, "Cyrus H. M'Cormick's Improved Reaping Machine," *Mechanics' Magazine*, 4: 209-210. Oct. 11, 1834.

To the Editor of the Mechanics' Magazine:

Dear Sir,—I send you a drawing and description of my Reaping Machine, agreeably to your request.

References—A, the platform; B, the tongue; C, cross-bar; D, hinder end of the tongue; ee, projections in front; F, broad piece on each side; G, circular brace; H, diagonal brace; I, upright post; J, upright reel post; K, braces to upright; L, projection to regulate the width of swarth; M, main wheel roughened; N, band and cog wheel of 30 teeth; O, band; p, small bevel wheel of 9 teeth; Q, do. of 27 teeth; r, do. of 9 teeth; s, double crank; T, cutter; V, vibrating bar of wood, with bent teeth; U, reel pulley; W, reel; X, wheel of 15 inches diameter; Y, reel post.

The platform A is of plank, made fast to a frame of wood, for receiving the grain when cut, and holding it until enough has been collected for a sheaf, or more. The projections in front, ee, are two pieces of the platform frame, extending about 1¼ feet in front, and one or more feet apart. On each outside of these pieces is to be secured a broad piece of wood, as at F, by screw bolts, as at 11, passing through them and the projection of the frame. From the end of the outer broad piece, nearest the platform, rises a circular brace, G, projecting forward, and secured to the reel-post, I, by a moveable screw bolt. About nine inches in front of the screw bolts, at 1 1, are two other *moveable* screw bolts, as at 2, passing through both broad pieces and the ends of both projections, allowing for a rise or fall in adjusting the height of cutting; and at about the same distance, further on, is to play an axis of a wheel to be hung between said pieces. Near each end of this axis is secured an arm with two screw bolts, as at 3 3, one of which is moveable, as will be seen; projecting before the wheel, where the tongue is made fast between them by means of two screw bolts passing through all at D. H is a diagonal brace. On the opposite side of the machine is another reel-post, Y, connected near the top with a piece, K, on each side, with a moveable screw bolt, and extending, one to the end of a piece, L, which is attached to the outside of the platform, and divides the grain to be cut, from that to be left standing, the other to the hind end of the platform. T is an upright post, secured to the braces of G and H, at 7, by a moveable bolt, bracing the reel-post Y by means of a piece, Z, passing diagonally over the reel. 5 5 is a strip of cloth about as high as the grain, for the purpose of keeping entirely separate the grain to be cut from that to be left. On the axis, hung between the hind pieces, is a wheel, M, of about two feet diameter, having the circumference curved with teeth to hold to the ground by. N is a cog wheel on the same axis, which serves also for a band wheel, on which and the pulley U the band O works. The cog wheel p working into the cog wheel N, has another cog wheel, Q, on its axle, which works into another small pinion, as at r, attached to the double crank s. These cranks are in a right line, projecting on opposite sides of the axis and in a line with the front edge of the platform. The lower of these works the cutter T, along the front edge of the platform, and the upper one the vibrating bar V, counter to each other. The cutter is a long blade of steel, with an edge like that of a reap-hook, and is supported on the under side by stationary pieces of wood at suitable distances apart. This blade is attached to the frame piece, below the edge of the platform, by means of moveable tongues or slips of metal; the bolt securing it to said frame-piece acting as a pivot, and that through the blade likewise, so that the motion is described in part of a circle. The vibrating bar is of wood, of the same length, and secured in the same manner, above the cutter, with iron teeth made fast in it, at about 2 inches apart, extending before the edge of the cutter, and bent round under it. This vibrating bar has been and may be made stationary, with bent teeth supporting the stalks on each side of the cutter, thereby dispensing with the upper crank; but the other is much preferable, as it reduces the friction and liability to wear materially, by dividing the motion necessary for one between the two, and counterbalancing each other.

In the upper end of each reel-post is a groove, or long mortice, to receive the end of the axis of the reel, which rests on an adjusting pin, subject to be moved higher or lower, to suit grain of different heights—rye, wheat, or oats, & c. The reel W is composed of two or more cross arms at each end of the axle, projecting about 3 feet each way, and connected at their ends by a thin board of about nine inches in width, which, by the arrangement of the arms, runs in a somewhat spiral direction along the axis (though it might be parallel), the right end bearing up first on the grain. This reel, by the motion given by the strap O as the horses advance, bears the stalks upon the cutter, and when separated lands them on the platform A, which advancing till a sufficient quantity is collected, is discharged as often as may be required by a hand with a rake at the right end of the platform. On the left end of the platform is a wheel, H, of about 15 inches diameter, that may be raised or lowered as the cutting may require, corresponding with the opposite side. The point of the tongue is secured to its place by passing through a pin, 6, that is fastened to the hames of each horse by means of leather straps.

I have made some alterations on the drawing, which I think you will readily understand. Two horses were not used to the machine until the last harvest; the necessary changes of which were only described to the draughtsman, and were not all understood. I directed that it should not exceed 5¼ inches, though I think it does one way. The wheel H I think has a wrong direction.

Very respectfully, yours, &c.
C. H. M'Cormick.

16

Irrigation Develops in the West

Modern irrigation agriculture began in the United States in July, 1847, when the first group of Mormon pioneers to reach Utah started diverting water from City Creek near the site of the present-day Salt Lake City.

Irrigation, or the diversion of water from a stream or a natural or artificial storage reservoir to arable land, was practiced in ancient times, notably in Egypt, Mesopotamia, and India. The Incas of Peru and the Indians of Mexico had developed extensive systems before Europeans arrived in the New World. Early Spanish explorers in the Southwest of what is now the United States found remains of extensive irrigation works that had outlived the civilization to which they belonged, and along the valley of the Rio Grande River and in other places they found the Pueblo Indians irrigating the soil just as their ancestors had done before them.

Spanish missionaries, drawing upon experiences in Spain and the American Southwest, introduced irrigation into California. The area irrigated around the missions was not extensive, nor did the practice receive particular attention. The Mormons probably were not familiar with the Spanish practices, although they may have known of Indian irrigation in New Mexico.

The Mormon settlers spread from Utah into parts of Arizona, Colorado, Idaho, Nevada, and New Mexico, and took their cooperative irrigation practices along with them. Other settlers moved into northeastern Colorado and began irrigating, starting in 1859. Irrigation went ahead so rapidly that it was necessary to develop institutions to settle conflicts over water. The controls developed in Colorado established patterns for water regulation in most of the West.

Western members of Congress realized rather early after irrigation was under way in their states that easy and inexpensive methods of diverting water were very limited and that the per-acre cost of irrigation was bound to rise. The first response was the Desert Land Act of March 3, 1877, under which a claimant could hold up to a section of land under promise to attempt to irrigate it. Although modified from time to time, the law was of little benefit to farmers interested in irrigation.

The Cary Act of 1894 granted each arid state up to a million acres of land to be sold at fifty cents an acre. The receipts were to be used to build irrigation works. By 1902, only about 250,000 acres had been claimed under the Cary Act. But at that time less than nine million acres of land were systematically irrigated in all of the West.

The increasing costs of irrigating additional land and demands for developing the public domain led to the passage of the National Reclamation or Newlands Act in 1902. Basically, the act provided that the United States should plan and construct irrigation projects and that the water users should pay back the cost of the projects over a period of years. Between 10 and 15 per cent of the land now irrigated in this country has been reclaimed under this act. In 1954, 20,500,000 acres of land in eleven western states were irrigated, while 29,500,000 acres in the entire United States were under irrigation.

Irrigation Begins in Utah

Orson Pratt, "Interesting Items Concerning the Journeying of the Latter-Day Saints from the City of Nauvoo, Until Their Location in the Valley of the Great Salt Lake (Extracted from the Private Journal of Orson Pratt)," *Latter-Day Saints' Millenial Star*, 12: 178-179. June 15, 1850.

July 21st—[1847]. No frost this morning, but a heavy dew. We resumed our journey, travelled 2½ miles, and ascended a mountain for 1½ miles; descended upon the west side one mile; came upon a swift running creek, where we halted for noon: we called this *Last Creek*. Brother Erastus Snow (having overtaken our camp from the other camp, which he said was but a few miles in the rear,) and myself proceeded in advance of the camp down Last Creek 4½ miles, to where it passes through a kanyon and issues into the broad open valley below. To avoid the kanyon the wagons last season had passed over an exceedingly steep and dangerous hill. Mr. Snow and myself ascended this hill, from the top of which a broad open valley, about 20 miles wide and 30 long, lay stretched out before us, at the north end of which the broad waters of the Great Salt Lake glistened in the sunbeams, containing high mountainous islands from 25 to 30 miles in extent. After issuing from the mountains among which we had been shut up for many days, and beholding in a moment such an extensive scenery open before us, we could not refrain from a shout of joy which almost involuntarily escaped from our lips the moment this grand and lovely scenery was within our view. We immediately descended very gradually into the lower parts of the valley, and although we had but one horse between us, yet we traversed a circuit of about 12 miles before we left the valley to return to our camp, which we found encamped 1½ miles up the ravine from the valley, and 3 miles in advance of their noon halt. It was about 9 o'clock in the evening when we got into camp. The main body of the pioneers who were in the rear were encamped only 1½ miles up the creek from us, with the exception of some wagons containing some who were sick, who were still behind. . . .

July 23rd.—This morning we despatched two persons to President Young, and the wagons which were still behind, informing them of our discoveries and explorations. The camp removed its position 2 miles to the north, where we encamped near the bank of a beautiful creek of pure cold water. This stream is sufficiently large for mill sites and other machinery. Here we called the camp together, and it fell to my lot to offer up prayer and thanksgiving in behalf of our company, all of whom had been preserved from the Missouri River to this point; and, after dedicating ourselves and the land unto the Lord, and imploring His blessings upon our labours, we appointed various committees to attend different branches of business, preparatory to putting in crops, and in about two hours after our arrival we began to plough, and the same afternoon built a dam to irrigate the soil, which at the spot where we were ploughing was exceedingly dry. Towards evening we were visited by a thunder shower from the west; not quite enough rain to lay the dust. Our two messengers returned, bringing us word that the remainder of the wagons belonging to the pioneer company were only a few miles distant, and would arrive the next day. At 3 p.m. the thermometer stood at 96 deg.

July 24th.—This forenoon commenced planting our potatoes; after which we turned the water upon them and gave the ground quite a soaking. In the afternoon the other camp arrived, and we found all the sick improving very fast, and were so as to be able to walk around. Towards evening another thunder shower from the south-west, but not enough rain to benefit the ground.

July 25th.—Sunday. To-day we held two meetings, at one of which we partook of the sacrament. Each one of the Twelve who were present, together with several others, expressed their feelings and exhorted the brethren to righteousness.

July 26th.—The brethren were quite busily employed in wooding their ploughs, harrows, &c., and in ploughing and planting, and in various branches preparatory to farming. Considerable good timber is discovered up the ravines which put down from the mountains, such as sugar maple, ash, oak, fir, and pine.

17

Commercial Fertilizers Appear Before the Civil War

During the 1840's and 1850's many farmers, particularly those living on the western prairies, were adopting new machines and looking for improved varieties of plants and livestock. Others, particularly in the South and East, were concerned with the declining productivity of their farms. Many remedies were advanced and some were used with considerable success. About 1840, the introduction of commercial fertilizer provided one answer to the problem.

Peruvian guano was the first commercial fertilizer to gain widespread popularity in the United States. The guano, composed entirely of the dried excrement of seafowls, was imported from the arid Chincha Islands off the coast of Peru. It was first brought to wide public notice in 1824 when John S. Skinner discussed it in his magazine, the *American Farmer*, but was not introduced commercially until 1843 when the first shipload arrived in Baltimore. It was widely used during the 1840's and 1850's, but declined in both quantity and nitrogen content after that time.

Many fertilizers were put on the market and widely advertised as competitors of guano. Some of them were odd mixtures of substances that were of little or no value; others were quite effective, and cheaper than guano. The first mixed chemical fertilizers manufactured commercially in the United States were placed on the Baltimore market in 1849. By 1860 there were seven factories in the United States. After the Civil War the manufacture, sale, and use of commercial fertilizer was greatly accelerated in the Old South. While it was not until much later that fertilizer changed the entire picture of American agricultural production, the foundations were laid in this early period.

Mixed Chemical Fertilizers are Advertised

Advertisements and Correspondence, *American Farmer*, ser. 4, vol. 4: 265-266; vol. 5: 97-98. February, September 1849.

Circular to the Farmers of Maryland

Your attention is called to a new article of Manure, manufactured in Baltimore, known as CHAPPELL'S FERTILIZER, OR AGRICULTURAL SALTS. This article is composed of the same materials as are found by analysis in the ash of plants. It consists of a mixture (in proper proportions) of *Bi Phosphate of Lime, and*

Magnesia (or bones dissolved in sulphuric acid,) *Sulphates of Ammonia, Potash, Soda, and Lime, Animal Charcoal, Silicates of Potash, Alumina and Magnesia*, and, as these constituents indicate, is intended to restore to the soil, all the inorganic materials abstracted by vegetation. It has been ascertained that a soil containing a sufficient quantity of these salts, is always fertile; and their absence constitutes what is called *"Worn-out Land."* The analysis of rich soils show a good supply, and poor land a deficiency.

The inorganic matter abstracted from the soil by the growth of different crops is the same, varying only in proportion, it is therefore evident that if we supply to the soil a sufficient quantity of each material thus abstracted, we restore its fertility.

The correctness of the above, has been fully sustained by the use of the agricultural salts, the last season. It has been used on *poor land*, and 25 to 28 bushels of wheat obtained, with a superior crop of clover. As a top dressing on wheat, 8 bushels additional has been realized. On the spring crops, of corn, oats and clover, the yield has been doubled.—it has been used on the same field, (as an experiment) with the best Peruvian Guano both on corn and oats, and the yield has resulted in favor of the Fertilizer. The most respectable reference can be given of its value and effects on poor land.

This article having been used with such favorable results, the manufacturer now offers it to agriculturists with the full confidence that it will largely repay for the outlay, and that it is the cheapest manure they can use.

On very poor land 2 barrels to the acre should be applied, on that in better condition, one, to one and a half barrels. It is calculated in using two barrels you supply to the soil sufficient salts for a rotation—as a top dressing, one barrel put on after a rain, or when the land is wet, and in all cases near the surface and not ploughed in, broadcast and harrowed when practicable. The Ammonia in this preparation is a Sulphate, and therefore not volatile as in Guano, the Bi Phosphates being soluble,—the rain dissolves them, and they thus saturate the soil with prepared food, ready for the nourishment of the plant; being rich in Sulphates, they are powerful absorbents of ammonia from the atmosphere.

As this Fertilizer can be manufactured only to a limited extent, and as the demand during the seeding season, during last fall, was much greater than could be supplied, it would be advisable for those who may wish to obtain a supply in time, to send in their orders and purchase at once.

Price $20 per ton of 2000 lbs. put up in barrels, of 300 lbs. each. Terms, cash on delivery. Address, P. S. CHAPPELL, Chemist, Baltimore.

Note.—Guano is deficient in alkalies and sulphates—this preparation has a sufficient supply, and for this reason on some soils, is superior to it for producing large crops. . . .

Kettlewell & Davison's Renovator

In asking the attention of the agriculturists of Maryland, and elsewhere, to the enterprise in which we have embarked, we congratulate ourselves upon the universal and active interest which prevails, throughout the State, upon the grave and important question of the best and cheapest means to continue the improvement of good, and the renovation of old and worn-out, lands. This energetic course had become absolutely necessary to the Atlantic farmer, as a matter of self defence. The new and rich lands of the West, with a virgin soil, yielding immense crops, and aided by the wonderful progress of internal improvement, makes the farmer of Michigan and Wisconsin the formidable rival of his competitor of Maryland and Pennsylvania. Thus pressed, it was not enough for the latter to remain stationary; the time had arrived when the "tiller of the soil" was required to act with that intelligence and promptitude which belongs to him as a class. The history of the agricultural improvement of Maryland, for the past few years, shows with what spirit and success—triumphant and conclusive—this reformation has been carried on. No branch of industry—and that the foundation of our National prosperity—has accomplished more already, or promises more useful results for the future, than those, in this State, who are engaged in the agricultural pursuits of life.

Such enterprise could not develope itself without calling into requisition every element directed to the same end. Science, capital, corresponding enterprise, a fair field open to all, was presented to every man who felt disposed to make the experiment. With such views, and not ignorant of either the suspicions or the prejudices we would have to encounter, we have invested our capital and character, in good faith and full confidence, with a stern determination to maintain the latter, if we risk the former, in the establishment of an extensive Agricultural *Depot* for the sale of simple and compound Chemical Manures. One of our firm having a consider-able personal interest invested in co-partnership with another party, in the practical details of farming, and the other, the chemist of one of the largest chemical factories in the city, we have entered upon our undertaking as a labor of love, hoping, however and be-lieving, that it will result to the mutual advantage of ourselves and the public. We present our Renovator in the most plain and prac-tical way in which we can place its merits before the public.

All soils contain naturally certain constituents which are removed by grass and grain crops, and appear in the bodies of animals fed on these crops, in the form of phosphate of lime, potash, soda, azo-tized matter, ammonia, &c. There are certain proportions in which these substances are removed by ordinary cropping.

The soil may contain a supply of all the materials referred to; but frequent cropping may have used up all those in a free state. Now, under these circumstances, we may renovate the land by supplying all those materials which are required for the crop, without drawing on the soil, but actually *resting it and keeping it covered*, while undergoing the process of disintegration; all of which, *experience* says is important.

A rotation of crops is not the *best* mode of accomplishing this object; for although all crops do not remove from the soil the same proportion of its elements, yet they are removed, and the land is impoverished. On the other hand, we are taught by experience that land exposed to the sun's rays is not improved by rest as when "covered." Guano will, in many cases, supply the deficiency of two of the elements necessary for the growth of a crop; but it is found frequently to fail, because *those two* elements are not wanted by this particular soil; and the experiment is a hazardous one, for the failure is not only a loss of time and labor, but the manure is an expensive one, and the crop is twice lost. Stable manure, plentifully applied, will general accomplish the object; but it is not always to be had in sufficient quantity; and many soils are injured by the admixture of so much vegetable matter, while the *salts* contained by the stable manure would have been beneficial *alone*. But, under the most favorable circumstances, we are prepared to prove that it is cheaper to apply one cart load of Salts, containing the extract of one thousand cart loads of stable manure, than haul out the latter, although it cost nothing. We call the attention of the public to the fact that we do not merely stimulate the growth of *one* crop by the application of an agent like guano or plaster; neither do we profess to have discovered some new combination or panacea for curing all the defects of drainage and bad cultivation; but we challenge the severest scrutiny to detect the absence or deficiency of any Salts that is required for the usual crops, in the proportions indicated by the best authority; in other words, we propose to put on the land exactly what will be taken off by the next crop. Take, for instance, one of the elements of our Renovator, phosphate of lime: eight pounds are removed from the soil in every ton of hay, wheat or straw, and one pound by every one thousand pounds of wheat or oats. Twenty pounds will supply an acre with this material for three crops of wheat, clover, &c. &c.; and one barrel of our Renovator will, consequently, provide more of this material than any six crops can remove from one acre. Moreover, we will engage to forfeit 200 barrels of our Renovator to any individual who will produce a barrel of our Renovator that contains less than the average in a hundred pounds of guano of phosphate of lime.

A bushel of green dung weighs 87½ pounds, of this 83½ per cent is Water, and only 2½ is soluble. One hundred pounds of dung contains *nearly* ¼ of a pound of Phosphate of Lime, so that one barrel of our Renovator is equal to about two hundred and fifty Bushels of pure dung with reference to Phosphates *alone*.

But if we compare the fixed soluble Salts, one barrel of our Renovator, represents more than four hundred bushels of dung; for one hundred pounds of dung do not contain ½ a pound of Salts. If it were possible to burn up the cartload of dung and collect the 8 lbs. of ashes, without losing the ammonia that would be volatilized, it is manifest that much labor would be saved in its application.

Now this we propose to accomplish in the use of the Renovator. All experience shows that the slow combustion or rotting of the dung when spread upon the field does not supply even this proportion of salts, for the straw or hay of the dung is frequently preserved for years without decomposition retaining the phosphates, &c., while the ammonia is evaporated and lost to the crop; whereas the ammonia of the Renovator is applied as a sulphate or fixed salts of ammonia more than 24 lbs. to the barrel. Apart from all this, the seeds of noxious weeds are spread broadcast upon the growing crops with every bushel of dung. It is estimated by the analysis of the ashes of the soap boiler that every barrel of our Renovator contains as much Potash as six bushels of their ashes; and the salts of lime in each barrel contain more pure lime than a bushel of the best quick lime from the Schuylkill. The Salts of Magnesia and Soda in each barrel will amount to 50 lbs., and the Sulphate will exceed seventy-five pounds in each barrel. Moreover we pledge ourselves always to supply the proportion as above in every barrel, and will make the forfeit referred to above to any one who can produce a barrel deficient in any of the articles as represented above.

We have before stated that our object is not to prescribe for all possible cases the same remedy; and if an apparent failure should occur in the use of our Renovator, we pledge ourselves to have the soil analysed and remedy the deffect; and, having the control of large quantities of Salts of Potash, Ammonia &c., not only in this city, but elsewhere, that were formerly thrown away, we will, if the agricultural community will avail themselves of the general re-sults of analyses of soils in any particular district, and note the element generally deficient, we will add it in larger proportions to our Renovator or supply it separately. These articles being much cheaper as manures than as they appear in commerce purified for internal use.

As before stated, we make no pretensions to originality, nor is there any mystery in our compound. We have the good fortune to command the materials, and the knowledge how to prepare them. We say that we have 24 lbs. of the Salts of Ammonia in every barrel of our Renovator; and we cordially invite all interested in the agri-cultural prosperity of the State to call at our Factory, on Hamburg street, and witness the process of distillation by which we command it. So with everything else; the whole process is open to any exami-nation which the farmer may desire to make. A statement appeared, sometime since, showing the enormous cost; and hence the impossi-bility of our manure containing the ingredients it does, and be sold at the price we ask.— There was more truth in this, than might be supposed. It came within one hundred per cent. of that high stand-ard, for if the farmer was to purchase the article separately and make the compound himself, he could not do so, at a cost less than between four and five dollars per barrel. This is truth.

And with this plain statement of our fertilizer we ask the patron-age of the public, with full confidence that time and experiment will confirm, as it has done heretofore, all, and more than we have said in its favor.

18

Cooperative Marketing of Farm Products

Cooperation in various forms exists in any society—farm or business, frontier or city. Such endeavors among colonial farm people included erecting buildings, constructing roads, making quilts, importing purebred cattle, and fighting Indians. There are reports of cooperative business activities among farmers early in the nineteenth century. In the 1850's, cooperative cheese and butter factories were established in New York and other states. By the end of the Civil War, the cooperative processing and sale of farm products had spread to many areas.

The Grange, officially known as the Patrons of Husbandry, founded in 1867, greatly stimulated cooperative activities. Local and state granges and finally the national organization sponsored cooperatives throughout the nation. As the Grange declined in numbers and influence, the Alliances undertook new cooperative activities, many of which have remained in operation until the present time.

From 1890 to 1920 the number of active enterprises increased to more than 12,000. Local cooperatives were established in nearly all the states and the cooperative method of marketing was adapted to most of the products for which sufficient quantities were available to permit carlot shipments. In 1895 one of the best known cooperatives, the Southern California Fruit Exchange, later the California Fruit Growers' Exchange and then Sunkist Growers, was organized. After 1902 the Farmers' Union and the American Society of Equity aided the cooperative movement, as did the American Farm Bureau Federation after 1919.

In 1920 enthusiasm was aroused for commodity associations operating over extended areas. These associations hoped to handle the entire output of important crops, with the objective of securing monopoly prices through monopoly control. This idea, widely promoted by Aaron Sapiro, dominated much of the cooperative movement for ten years, but the associations could not live up to such high expectations. They never controlled a sufficient portion of any product, with spectacular exceptions in fruits and vegetables, to exert a decisive influence on the market.

During the post–World War I period, the movement was aided by legislation which definitely authorized the establishment and operation of agricultural cooperatives, and provided certain types of governmental assistance, culminating in the Federal Farm Board in 1929. National councils and federations developed. After the decline of the large-scale commodity associations, emphasis was placed upon sound business practices. The cooperatives emphasized service and savings rather than large-scale reform. After World War II, many cooperatives grew larger and carried on more complex operations, with a continuing emphasis on sound business operations.

Beginning of a Cheese Cooperative

X. A. Willard, "American Dairying; Its Rise, Progress, and National Importance," U.S. Department of Agriculture, *Annual Report*, 1865, pp. 432-433 (Washington, Government Printing Office, 1866).

About this time (1860) the associated dairy system began to attract attention. Several factories were in operation in Oneida county, and were turning out a superior article of cheese. The system had been first inaugurated by Jesse Williams, a farmer living near Rome, in that county, and was suggested from mere accidental circumstances. Mr. Williams was an experienced and skillful cheese maker, and at a time when the bulk of American cheese was poor. His dairy, therefore, enjoyed a high reputation, and was eagerly sought for by dealers. In the spring of 1851, one of his sons, having married, entered upon farming on his own account, and the father contracted the cheese made on both farms at seven cents per pound, a figure considerably higher than was being offered for other dairies in that vicinity. When the contract was made known to the son, he expressed great doubt as to whether he should be able to manufacture the character of cheese that would be acceptable under the contract. He had never taken charge of the manufacture of cheese while at home, and never having given the subject that close attention which it necessarily requires, he felt that his success in coming up to the required standard would be a mere matter of chance. His father therefore proposed coming daily upon the farm and giving the cheese making a portion of his immediate supervision. But this would be very inconvenient, and while devising means to meet the difficulties and secure the benefits of the contract, which was more than ordinarily good, the idea was suggested that the son should deliver the milk from his herd daily at the father's milk-house. From this thought sprung the idea of uniting the milk from several neighboring dairies and manufacturing it at one place. Buildings were speedily erected and fitted up with apparatus, which, proving a success, thus gave birth to the associated system of dairying now widely extended throughout the northern States.

The system of associated dairies, during the last eight years, has been carried into the New England States and into the Canadas. It is largely adopted in Ohio, and has obtained a foothold in Wisconsin, Illinois, Iowa, Kansas, and other States. It is known abroad as the "American system of dairying," and its peculiarities are so well adapted to the genius of our people as to give it a distinctive character of nationality.

19

Grimm Alfalfa Brought to Minnesota

The introduction of new or improved varieties and breeds of plants and livestock has played an important part in the development of American agriculture. Some introductions have been by individuals in a conscious effort to aid themselves or others. Sea-island cotton was such an introduction. Others, such as the navel orange, were made by the Department of Agriculture. Still another group of introductions, many of which never became widely known, were those of seeds brought by immigrants to their new homes. Grimm alfalfa, brought to Minnesota in 1857, and durum wheat, brought to the Dakotas as early as 1864 by Russian immigrants, were in this group.

In 1857, Wendelin Grimm left his native home of Kuelsheim, Germany, for Minnesota, where he bought a farm in Carver County. Among the possessions he brought with him was a bag of alfalfa seed, weighing not more than twenty pounds. Grimm planted the seed in the spring of 1858. Some of the plants winterkilled, but he saved the seed from those that survived and replanted the field. After years of persistence, the alfalfa became acclimatized and no longer winterkilled.

Farmers in Grimm's neighborhood secured alfalfa seed from him, but little was known of the variety outside of Carver County for many years. About 1880, Arthur B. Lyman of Excelsior, schoolteacher and farmer, became impressed with the alfalfa in Carver County and persuaded his father to plant a field to the crop. It winterkilled because ordinary seed was used, but about ten years later Lyman obtained seed from the Grimm neighborhood and the crop was a success.

In 1900 Lyman told the story of his discovery to Professor Willet M. Hays, head of the Agricultural Experiment Station of the University of Minnesota. Hays and Andrew Boss made an investigation of the crop and began to grow it at the experiment station. Lyman was invited to read a paper on the subject before the Minnesota State Agricultural Society in 1904. Other experiment stations tested the alfalfa and confirmed its hardiness and superiority over many other forage crops as a general feed crop for the Northwest. Gradually, it became the outstanding forage crop in the area, and subsequently was used as basic material in breeding newer varieties of alfalfa.

Lyman Reports on Grimm Alfalfa

A. B. Lyman, "Alfalfa Seed," Minnesota State Agricultural Society, *Annual Report*, 1903, pp. 38-44 (Minneapolis, Minnesota State Agricultural Society, 1903).

The first requisite in growing alfalfa seed in Minnesota is to grow a variety that does not winter kill. There are one hundred acres of such a variety growing on our farm at Excelsior, Minn. Also several hundred acres on neighboring lands, all of which are grown for seed.

This hardy variety was brought to Carver county over forty years ago by a German settler and as near as we can learn, came originally from Norway.

Some ten or twelve years ago there was an article published in one of the Minneapolis papers stating that alfalfa could not be grown in Minnesota except in Carver county, and attributed our success to soil conditions. In this the writer was mistaken as common alfalfa is not a success with us. Last winter fields of common alfalfa were nearly ruined by winter killing; yet strawberries wintered in perfect condition with no covering.

The report of the Kansas State Board of Agriculture of 1900, states that "the severe winter of 1898-99 killed off one-half of the alfalfa of Kansas, Nebraska, Colorado and Wyoming."

The winter of 1898-99 killed all the fields of common alfalfa seeded in our county, yet there were no loss of fields of our hardy variety even where the fourth crop had been severely pastured by sheep and cattle the previous fall. The spreading of this valuable variety through the Northwest has been slow because price of seed has been governed by the price of western seed, and there was no stimulus to seed growing. Farmers having ten or fifteen acres would cut the three crops for hay; many times fields that if left would have produced heavy crops of seed have been cut for hay. During the Horticultural summer meeting at the State Experimental Station in 1900, Prof. W. M. Hays learning that I had said that we had a local hardy alfalfa, came to me and had me tell him all I knew about it. Prof. Hays was much interested and came out the following August to see for himself. We had known for a number of years that we had a local hardy variety of alfalfa but didn't realize the importance of growing for seed until after meeting Prof. Hays.

We had at that time on our farm but one field of eight acres seeded in 1894, and have since increased the amount to over one hundred acres. The yield of alfalfa seed depends greatly on weather conditions at blooming time. Heavy rains such as we had the past two seasons are very unfavorable. The second crop is generally the best for seed, yet we have known the third crop to seed heavily in seasons of warm fall weather. The past two falls have been too cool for third crop seed. The bees are great workers on alfalfa blossoms and are a help to seed growing. The upland produces more and better seed than rich low land.

We have cut the seed crop at different seasons with the mower, self binder and self rake; and of the three methods we prefer the self rake.

The mower is too wasteful and much seed is broken off by the team in both mowing and raking. Cutting with the self binder was quite satisfactory and the self rake the best of all. Alfalfa to be ready for seed harvest must have the seed fully developed in the pods, if left too long there is loss in shelling.

If the weather is favorable one or two days after cutting we go over the fields and place two or three dumps in one, Seed alfalfa cures readily as it is nearly mature when cut.

In stacking great care must be taken to prevent loss in shelling, we have used slides 8x16 feet, made of one inch lumber. A team can haul quite a load and it can be loaded without anyone on the load. Of late years we have used the basket rack, size 9x16, and unload with a stacking derrick.

In stacking make the stacks narrow with the sides and ends perpendicular and cover with wild hay. If a machine can be had the alfalfa can be threshed when taken from the field and save the work of stacking. Unlike the red clover, the alfalfa should be threshed or stacked and not left in the field for a long time. The chaff after threshing is good feed, not as good as first-class alfalfa hay but better than timothy hay and will stand heavy rains without injury. We build a stack bottom for each seed stack to prevent loss from moisture. In the matter of threshing there is a great difference of opinion. Many thresh with a common threshing machine, but we have always had the work done with a clover huller. The sieves of the seed cleaner should be somewhat larger than those used for red clover as the alfalfa seed is larger and will carry over into the straw. Some difficulty is experienced because the alfalfa "chops up" so and the broken parts return over and over through the elevator. Sometimes threshers dampen the stacks to prevent this.

The seed after threshing must be run through a seed cleaner. For this purpose we have an exclusive grass seed cleaning machine —the Clipper. Many do not yet realize the value of alfalfa as a farm crop and never can, until they have grown and fed it to their stock.

In 1892 we sent two average samples to our Experimental Station. One sample first crop which tested 15 per cent. crude protein and one sample, second crop, which tested 17.62 per cent.

We find extreme fall pasturing with sheep or cattle does not harm the stand of alfalfa and that it is an excellent way to get red clover out of the alfalfa fields; however, this may not be universally true.

A member: I would like to ask Mr. Lyman how long he has grown that seed?

Mr. Lyman: We have fields in our county there twenty-eight years old; yes, thirty-two years old now,—that are still in a good state of preservation. I have never known a field to winter kill.

Member: The reason I ask, I have known Mr. Lyman some forty-five years, and I have known this alfalfa to grow around here, but I believe it is the same as was brought in there originally by Swiss and called "everlasting clover."

Mr. Lyman: Well, it was brought in by Germans.

Member: Well, they speak the German language, but it was brought in from Switzerland. That is my information. When they first commenced to plant it some of them were badly discouraged, and I think Mr. Lyman will remember that, but finally they made a success of it, and I attribute that success to its having acclimated itself to the country, but I can remember that clover growing in that country, well I should say pretty close to forty years.

Another member: I would like to ask the gentlemen a few questions. What kind of alfalfa was this you have been raising?

Mr. Lyman: Why, it is simply a variety that does not winter kill. Common alfalfa winter kills. It is a variety that makes a different growth from the common alfalfa. Common alfalfa will grow taller. I have seen fields side by side, and there is a difference; it is a leafy plant and more of a dwarf plant. I don't know the name of it.

Question: Was that raised on level ground?

Mr. Lyman: On all kinds of ground. It seeds better on high ground, but so far as growing is concerned it doesn't make any difference. But some fields I have noticed have been injured by standing water.

Question: Is it liable to winter kill on knolls?

Mr. Lyman: No, I have noticed fields growing for years and it won't winter kill. During the fall of 1898 we allowed sheep and horses to run on our alfalfa; that winter you know, the winter of 1898 and '99 many fields of the common alfalfa were wiped out of existence, while fields of this local variety were not killed at all.

Question: Does it seem to grow thicker as the years go by, or does it get weedy in spots?

Mr. Lyman: I don't think the alfalfa thickens, but it holds its stand. The stand remains about the same.

Question: How much seed per acre does it yield, and about how often do you get a seed crop?

Mr. Lyman: The past three years our alfalfa seed crop has been light. This year there was no seed. Last year there was some, and the year before some. I have known years when the seed crop was heavy. There has been no incentive to seed production. The farmers would save an acre or two here or there for a neighbor or for themselves. I have known the seed some years to yield eight bushels to the acre. I think the average would be a seed crop of two bushels to the acre. That is a very conservative estimate.

Question: What is the soil?

Mr. Lyman: Well, we have a variety of soil: the black loam

with clay subsoil, and we have the sandy soil; then we have a very rich soil, and the clay hills. . . .

Question: In seeding down, what do you seed per acre?

Mr. Lyman: The last two years we haven't used but seven pounds of seed to the acre, but perhaps it would be well to seed 10 or 12. Twelve pounds to the acre is a very large amount for this kind of seed. Seed of this variety is considerable smaller than the common western alfalfa. If you seeded 12 pounds of this seed to the acre you would be seeding considerable more than of the common variety. I think ten pounds to the acre would be a good amount of seed. I would sow it in the spring. The seed crop the last two years has not been good owing to the wet weather.

Prof. Hays: Mr. Lyman, will you tell them how much hay you got per acre cutting three times this year, and how much money you got for it?

Mr. Lyman: Well, it will always cut three good crops, and the Germans make it a practice to pasture the fourth crop. They cut three crops of hay and then turn the cattle in on the fourth crop. I should judge that the three crops would cut easily four tons to the acre, probably more.

Question: What does it bring on the market?

Mr. Lyman: It generally brings $14 a ton. The buyers before they know its feeding value will not pay what it is worth. If I was growing alfalfa at home I would feed it to my stock and sell the other hay, as it is very rich in food value.

Prof. Hays: This is a young man I want to make an example of. When he told me he had discovered this hardy alfalfa, I said to him, "You co-operate with the experiment station and I will co-operate with you, and we will give you a reputation as a seedsman," And if any of you have boys that can discover anything of this kind, and the station can help them to become notorious and get a little money out of it, I am going to aid him. The only way to push the seed growing business is to get good prices for the seed. I expect to co-operate in helping Mr. Lyman distribute this seed where it will be used for growing seed. We expect to sell it at a reasonable price, and possibly distribute some of it through the Department of Agriculture, that it may be grown in other places and the seed produced even more abundantly than in Minnesota. The trouble with growing alfalfa seed here is that it is a cold country and the seed does not produce very well. There are some years when even this alfalfa does not produce much seed, but ever since I saw these fields and saw the evidence among the Carver county farmers that this was a hardy variety, it has been a very interesting matter. I might say for Mr. Lyman that he has had an option on the seed for two or three years. But the seed crops have been so poor, owing to these peculiar years that alfalfa would not produce much seed. Earlier this variety in Carver county produced from 3½ to 4 bushels of seed per acre.

I want to say further, gentlemen, that we have begun breeding this variety of alfalfa, and we will breed it just as extensively as we can get funds to use in propagating and breeding it, and make it still more hardy and make it a free seeding variety under our cold conditions. If we can turn this state into an alfalfa country like California or Colorado, it is a good business proposition to do so.

Question: What is the seed worth per bushel?

Prof. Hays: There is no settled value now. When the seed is available it will be worth what it cost Mr. Lyman and a good respectable profit besides. You can raise this seed and in turn get a high price for it, and at the same time distribute the seed more widely. If we have a good variety, let us put a high price on it so that the men raising it for seed can make a profit. It is just as true with wheat and corn as with alfalfa, that high prices for seed of a variety highly accredited will greatly assist in bringing about its wide introduction.

Prof. Spillman: Mr. President, I am glad to see Professor Hays take the stand that he does. We haven't the free distribution of seed in the Department of Agriculture except that which is distributed by the Congressmen. The Department no longer distributes seeds free. I want to say a word about growing alfalfa seed. I cannot help but be impressed with this paper read by Mr. Lyman this afternoon as of vital importance to the future of agriculture in the State of Minnesota and in the Dakotas. We have been searching the world for a variety of alfalfa that would do just what this variety does. We sent a man to Turkestan this summer at great expense to get something of that kind, but here we know we have what we sought. Let me make a suggestion which we have gleaned from our experience in growing alfalfa seed. We engaged a farm to grow forty acres of Turkestan alfalfa seed. We sowed it in the usual way, and I found around the margin of the field it grew some seed, but in the middle of the field there was no seed, and I noticed among the plants in our experimental grounds that the marginal plants yielded a great deal of seed while the central plants yielded almost no seed, and now we plant in rows of 18 inches apart and we get four times as much seed per acre by that method of planting as we do by planting in the ordinary way for hay. That is when the plants are given room to grow and develop, they produce four times as much seed as when planted thickly. I merely throw out this suggestion to some of you who may plant alfalfa seed. The value of that seed represents more than a million dollars to the State of Minnesota. The alfalfa plant according to my estimation is going to be in the future the most important forage plant on the American continent, unless it is possibly corn; but within the next fifteen years, if it continues half of its present prosperity, it is going ahead of every other forage plant in this country except corn, and I would not be surprised if some day it exceeded the value of corn. We have been searching for protein to feed our live stock. Now alfalfa is the ideal protein plant. When you have alfalfa hay you don't have to buy linseed oil cake; in fact cornmeal is worth more than linseed oil cake when you are feeding alfalfa hay. Now that means a great deal to the Minnesota farmers. (Applause.)

Prof. Hays: I just want to say one word in reply to a question in regard to the soil suitable for growing alfalfa. Alfalfa does well on any good corn soil. You know what that means. You know you can grow corn on almost any soil in Minnesota. The only place that alfalfa ought not to be sown is where it is wet. Alfalfa will not stand wet weather; and furthermore it is like the turkey, it is tender when it is young. You want to sow it where it will have a good chance in its early growth, for two or three months, and it is better to sow without a nurse crop, because it will catch better. If you can raise some of this seed and can offer it at any reasonable price you will be pretty sure to find a market for it in Minnesota, Wisconsin and East to Maine.

Prof. Spillman: In planting alfalfa seed for hay I wouldn't think of planting it in rows, but when planting for seed only, plant in rows. I have seen great fields that if they had produced two bushels of seed to the acre, would have been more profitable than the hay crop, because of the high price of this seed of a rare variety, while the same crop the same year on the same ground if sown in rows would have produced a far heavier crop of seed at a much greater profit. Don't get the idea that I would recommend sowing in rows for hay, because it would not produce good hay in that way.

Question: How soon do you sow in the spring?

Prof. Spillman: If you permit me to answer that question. I cannot give any dates, because the seasons vary so much in different years; then the same date that applies here would not apply 100 miles north of here. There are some that sow early in the spring; some in the middle of spring, and some late in the spring. My practice has been to sow very early in the spring; earlier than corn; in barley sowing time.

The Chair: We have heard considerable talk on this alfalfa question, which goes to show the amount of interest you all have in the question of seed. We have here what we term the Minnesota Field Crop Breeders' Association. We have today adopted a constitution and by-laws, and put the fees at one dollar per year. We have a good many subjects to bring up that we know are of vital interest. Now there are farmers here that have been growing grain perhaps for years that have been raising live stock, and previous to getting into live stock they raised wild oats, and quack grass, and things like that, until they are unable on those fields to get any good clean seed, and now after raising live stock for a few years they have cleaned those fields up. Now the question arises, where are you going to get good, clean seed that is absolutely pure, to put on those lands? For this purpose we have organized the Field Crop Growers' Association for the dissemination of knowledge as to the best seeds, and distributing among the people such seed as has been spoken of this afternoon, and for the encouragement of the best varieties of the different crop seeds raised, and we find by increasing our knowledge in this work, and by being able to furnish the seed, we are not only doubling the yield of our land but producing better food for our live stock.

PART IV

*The First American Agricultural
Revolution, 1861-1914*

20

Establishment of the United States
Department of Agriculture

Proposals for an agricultural branch of the national government were made as early as 1776. George Washington recommended the establishment of such an agency in 1796, Elkanah Watson later urged a related plan, and John Quincy Adams gave the idea some support by directing consuls and naval officers abroad to send home seeds and improved breeds of domestic animals.

In 1836, Henry L. Ellsworth, Commissioner of Patents, on his own initiative undertook to distribute seeds obtained from abroad to enterprising farmers. In reporting his activities to Congress, Ellsworth suggested that greater provision be made for the agricultural interests of the nation. Three years later Congress appropriated $1,000 of Patent Office fees for collecting agricultural statistics, conducting agricultural investigations, and distributing seeds. Ellsworth then established an Agricultural Division in the Patent Office, which in 1840 distributed 30,000 packages of seeds, and in 1842 published some of the farm statistics that had been collected in connection with the census of 1840. By 1854 the division employed a chemist, a botanist, and an entomologist, and was conducting experiments. In 1856 a 5-acre garden was obtained and investigations into the cultivation of sorghum and tea were begun.

Farm editors, agricultural leaders, and officers of the numerous county and state agricultural societies were far from unanimous in their praise of the efforts of the Commissioner of Patents to aid agriculture. Some believed that agriculture should be represented by a separate agency; others were opposed to any effort by the federal government to aid farmers as a group. Leadership in the movement for the establishment of a department of agriculture was assumed by the United States Agricultural Society, established in 1851. Its resolutions and memorials to Congress, combined with the pledges of the Republican Party in 1860 for agrarian reform, led to the establishment of the department.

On May 15, 1862, President Lincoln signed a bill creating an independent Department of Agriculture, headed by a Commissioner responsible to the President. Congress stated in the bill: ". . . there is hereby established at the seat of the Government of the United States a Department of Agriculture, the general designs and duties of which shall be to acquire and to diffuse among the people of the United States useful information on subjects connected with agriculture in the most general and comprehensive sense of that word, and to procure, propagate, and distribute among the people new and valuable seeds and plants." The act further directed "the Commissioner of Agriculture to acquire and preserve in his Department all information concerning agriculture which he can obtain by means of books and correspondence, and by practical and scientific experiments, (accurate records of which experiments shall be kept in his office,) by the collection of statistics, and by any other appropriate means within his power; to collect, as he may be able, new and valuable seeds and plants; to test, by cultivation, the value of such of them as may require such tests; to propagate such as may be worthy of propagation, and to distribute them among agriculturists." This law, very broad in scope, has remained the basic authority for the Department to the present time. The Department was raised to cabinet status in 1889.

Commissioner Ellsworth Discusses Government Aid to Agriculture

U.S. Patent Office, *Annual Report*, 1837, pp. 4-6 (Washington, 1837).

Of late, however, inventors have directed their attention, with peculiar interest, to the improvement of the implements of *agriculture*, and many labor-saving machines have been patented, which are of the highest utility to the husbandman. These are rapidly increasing; and it is scarcely possible to conjecture to what extent the labor of the agriculturist may be diminished, and the products of the country increased, by these improvements.

Already, the process of sowing, of mowing, and of reaping, is successfully performed by horse-power; and inventors are sanguine in the belief (and probably not without reason) that the time is not far distant when ploughing machines will be driven by steam, and steam-power applied to many other operations of the husbandman. Implements of this kind will all be collected and exhibited at the Patent Office, and, from the resort of thousands to the seat of Government during the session of Congress, a knowledge of their use and practical application will be extended over the whole country. A subject intimately connected with this, is the aid which husbandry might derive from the establishment of a regular system for the selection and distribution of grain and seeds of the choicest varieties for agricultural purposes.

For commerce and manufactures, much has been done; for agriculture, the parent of both, and the ultimate dependence of the nation, much remains to be done. Husbandry seems to be viewed as a natural blessing, that needs no aid from legislation. Like the air we breathe, and the element of water, which sustain life, the productions of the soil are regarded by too many as common bounties of Providence, to be gratefully enjoyed, but without further thought or reflection. Were the two former susceptible of the same improvement with the latter, who would not rejoice to enroll his name high on the list of philanthropists, by making the first experiment?

This subject has been forced on the attention of the undersigned by those who are engaged in improving our implements of husbandry. The Patent Office is crowded with men of enterprise, who, when they bring the models of their improvements in such implements, are eager to communicate a knowledge of every other kind of improvement in agriculture, and especially new and valuable varieties of seeds and plants. Hence, the undersigned has been led to receive and distribute, during the last two years, many articles of this kind which have been committed to his care; and experience has induced him to believe that there is no spot in the Union so favorable to this object as the seat of Government.

The great desideratum at the present time seems to be, that some place should be designated and known as the depository of all articles of this kind, and from whence they may be dispensed to every part of the United States.

Our citizens who are led by business or pleasure into foreign countries, and especially the officers of our navy and others in public employment abroad, would feel a pride in making collections of valuable plants and seeds, if they could be sure of seeing the fruits of their labors accrue to the benefit of the nation at large. But, hitherto, they have had no means of distributing, to any extent, the valuable productions of other climates, which patriotism or curiosity has led them to introduce into our country. To a great extent, they have perished on their hands, for want of some means of imparting to the public the benefit they had designed to confer. Those who have not considered the subject in its wide details, are very imperfectly qualified to judge of its importance.

The introduction of a new variety of wheat promises the most gratifying results in securing that important and indispensable production from the destructive effects of our severe winters.

A short time since, the most eastern State of our Union was, in a measure, dependent on others for the bread-stuffs. That State is now becoming able to supply its own wants, and will soon have a surplus for exportation; and this is effected by the extensive introduction of spring wheat. Among the varieties of this wheat, however, there is great room for selection: there is at least 20 per cent. difference, if regard is paid to the quality and quantity of the crop.

From experiments made the last summer, there can be no doubt that the crop of Indian corn may be improved at least one-third, without any extra labor; and this, effected by a due regard only to the selection of seeds.

And here it may be mentioned, that an individual has devoted twenty-five years to this single object; and, from our common Indian corn, has produced a new variety, which, if distributed as it ought to be, may prove a great benefit to the husbandman and to the country.

From the samples transmitted to the Patent Office, especially from the shores of lake Superior, there is a moral certainty of a good crop of corn in the higher latitudes, if proper attention is paid to the selection of seeds. Inattention to this subject has lost to the Northern portion of our Union many millions every year. The quantity of flour (wheat or other kind) consumed in the United States is estimated, on the highest authority, at five thousand five hundred millions of pounds: one-half of this is supposed to be wheat; which, at three cents per pound, amounts to over eighty million of dollars; and the remainder, at one and a half cent only, amounts to over forty millions. If to this be added the vast quantity distilled and employed in the arts, and consumed by domestic animals, a conception may be formed of the importance of our crop of grain. If, then, the quantity should be increased only 10 percent. by improving the seed, the annual gain to the country, from this source alone, would not be less than from fifteen to twenty millions of dollars. It is unnecessary to carry out this estimate to the other productions of the vegetable kingdom; the result would be the same in all. The well-directed efforts of a few years might give to this generation what would not otherwise be enjoyed in the present century.

It may not be improper to add, that, if this nation should desire to make her metropolis the seat of science and the arts, this might be easily accomplished. The collections of mineralogical specimens from every section of our widely-extended territory, will, it is believed, furnish a most interesting exhibition, illustrative of the geology of the country and of its mineral resources.

The natural and practical sciences, as well as the arts, have usually found their best patron in the munificence of a wise Government. An apartment in the new building could be appropriated to the above object, in connexion with an agricultural depository.

The undersigned will be pardoned for offering these considerations in favor of agriculture, as they have been forced upon him in the discharge of his official duties; and as Congress has required him to make such suggestions, respecting the interests committed to his care, as may seem important to the public good, he will continue to do all in his power to promote the secondary, though important, object which has thus become, in some degree, connected with the Patent Office; in the full belief that Congress will find it for the public interest, either now or at some future period, to give a more definite character to the measures which have thus been commenced for this most important object.

21

Agricultural Colleges Encouraged by Morrill Land Grant Act of 1862

Many agricultural leaders early saw the need for agricultural education, and in the early 1800's, agricultural societies and farm journals pointed out its desirability. A few agricultural schools and academies, of which the Gardiner Lyceum of Gardiner, Maine, established in 1821, was one of the first, were founded in the first half of the nineteenth century. During the same period, a number of private colleges gave instruction in agriculture and in the application of science to agricultural problems.

The efforts of private institutions were limited, and the proponents of agricultural and industrial education which would be available to all citizens looked to the state governments for aid. State agricultural colleges were established on a permanent basis in Pennsylvania and Michigan as a result of acts of the state legislatures in 1855, in Maryland by an act of 1856, and in Iowa by an act of 1858.

While efforts were being made to establish state-supported institutions, a number of leaders were urging that the federal government assist in making agricultural education generally available. On January 21, 1841, Alden Partridge, president of Norwich University, proposed to Congress that it appropriate funds from the proceeds of the sales of public lands, to be distributed among the states in proportion to their representation in Congress, for the endowment of institutions which would teach the natural and economic sciences as applied to agriculture, engineering, manufactures, and commerce. This appears to be the first definite proposal to Congress of its type.

The activities of Jonathan B. Turner of Jacksonville, Illinois, some ten years after Partridge made his proposal, aroused national interest. Turner suggested in 1848 that agricultural instruction be added to the classical schools, but in 1850 he presented a much broader plan at a Pike County teachers' institute and at a public meeting at Griggsville. His most important statement was at a farmers' convention at Granville, November 18, 1851, where he proposed the establishment of a state-supported industrial university. His address was printed in the *Prairie Farmer* for February, 1852, in the United States Patent Office Report for 1851, and in a number of papers. In the *Prairie Farmer* for March, 1852, Turner suggested that Congress grant public lands to each state for the establishment of industrial universities. In 1853, the Illinois legislature approved a petition to Congress asking for the donation to each state of public lands valued at not less than $500,000, probably the first such public petition. Later, the Illinois plan was discussed and adopted by the United States Agricultural Society.

The influence of Turner, either directly or through the United States Agricultural Society upon Justin S. Morrill, representative in Congress from Vermont, cannot be determined. Morrill claimed complete authorship of his bill for donating public land to the states for colleges of agriculture and the mechanic arts, first introduced on December 14, 1857. The land grant bill was passed in 1859 but was vetoed by President Buchanan on February 26. Reintroduced in 1861, the bill became law with President Lincoln's approval on July 2, 1862.

Credit for this uniquely effective legislation cannot be assigned to any one man. Rather, as Earle D. Ross has so aptly stated, "the act was an epitome and composite of a decade of formative discussion."

Illinois Legislature Petitions Congress to Grant Land for Colleges

"Industrial Education," *Prairie Farmer*, 13: 114. March, 1853.

The friends of this measure will be glad to see, by the accompanying joint Resolutions of our General Assembly, that this principle has been unanimously endorsed by our law makers. An act establishing an Industrial University for Illinois, will doubtless be passed, in good time; whether Congress comes again to our aid, or not. But this measure contains too many popular elements not to find favor with a land-giving Congress, if pressed forward in season. The excellent memorial, on which these resolutions were based, was drawn up by professor Turner, by request of the committee, and signed by the President, and presented in the Senate after the adjournment of the recent industrial convention.

In the House, on Friday, Feb. 5th, Mr. Denio offered the following joint resolution, which was unanimously adopted:

Whereas, The spirit and progress of this age and country demand the culture of the highest order of intellectual attainment, in theoretic and industrial science; and whereas, it is impossible that our commerce and prosperity will continue to increase, without calling into requisition all the elements of internal thrift arising from the labors of the farmer, the mechanic, and the manufacturer, by every fostering effort within the reach of government; and whereas, a system of industrial Universities, liberally endowed in each State of the Union, co-operative with each other, and with the Smithsonian Institution at Washington, would develop a more liberal and practical education among the people, tend the more to intellectualize the rising generation, and eminently conduce to the virtue, intelligence and true glory of our common country; therefore, be it

Resolved, by the House of Representatives, the Senate concurring therein, That our Senators in Congress be instructed, and our Representatives be requested, to use their best exertions to procure the passage of a law of Congress donating to each State in the Union an amount of public lands not less in value than five hundred thousand dollars, for the liberal endowment of a system of Industrial Universities, one in each State in the Union, to co-operate with each other and with the Smithsonian institution at Washington, for the more liberal and practical education of our industrial classes and their teachers; a liberal and varied education, adapted to the manifold wants of a practical and enterprising people, and a provision for such educational facilities, being in manifest concurrence with the intimations of the popular will, it urgently demands the united efforts of our national strength.

Resolved, That the Governor is hereby authorized to forward a copy of the foregoing resolutions to our Senators and Representatives in Congress, and to the Executive and Legislature of each of our sister States, inviting them to co-operate with us in this meritorious enterprise.

22

Homestead Act Passed

The Ordinance of 1785, which established basic principles for the survey and disposal of the public domain, was modified in 1787 in an endeavor to increase sales. Thereafter, the land laws were amended and rewritten every few years, nearly always with the avowed aim of enabling settlers to acquire farms upon more favorable terms. Much land was acquired and sold by speculators, which led to agitation for greater changes in the system.

The culmination of the changes was the passage of a law giving land to actual settlers. The idea was not new; it reached back to colonial days. Petitions for donations were made to the Congress from 1797 on. In 1825, Senator Thomas Hart Benton of Missouri proposed that Congress investigate the idea of giving land to settlers. From that time on, the idea was before Congress at frequent intervals. The Committee on Public Lands of the House of Representatives issued a report in 1828 that clearly foreshadowed the Homestead Act.

Westerners were joined in their support of the homestead idea by many eastern workingmen and reformers. In the late 1830's, George Henry Evans, a labor leader and reformer, developed a land policy which called, basically, for giving land to settlers, with a limitation on the amount of land which might be owned by any one person. Evans organized the National Reform Association in 1844 to carry forward this and other plans. The plan won the support of Horace Greeley, publisher of the *New York Tribune*, who had expressed an interest in western settlement in 1837 when he urged "Go West, young man, go forth into the Country." The constant publicity given by Greeley kept the matter before the public.

In 1848 the Free Soil Party adopted a plank favoring free land. The issue became involved in the sectional struggle in the 1850's, with the Congressmen and Senators from the South consistently voting against the various homestead bills. A bill passed both houses of Congress in 1860, but President Buchanan vetoed it.

The Republican Party, in its 1860 convention, declared for both homesteads and a protective tariff as a compromise between the West and the East. Lincoln's inauguration did not mark the immediate enactment of the homestead bill, for it was not until the Southern delegations withdrew from Congress that the Republican Party had enough votes in both houses to insure its passage. The Homestead Act became law on May 20, 1862. It provided for the giving of 160 acres of the public domain to any person who was the head of a family or over 21 years of age and who was an American citizen or had filed intentions of becoming one. A patent to the land was issued the settler after he had resided on it for five years, had made improvements on it, and paid a nominal registration fee. The settler could gain full title after six months' actual residence and suitable improvement by the payment of $1.25 per acre.

The Homestead Act did not achieve all that its proponents had hoped. It was completely inadaptable to the region to which it applied. In the arid West, 160 acres was too much land for irrigated farming and too little for dry farming or grazing. In addition, the act was not coordinated with other land legislation, which worked at cross purposes for decades. Nevertheless, the Homestead Act stood as a symbol of American democracy to native-born and immigrant alike.

Theory of the Homestead Expressed in Congress in 1828

U.S. Congress, *American State Papers, Public Lands*, vol. 5, pp. 447, 449 (Washington, Gales & Seaton, 1860).

Mr. DUNCAN, from the Committee on Public Lands, to whom was referred a resolution directing an inquiry into the expediency of reducing and graduating the price of public lands, and of making donations to actual settlers, reported:

That their most diligent attention to the subject has been excited, as well on account of the magnitude of the national interests involved in the inquiry as on account of the strong solicitations of the legislative memorials of the several States and Territories of the United States, and the petitions of the people which have been presented to Congress so repeatedly upon this subject. . . .

That small tracts of eighty acres be given to the heads of such families as will cultivate, improve, and reside on the same for five years. This proposition has recommended itself to the consideration of your committee by a knowledge of the fact that there are many families who are neither void of industry nor of good moral habits, who have met with a usual share of the difficulties always accompanying the settlement of a new country, and who, living very remote from market, never expect to see the day arrive when they will be enabled to save enough, with all their efforts, from their means of actual support, to purchase a farm and pay for it in cash. Besides, your committee believe that such small earnings applied to the improvement and cultivation of small tracts, scattered through the public domain, would be as advantageous to the public as though they should be paid directly into the treasury. No axiom in political economy is sounder than the one which declares that

the wealth and strength of a country, and more especially of a re-
public, consists not so much in the number of its citizens as in their
employments, their capability of bearing arms, and of sustaining
the burdens of taxation whenever the public exigencies shall require
it. The poor furnish soldiers, and an experience shows that the
patriotism which exists apart from an interested love of country
cannot be relied upon. The affections of good citizens are always
mingled with their homes and placed upon the country which contains their fields and their gardens. . . .

23

First Grange Organized

The Patrons of Husbandry, popularly known as the Grange because
its branches were called Granges, was organized in 1867 through the
efforts of Oliver Hudson Kelley. It became the first nationwide organization to reach a large number of farmers. In his first printed circular
Kelley suggested that the main objective of the order would be to encourage and advance education in all branches of agriculture, but he
also emphasized in other writings the establishment of a cordial and
social fraternity among farmers all over the country which would be
promoted by secret rituals and degrees.

    As local and state granges became active, some of their leaders under-
took to promote cooperative buying and selling. It was but a short step
then to organize political activity, aimed primarily at railroad regulation, particularly by the states. This activity, the mainspring of the
Grange from about 1871 to 1880, resulted in some immediate success and
eventual success for most of the programs advocated. However, the
Grange itself began to decline as a political force and in membership
after 1875. Most of its economic activities were discontinued, and it
became stabilized as a social and fraternal order with a continuing educational program. Little change in membership occurred until the early
1900's, when a period of steady growth began. In 1919 the National
Grange opened a legislative headquarters in Washington, which has
been maintained since that time.

Kelley Discusses Organization of the Grange

Oliver H. Kelley, *Origin and Progress of the Order of the Patrons of Husbandry in the United States; A History from 1866 to 1873*, pp. 11-15, 17-20, 38-40, 44-45, 48, 123, 129-130, (Philadelphia, J. A. Wagenseller, 1875).

It is generally acknowledged that the idea of the Order of the Patrons of Husbandry originated with the writer. From its inception he has given it his whole attention, and hence claims to be thoroughly informed regarding the work, as it progressed, up to the time of permanent organization of the National Grange, at Georgetown, D. C., in January, 1873. Repeated calls from many associates, for authentic history, prompts him to comply, and he has woven together, in these pages, facts that he hopes will be interesting, and which show an instance of success, through perseverance, in a good cause.

Excessive drought in Northern Minnesota during the years 1862-63, by which I was a considerable sufferer, and the favorable reception of my newspaper contributions, induced me to accept a proposition to spend the winter of 1864 in Washington, and through the favor of Senator Ramsey, I received a clerkship in the Department of Agriculture. . . .

January 13th, 1866, I left Washington on my long cherished trip, bearing the following commission:

Department of Agriculture,
Washington, D. C., January 1st, 1866

To O. H. Kelley, Esq.:

Sir:—The relations of the Southern States with the Government for several years past having prevented this Department from obtaining the usual statistical and other information from those States, and a prevailing desire for reliable information being manifested on the part of the people, I have determined, with the advice and authority of his Excellency, the President of the United States, to appoint you an Agent of this Department, to proceed immediately through the States lately in hostility against the Government, to procure such information, and report the same to this Department for publication. Having reference to the enclosed instructions, you will immediately enter upon the discharge of your duties as such Agent.

Isaac Newton, Commissioner

My instructions required me to communicate at regular intervals with the Commissioner, which was done promptly, also taking the precaution to keep for myself a daily record of my trip and observations. . . .

While traveling, I was enjoying a lively correspondence with many at the North, and mentioned, in a letter to my niece, Miss C. A. Hall, the idea of a Secret Society of Agriculturists, as an element to restore kindly feelings among the people. At Mobile I received her reply, in which she expressed sympathy for the women of the South, and much encouraged my suggestion that an organization of the farmers of the country might prove a blessing. At Savannah I met P. H. Woodward, with whom I spent several days, and then accompanied him to Augusta and Atlanta. From January until May, I was in motion through the several States. The idea of association was fast getting fixed in my mind, and I remember comparing the Mississippi and its tributaries to a national organization and its subordinates. . . .

Mr. Saunders informed us of his intended visit to St. Louis, to attend the meeting of the United States Pomological Society, and said if we would give him in writing an outline of the proposed society, he would submit it to some of those he should meet, and see how it would take.

I gave him the following

OUTLINE OF THE ORDER:

August, 1867.

William Saunders, Esq.,—Dear Sir:

Notwithstanding a large majority of the people of this country are directly engaged in Agriculture, I regret to say in my travels North and South, East and West, I find there is a great lack of interest on the part of farmers,—a visible want of energy on their part to favor progressive agriculture. Where we find one who reads agricultural books and papers, there are ten or more who consider "book farming," as they term it, nonsense. This average is too small. In one of our Western States, after making a general investigation, I found the circulation of *purely* agricultural papers was but one to every two hundred and thirty inhabitants; and libraries of fifty bound volumes were exceptions, yet but very few who could not read and write. Their system of farming was the same as that handed down by generations gone by, with the exception that economy prompted them to use reaping and threshing machines. Of the science of agriculture, the natural laws that govern the growth of plants and kindred subjects of pleasing and vital interest to farmers, when once they turn their attention to them, there was ninety per cent who were totally ignorant.

Agricultural editors have worked faithfully for years, to induce our rural population to read and think—their increasing circulation (that of older papers) indicates that they have made some progress, but we see there is something wanted to produce an excitement which, when once created, we can throw on fuel and increase the flame.

Agricultural societies have done much good by establishing fairs; yet these are generally the work of a few right-minded, enthusiastic men, aided oftentimes by aspiring politicians. At these fairs the great attractions generally are implements and works of art, while the products of the soil offer the least attractions, and to bring the farmers out in any numbers, it is actually necessary to introduce, as a prominent feature, horse-races and numerous side-shows.

I think we can revolutionize all this, and I suggest the project of organizing an Order to embrace in its membership only those persons directly interested in cultivating the soil. I should make it a secret order, with several degrees, and signs and passwords. The lectures in each degree should be practical, appertaining to agricultural work, at the same time convey a moral lesson. While the order would aim to advance agriculture to a higher rank, by encouraging education, it would at the same time naturally embrace the benefits to its members guaranteed by Masonry. Every tool used by farmers and gardeners could be emblems of the Order in some degree, and each convey a practical and moral illustration. Being a rural organization, lodge furniture need not be extravagant, yet appropriate.

Of membership, I should advocate both sexes being admitted, having separate degrees for the ladies, yet all meet in common. Making the expense of each degree but one dollar, would place it within the means of all. The secrecy would lend an interest and peculiar fascination, while the material for manufacturing new degrees to keep up an interest, would be inexhaustible; and here I can safely say no Order could surpass this in sublimity of the degrees that can be introduced.

My plan of work is this: Having a complete, but temporary organization of an United States lodge, dispensations are to be granted to lecturers to organize in several counties in each State; these county organizations to elect one delegate each to the State organization, and the State organization one each to the United States. As soon as the majority of the States shall be represented, the temporary organization shall be permanently organized by the United States delegates. A small fee from each membership shall be annually paid to the united organization, and this will defray its expenses.

The grand head of the organizations will be an auxiliary to the department of agriculture; and as soon as this shall become a permanent department, with its Secretary in the Cabinet, it seems to me Government can aid materially in advancing the agricultural interests of the entire country. I should object to any State, or United States delegate, holding any Government or State political appointment, while serving in that capacity, and thus keep it free from contamination. I should advocate the department sending out agents, men of known ability, for the collection of statistical information, who should be versed as botanists, horticulturists, entomologists, etc., who should deliver free lectures for the organizations, and to which the Order should invite the public. In this way, by practical lectures properly illustrated, a vast amount of good could be affected through appropriations of Congress, and hardly any member of Congress would wish to vote against appropriations that would be called for by the department.

There is nothing now that binds the farmers together, and I think such an Order would, with the most cheerful results. Its tendency would be to encourage the circulation of our agricultural newspapers, which insure the co-operation of the editors. It will increase the demand for fruit trees and nursery products, securing the support of horticulturists, etc. We only need to secure the approval of our leading agriculturists. If such gentlemen as Col. Wilder, Barry, yourself and others, besides the editors of the agricultural press, will endorse the movement, it can possibly be inaugurated by the middle of September.

Trusting these views will meet with your approval, I remain

Your sincere friend,

Fraternally,

O. H. Kelley.

P. S.—I venture to enclose the initiatory degree for your perusal. . . .

I scratched off the following for a rough circular, which was the first ever sent out. Of these I had three hundred printed at Polkin-horn's, on Seventh street, Washington, November 1st:

"A number of gentlemen engaged in Agriculture and its kindred branches in different States, are now perfecting a Ritual for an Order, to be composed wholly of persons, male and female, directly interested in Agricultural pursuits.

"The Order will secure to its members all the advantages of Masonry, but while that is speculative, this will be operative; its main object being to encourage and advance education in all branches of Agriculture.

"The Order will have its 'Lodges,' known as 'Temples of Industry,' or similar appellation. The work in a 'Temple' will be divided into four degrees.

"The ceremonies of passing from one degree to the other are made pleasing and instructive. Every tool used in Agriculture has its appropriate lecture, the aim being to instruct practically and morally in every possible way, and also add an interest to the most noble of all occupations—the cultivation of the soil.

"It is believed that by admitting the young folks of both sexes at fourteen or sixteen years of age, it will have a tendency to instill in their minds a fondness for rural life, and prevent in a great measure so many of them flocking to the cities, where all occupations are now crowded, and at the same time depriving the country of that class of young men so much needed there.

"The ceremonies in the degrees for the ladies are slightly different but of the same nature, and intended to lighten and render their household duties more pleasing.

"The whole, it is believed, will do much towards elevating our occupation, as well as establishing a unity of sentiment among the farmers of the country, and materially increase the circulation of publications devoted to the interests of agriculture, and consequent increase of knowledge.

"Politics and Religion are *not* subjects of discussion. Private work of the Order will occupy one evening each month. Public meetings for lectures and discussions are proposed to be held once a week.

"Libraries and Museums (the latter to contain among other things samples of each year's crop of all cereal productions,) are considered necessary appendages to each Temple.

"It is designed to have at least one Temple in each county, with one delegate from each to the State Temple: these will send one delegate each to the National Temple, which is to be the head of the Order. Persons holding office under Government cannot be delegates to either the State or National Temple.

"Should such an organization meet your approval, and you see fit to offer any suggestions to enable the originators to make further improvements, before it is introduced to the public, the same will be most cordially received and duly considered.

"Please address"

These I signed and sent out to any persons whose Post-office address I received, and my memorandum book shows twenty-eight from Mr. Saunders,—thirty-nine from Ireland and others, and the balance to names I found otherwise. . . .

October 24th, Bartlett wrote me he was busy digging potatoes, and I must be patient. I replied as follows:

November 1st, 1867.

Dear Brother:

To facilitate correspondence with others whom we wish to interest in our Order, we have had three hundred of the enclosed slips printed, which can be put in letters. Those enclosed, use as you see fit.

The name of the "League of Husbandry" has been suggested as a name for the Order. It is submitted for your opinion. If any original name in the place of "League" could be substituted, it would be better. "Husbandry" comprises the work nicely, according to Webster. Within a week, we propose to send out about two hundred of these printed slips to Agricultural Editors and others, for their opinions of the work.

Yours truly,

O. H. Kelley.

November 4th, in a short letter I wrote to Bartlett, I find the following:

"How would it do to call the 'Lodges' 'Granges?' For instance, 'Blue Fly Grange of the League of Husbandry.' Grange and Husbandry being used according to Webster's Unabridged."

This word grange I took from the name of a novel, advertised at that time. In his reply of November 6th, he writes:

"I have written the first degree work (except the lecture of Bacchus), making such alterations as my fancy dictated. I shall take hold of the third and fourth degree work now, but would prefer to have the second degree before doing much with them, so they will not clash. I have received the printed slips, and will try to make good use of them. How about the name? How would 'Patrons of Industry' be? I almost fancy it to be good. I believe it is original, at any rate.

Fraternally,

Anson Bartlett.

That will settle the question as to where the name originated, for, on the receipt, I substituted the word "Husbandry. . . ."

At a meeting, called by previous notice, held at the office of Wm. Saunders, November 15th, 1867, at 4 P.M., for the purpose of organizing an Order of Agriculture in the United States, by unanimous consent, Wm. M. Ireland was called to the Chair, and O. H. Kelley chosen Secretary. The object of the meeting having been stated, the work that had been done since August 5th was laid before the meeting. . . .

It was decided that the name of the Order be "Patrons of Husbandry," and the branches of it to be known as Granges, instead of Lodges. . . .

During the last of August, I had met Col. D. A. Robertson, of St. Paul, at various times, and had several conversations relative to the Order. . . .

Among other advantages which may be derived from the Order, can be mentioned, systematic arrangements for procuring and disseminating, in the most expeditious manner, information relative to crops, demand and supply, prices, markets, and transportation throughout the country, and for the establishment of depots for the sale of special or general products in the cities; also for the purchase and exchange of stock, seeds, and desired varieties of plants and trees, and for the purpose of procuring help at home or from abroad and situations for persons seeking employment; also for ascertaining and testing the merits of newly invented farming implements, and those not in general use, and for detecting and exposing those that are unworthy and for protecting, by all available means, the farming interests from fraud and deception of every kind.

In conclusion, we desire that agricultural societies shall keep step with the music of the age, and keep pace with improvements in the reaping machine and steam engine. In this Order we expect to accomplish these results. Every Grange is in intimate relation with its neighboring Granges, and these with the State Grange, and the State Granges are in unity with the National Grange. Valuable information, and benefits enjoyed by one, are communicated to all. The old style of Farmers' Clubs, like the old sickle and flail, were very good in their day, but they are of the past, and are too far behind all other enterprise in the progress of civilization. Hence the necessity of this new Order.

O. H. Kelley,
Secretary of the National Grange.

It was on this circular we based the real foundation of the Order, and on North Star Grange as the leader in a forlorn hope. To Col. D. A. Robertson is the credit due for establishing this Grange, which, up to this date, has never missed a meeting.

24

Science of Human Nutrition Established

Mankind is the ultimate consumer of all the products of agriculture. In many countries, at many times, famine and starvation have resulted when food has not been available in sufficient quantity to sustain life. The United States has been spared this disaster, except in isolated instances, yet many Americans have lived shorter, less productive lives because they lacked knowledge or could not afford a diet that would provide energy and health.

Until well into the nineteenth century, people commonly thought that all foods had much the same value. During the 1830's, a reformer, Sylvester Graham, urged Americans to eat plainer, bulkier foods. He obtained converts to his theories, and medical men began to concern themselves with food problems. However, most people regarded those concerned with such matters as cranks.

The beginnings of the modern science of nutrition came in 1869, when Wilbur O. Atwater received a Ph.D. degree from Yale University on a thesis dealing with the chemical composition of different varieties of maize. Atwater then studied chemistry in Germany, and, after serving as director of the first state agricultural experiment station, became the first director of the Office of Experiment Stations of the U.S. Department of Agriculture.

While working in the Office of Experiment Stations, Atwater devoted much time to nutrition studies and encouraged others to carry on research in the same field. Atwater published tables showing the chemical composition of foods, developed ideal diets to meet varying needs, and, with others, developed the respiration calorimeter for the study of the energy relations of nutrition to the human body.

On a broad basis, nutritionists were concerned with obtaining the best possible returns in economic progress and social welfare from the national food production. The problems included determining what the body needs in its food, what nutrients the different foods supply, how the nutrients are utilized by the body, what diets are actually used in different regions, and what foods and methods of food preparation furnish the most economical and healthful diet. Fifty years after Atwater's death, scientists were still concerned with these basic problems.

An Analysis of an American Food Appears

Wilbur O. Atwater, "On the Proximate Composition of Several Varieties of American Maize," *American Journal of Science and Arts*, ser. 2, 48: 352, 358-360. November, 1869.

The four varieties of Indian corn analyzed are as follows:

A. *Early Dutton Corn.*—An early variety, yellow in color, twelve rowed, kernels rather small. Ears medium size. One of the most common varieties of early corn in New England.

B. *The common Yellow Corn* of New England and the eastern States, also called Canada Corn.—Eight rowed, kernels and ears of good size.

C. *King Philip Corn,* sometimes called Rhode Island Corn.—Brown-red color, eight rowed, ears and kernels often quite large.

D. *Stowell's Evergreen Sweet Corn.*—Specimens are sold under this name, having twelve and sixteen rows, ears short and thick.

Preparation for analysis.—The corn ground in an ordinary drug mill. The mill was carefully cleaned by grinding corn therein until the meal came through clean in appearance. For the ash-determinations, a portion of each sort was coarsely crushed in the mill. Another portion was then ground quite fine for the other investigations, in which the result could not be appreciably affected by an amount of impurity from the mill, not detectable by the eye. Considerable care was taken to insure a thorough mixture of the material, it having been noticed on cleaning the mill before the grinding of each specimen that a portion of the finely divided substance adhered to the interior, which portion it was feared might come from the softer and more easily pulverized part of the kernels. In a number of cases it was found necessary to grind the meal still finer with sand in a porcelain mortar. The specimens for analysis were all ground at the same time, and set aside for use in well closed bottles. . . .

The complete (mean) analyses stand as follows, taking the sugar and gum as estimated with Fehling's solution and reckoning starch by difference:—

	A.	B.	C.	D.
				Stowell's
	Early	Common	King	Evergreen
	Dutton.	Yellow.	Philip.	Sweet.
Water, ...	8.08	10.52	9.79	10.86
Albuminoids, ...	9.62	9.72	11.87	11.10
Sugar, ...	3.00	4.78	3.05	11.64
Gum, ...	4.22	2.36	4.80	4.64
Starch, ...	65.40	64.49	62.23	49.58
Fat, ...	5.67	4.42	4.45	7.66
Cellulose, ...	2.52	2.40	2.21	2.63
Ash, ...	1.52	1.31	1.60	1.89
	100.00	100.00	100.00	100.00

Subjoined are the mean percentages of the proximate elements calculated upon dry substance:

	A.	B.	C.	D.
Albuminoids, ...	10.46	10.86	13.16	12.45
Sugar, ...	3.26	5.34	3.38	13.06
Gum, ...	4.59	2.64	5.32	5.21
Starch, ...	71.13	72.08	68.99	55.62
Fat, ...	6.16	4.94	4.93	8.59
Cellulose, ...	2.74	2.68	2.45	2.95
Ash, ...	1.66	1.46	1.77	2.12
	100.00	100.00	100.00	100.00

In these analyses the percentage of water and ash alone can be regarded as quite correct. The percentage of albuminoids must be considered as a close approximation to the truth. The figures given for "sugar" and "gum" (aqueous extract) are likewise probably not far from right. They include, however, a little of some soluble albuminoid and possibly soluble starch—the "amiduline" of F. Schulze and "amylogen" of Jessen. The cellulose is much lower than most chemists have found. Thus Poggiale, Payne and Polsen obtained respectively 4.5, 9 and 14.9 to 20.4 per cent of fiber. That these figures are erroneous must be concluded from simple ocular investigation. Fresenius, using Peligot's method obtained 1.5 per cent. Bibra rejects Peligot's method as yielding too little cellulose, but the numerous analyses executed by the German Agricultural Chemists within recent years indicate that its results do not vary widely from the truth. The error in the percentage of starch (insoluble), which is determined by difference, cannot probably exceed 2 or 3 per cent.

The only detailed investigations upon Indian corn by American chemists with which I am acquainted, are those of J. H. Salisbury, Trans. N.Y. State Ag. Soc., 1848, p. 678, and those of C. T. Jackson, U.S. Patent Office Report, 1857, p. 160, and Geology of New Hampshire, pp. 256 et seq. These investigations, the former of which, especially, was quite extended, were unfortunately made for the most part by methods too imperfect to yield valuable results. I append an analysis by Salisbury, above report, p. 779, of "Yellow Corn," the same variety as B of the present article, also one of "Rhode Island Sweet Corn," same report, p. 784.

	Yellow Corn.	R.I. Sweet Corn
Water, ...	11.18	10.22
Albumen, ...	6.46	13.00
Casein, ...	.12	2.64
Zein or gluten, ...	7.32	3.68
Sugar and extract, ...	11.87	18.08
Sugar, ...	.65	2.72
Dextrin or gum, ...	6.28	12.32
Starch, ...	42.03	15.16
Oil, ...	4.35	9.92
Fiber, ...	9.36	12.80
Matter separated from fiber by weak solution of potash, ...	.44	.24
Ash, ...	not given	not given
	100.06	100.78

The following is an analysis by Jackson, Patent Office Report, 1857, p. 161, of King Philip Corn.

Water, ...	10.0
Gluten or zein, ...	5.0
Casein and albumen, ...	2.0
Dextrine and glucose, ...	1.5

Starch, ... 54.5
Fat oil, ... 4.2
Cellulose, ... 17.3
Undetermined, ash, &c., ... 2.0
                                                          ————
                                                          100.00

As seen above, Dr. Salisbury found in Sweet Corn 12.32 per cent of dextrin or gum and 13.00 per cent of albumen, and in the article referred to attributes the shrivelling of the kernels to the loss of water in the drying of these bodies. It cannot be doubted that the estimations were erroneous.

In "The Geology of New Hampshire," page 259, Dr. Jackson reports the amount of oil in different varieties of corn as varying from 6 to 11 per cent, the latter amount being found in the Canada Corn (B of this paper). In the same article, p. 257, he states that the oil in this variety as in several others, is confined chiefly to the endosperm, whereas Lenz and myself find it nearly all in the chit. On page 258 Dr. Jackson "is able to prove that the popping of corn" is due entirely to the decomposition of the oil and the formation of carburetted hydrogen gas. But it is a matter of experience that sweet corn which is remarkable for its large content of oil, expands only very slightly in "popping". On page 257, Dr. Jackson mentions "a beautiful and new application of chemistry" by which the use of qualitative tests, "iodine," "sulphate of ammonia," &c., "we may easily cause any grain to point out the extent and precise limits of each of its ingredients and by the eye we can form a pretty correct estimate of their relative proportions in different seeds." It would be ungracious to notice these statements, were it not that they are frequently quoted as a part of our standard knowledge on this subject.

It will be seen from my analyses that the three first varieties of corn which are quite similar in general appearance and in the consistency and structure of the kernel, are almost identical in composition, while the sweet corn is much poorer in starch and richer in sugar and gum as well as in fat. I hope to have an opportunity in the future of extending my investigations in this direction so as to accomplish more perfect separations and also to examine a large number of varieties of American maize.

25

Bonanza Farming in the Red River Valley

Large-scale farming has been a characteristic of American agriculture. From the first settlements, American farms were on a large scale as compared with European farms because land was available at little or no cost. As agricultural tools and techniques improved, farmers, particularly in the West, tended to operate larger tracts rather than to intensify efforts on smaller units. The changes in agriculture centering around the Civil War accelerated this tendency.

The Red River Valley in North Dakota and Minnesota became, during the 1870's and 1880's, one of the world's most spectacular examples of large-scale farming. The region was particularly suited to growing hard spring wheat. This wheat came into great demand after 1870 when a new process made it possible to produce a fine grade of flour at one grinding. In 1874 the Hudson's Bay Company brought a horse-powered thresher into the Valley, and in the same year a flour mill was erected at Moorhead, Minnesota. Meanwhile, the Northern Pacific Railroad was forced to suspend its road building at Bismarck, North Dakota, because of financial difficulties. The Panic of 1873 made it impossible both for the railroad to raise money and to sell the land it had been granted by the federal government. The general land agent of the railroad persuaded the president and a director of the company to exchange some of their railroad bonds for eighteen sections of land in the Valley.

In the spring of 1875, Oliver Dalrymple, an experienced wheat farmer of Minnesota, contracted to take charge of the land owned by the railway officials. He plowed two sections of prairie sod that summer, and harvested 32,000 bushels of wheat in 1876, a yield of 23 bushels to the acre, as his first crop. Dalrymple got 25 bushels to the acre from 4,500 acres in 1877. The spectacular yields, the extensive use of machinery, and the appearance of many accounts of Dalrymple's achievements, such as the one reprinted here, led others to undertake similar operations. In 1880 there were 82 farms of more than 1,000 acres each in the Red River Valley. A large number of them contained more than 10 sections. Large holdings increased in number for some years, although after 1883 a series of dry years and low prices discouraged the bonanza farmers. By the 1890's most of the large single-crop farms had given way to smaller, diversified holdings.

Dalrymple's First Year

"Wheat Growing in Pembina," *St. Paul and Minneapolis* (Minn.) *Pioneer-Press and Tribune.* Aug. 13, 1876.

A gentleman who came down from the North Pacific yesterday, gives the following interesting notes in relation to Dalrymple's great wheat farm at Casselton:

The amount of ground sown to wheat this spring was thirteen hundred acres. Harvesting commenced on Monday, with nine Wood's Self Binders. The machines are run for fifteen hours without rest, except the ordinary stops for oiling, lunch and dinner, and the result per day is one hundred and eighty acres. One man is employed to each team, and twelve men follow the machines, shocking the wheat as fast as it is cut. The entire thirteen hundred acres were to be cut and shocked during the week; stacking and threshing will of course follow. Mr. Dalrymple informed the gentlemen that the cost of the wire for binding would not exceed thirty-five cents per acre. The cost of the nine three horse teams, and of the twenty-one men required to manage the teams and shock the grain can be readily estimated. It will be seen that Mr. Dalrymple is harvesting his crop for about one fifth of the cost required under the system in vogue ten years ago. At the time harvesting commenced it was estimated the yield per acre from the entire tract would be not less than twenty bushels to the acre. Grasshoppers had done but little damage; the excessive hot weather came too late to blast the crop, and everybody who saw the waving grain pronounced big wheat farming on the North Pacific a success, but on Tuesday a fearful gale passed over the Red river country, followed by a severe wind on Wednesday, which whipped from the standing grain, it is estimated, from two to four bushels to the acre, knocking off not less than $3,000 which would otherwise have been realized in the shape of clear profit. As it is the profit on the Dalrymple operations this year will be simply immense. The entire cost of breaking, sowing, reaping, threshing and marketing will not exceed nine dollars per acre. Estimating the value of wheat at eighty cents per bushel, and the yield at seventeen bushels per acre, we have a clear profit of $6,980 for this year's operations. But this is but the beginning. The farm on which this crop was grown consists of thirty thousand acres, on which next season there will be sown to wheat nine thousand acres, the sod for it having been broken this season.

During the breaking season Mr. Dalrymple had as high as one hundred teams at work. The furrows turned were six miles long, and the teams made but two trips a day, traveling with each plow, to make the four furrows, twenty-four miles. The location of this farm is eighteen miles west of Moorhead, Minn., in the proposed new territory of Pembina, and this is not the only big farm in the vicinity, but it is the "boss farm" of a dozen or more running from six hundred to several thousand acres.

26

Sugar Beets Cultivated Successfully and Vertical Integration in Farming Begins

The manufacture of sugar from the sugar beet was established in France and Germany early in the nineteenth century, largely through the encouragement of Napoleon Bonaparte. The industry languished with Napoleon's downfall, but was revived in the 1820's in France and in the 1830's in Germany.

The first experiments in the United States were made in the 1830's. Interest, however, remained dormant until 1863 when a factory was established in Illinois. This failed after six years, as did factories in Wisconsin and California until the erection of one at Alvarado, California, in 1879, which proved to be a profitable undertaking. After 1890, when the federal government adopted the policy of taxing imported sugar, production increased sharply. By 1900 the leading states in beet sugar production were California, Michigan, Utah, and Nebraska. In 1919 the leading states were Colorado, Michigan, Utah, and California, and in 1954, California, Colorado, Idaho, and Minnesota.

The year before the establishment of the successful factory at Alvarado, the Maine Sugar Beet Company established a factory near Portland, Maine. Although this factory did not survive, it was studied by an expert of the United States Department of Agriculture. The resulting report indicates that this factory inaugurated the practice of contracting with farmers for a specific acreage of sugar beets that would be raised by seed furnished by the company. This plan of operation, adapted from French practices, has persisted to the present.

A similar method of contracting was used by canning companies some forty years later. However, it was not until the mid-1940's when a modified plan of contracting for the raising of broilers was developed, with virtually everything furnished by the processor but the labor required for raising the chickens, that particular attention was given the subject. As this method of production and marketing was extended to other farm products in the next decade, it became the subject of special concern at the end of the 1950's under the term "vertical integration."

Sugar Beet Company Contracts for Production

William McMurtie, *Report on the Culture of the Sugar Beet and the Manufacture of Sugar Therefrom in France and the United States,* United States Department of Agriculture Special Report 28, pp. 171-173 (Washington, Government Printing Office, 1880).

The inauguration of the enterprise of growing beets for the production of sugar in the vicinity of Portland, Me., occurred in the spring of 1878 under the influence of the Maine Beet Sugar Company, which issued notice of organization on April 23, and was granted a charter by the State legislature May 11.

The plan of the company was to secure a limited crop in 1878, and work it with as inexpensive apparatus as could be procured and made effective to be used in connection with the Forest City Sugar Refinery. The German idea which has governed former experiments of this kind in this country, that of purchasing for the company a quantity of land sufficient to furnish the necessary supplies for a factory, was considered impracticable, and they determined to depend upon contracts to be made with the farmers for their supplies, and though the enterprise is a new one to the farmers large numbers appear to have been willing to cultivate small areas, but on account of an unfortunate delay in securing the seed for distribution (it had been ordered in Germany) and the consequent very late planting the crop was not a good one, and, therefore, not very profitable to the growers, and only about 1,000 tons were obtained to be worked up in the factory last year. The company suffered another discouraging experience in the way of the mode adopted for the preservation of the roots for working late in the season. The method proposed was to slice the roots and dry them, and by this means it was expected that larger quantities could be obtained from the fact that they could be transported greater distances, but the experiment resulted in disastrous failure. The drying oven experimented with was estimated to cost $800, but actually cost $5,000. It was stated to have a capacity of 25 tons per day and would dry but 7 tons, and the cost of working was about $6.50 per ton. The experiment was made in the Aroostook upon 500 tons of roots under the most favorable conditions, proving conclusively that the method is too costly to be employed for the purpose. Besides the cost involved in drying the roots, it was found more difficult to extract the sugar from the dried slices in the factory than from the roots worked in the green state.

But after all these discouraging circumstances the results obtained in the factory did much to counterbalance them. The roots produced and delivered, contained an average of 12½ per cent. of sugar and yielded nearly 10 per cent., in the extraction, of sugar of good grade, convincing the company that good roots could be produced, and that if sufficient quantity could be obtained for work in the factory the enterprise could be carried on with profit to all concerned. They, therefore, proceeded to make arrangements for securing the machinery and apparatus necessary for working 150 tons of roots in 24 hours, and roots sufficient to supply a factory of this capacity. The process for extraction adopted is Robert's diffusion process, for which the apparatus of the most approved patterns, and with the latest improvements, was purchased at Halle in Germany. The works are adapted to the extensive buildings of the Forest City Sugar Refinery, and the glass-house adjoining, and will be ready for active work by the middle of October. It was proposed to make use of the vaults of the glass-house as a place for storage of roots during the winter, but upon later consideration, this, it was thought, would be found impracticable on account of the danger of collecting too large a quantity of roots in a single mass, and subjecting them in this way to the possibilities of heating, sprouting, or decay, and consequent loss in their sugar content. Arrangements will, therefore, be made with the farmers for storing the roots in trenches and delivering them as they may be needed.

As before stated, the German method for obtaining supplies, that of purchasing large areas of ground to be devoted to the culture, was considered impracticable on account of the large investment of capital involved, and the method followed by the French, though somewhat modified, has been adopted.

The company appointed agents to call upon the farmers and make contracts with them for the roots produced on a given area, to be delivered either at the factory or the nearest shipping point. In this way contracts were made with about 1,700 farmers for the roots of 1,250 acres of land. When the agent of the company made the contract he delivered to the farmer the quantity of seed desired, to be paid for in the fall in beets from the crop produced.

The following are the forms of contracts employed in all the dealings with the farmers:

_____ _____P.O., Me.,_____ ___, 1879.

I agree to raise for the Maine Beet Sugar Company_____acre___ of sugar-beets from seed furnished by them, and to deliver the beets next fall on the cars at_____railroad station for five dollars per ton of 2,240 pounds of unwashed beets, as they come from the field.

_____ _____.

OFFICE MAINE BEET SUGAR COMPANY,

Portland, Me.,_____ ___, 1879.

We agree to buy of_____ _____all the sugar-beets raised by him on_____acre___from seed furnished by us, and to pay for the beets cash on delivery on the cars at_____railroad station next fall, five dollars per ton of 2,240 pounds of unwashed beets as they come from the field.

MAINE BEET SUGAR COMPANY,

Per_____ _____, Agent.

$_____.]   _____ _____P.O., Me.,_____ ___, 1879.

For value received in sugar-beet seed, I promise to pay the Maine Beet Sugar Company, or order, in October next, _____dollars and _____cents in cash, or in sugar beets at the rate of five dollars per ton of 2,240 pounds of unwashed beets delivered on the cars at_____ railroad station.

_____ _____.

The company agreed to pay $5 per ton for the roots delivered at the nearest shipping point (railroad station or wharf), and made arrangements with the freight agents at different points to receive, acknowledge, and forward the roots to the factory. If they be delivered by the farmer directly to the factory, the price paid is $6 per ton. The quantity delivered directly will, however, be small. The companies governing the railroads centering in Portland allow very generous terms for transportation of the roots, and for any distance not exceeding 50 miles the rates are 50 cents per ton; while for distances of over 50 miles, and not exceeding 110 miles, the rates are 80 cents per ton. This admits of obtaining roots from very long distances, and they have this year been grown in small crops in the entire section extending from Farmington on the north to Haverhill, Mass., on the south, and from Orono on the east to Concord on the west. The pulp will be carried back to the farmers at the same rates for freight, and will be sold to the producers of roots at $1 per ton, which will afford them a cheap source of valuable cattle food.

In order that the farmers with whom contracts for roots were made might be instructed as to the methods of culture to be followed, the agents of the company delivered to each one, and to all others who might desire them, copies of the following circular:

HOW TO RAISE SUGAR BEETS.

PORTLAND, March 31, 1879.

To the farmers of Maine:

The Maine Beet Sugar Company is now ready to contract with farmers to supply them with genuine sugar-beet seed, and to pay them $5 per ton for the crop of beets, cash, on delivery at the nearest railroad station, or $6 per ton, cash, on delivery at the Forest City Sugar Refinery in Portland, either by wagon or vessel. The seed will cost 20 cents per pound, payable next fall in cash or beets. Fourteen pounds of seed will plant one acre.

Almost every farmer has raised beets, or mangel-wurzels, which require similar cultivation. In order to get a good crop, say 20 tons or more per acre, the needful conditions are, early planting, good manuring, deep plowing, thorough harrowing, plenty of seed, timely thinning-out, careful hoeing and weeding. With these seven conditions, a good crop is certain. . . .

27

Cattle Industry of the Great Plains

Herding cattle on the Great Plains has been more romanticized than any other side of American agriculture. The range cattle industry boomed from about 1870 to 1885 and was then replaced by cattle ranching, but it has been remembered and romanticized in tens of thousands of novels, songs, moving pictures, and television episodes.

The range cattle industry of the West began in the 1690's when Spanish missionaries brought cattle into the Southwest. The mission herds multiplied and served as foundation stock for Texas herds, which, by 1865, totalled about six million head. These cattle could be bought at almost any price, yet livestock was scarce in the North and prices were high. The Texans began driving their herds to railheads in Kansas for shipment to the East. Within a few years, many Texas cattle were being driven to the northern plains for fattening before shipment to Chicago for slaughter.

The range cattle industry, as distinguished from the succeeding ranch cattle industry, was based upon free grass. The cattlemen ranged their herds over the public domain, sometimes holding particular areas by custom or force. The Homestead Act of 1862 granted 160 acres of land to farmers, yet made no provision for the rancher, who needed much more than 160 acres to maintain a herd of cattle on the Great Plains. The free grass that the cattlemen held was likely at any time to be claimed and plowed by homesteaders.

Since the average cattleman had no incentive to protect his range, he tended to the other extreme of overstocking and consequent overgrazing. This situation, combined with the homesteading threat, left the cattle industry in a vulnerable situation. Low prices and bad weather tipped the scale and brought an end to the open range livestock business.

Late in 1884 the price of livestock in Chicago dropped sharply. Many growers decided to hold their young cattle rather than ship them on a declining market. The winter of 1885-1886 was very severe in Texas, New Mexico, and Kansas and cattle losses were high, partly because of extreme overstocking. Meanwhile, prices on the Chicago market continued to decline.

During the spring and summer of 1886, many cattle were shipped from the southern to the northern plains. The summer was hot and dry and some cattlemen became alarmed and shipped their stock to market, but the range was still overstocked. Then, in November 1886, the worst winter weather in the history of the plains set in. Snow was so deep that starving animals could not paw down to grass, and many creeks and water holes froze so solidly that the cattle could not drink. Not until March was there any alleviation, but by then many ranchers had lost most of their cattle.

The great losses, combined with continued low prices and the continuing encroachment of the farmer, had a number of effects. Eastern and foreign investors stopped their blind speculation in livestock. Better business methods were followed by the ranchers and they improved the quality of the livestock. Above all, the losses of 1886-1887 convinced many ranchers that cows and calves could not be run on the northern range without provision for feed and shelter, and that better use must be made of the grass. This marked the end of the open range.

The ranch cattle industry developed gradually. Stockmen acquired land either by purchase or lease, fenced their lands, drilled wells and built water storage reservoirs, divided their range into summer and winter grazing areas, cut meadow grass for hay, began irrigating hay land and growing alfalfa, and began to develop better beef cattle by controlling breeding. Not all of these changes were made at any one time in any one place, but they continued throughout the plains until the range cattle industry was entirely displaced by the ranch cattle industry.

The Winter of 1886-1887

"Editorial," *Rocky Mountain Husbandman* (White Sulphur Springs, Mont.), Aug. 18, 1887, p. 4.

The truth in regard to the cattle losses of the northwest during the past winter is only beginning to be known. When the winter first broke the loss was supposed to have been 50 per cent. But when the cattlemen got out on the range they soon contradicted this and set the loss at from 20 to 30 per cent, but later advices placed it back to 50 again, and now it is stated on good authority that it was no less than 75 per cent loss in many localities. On the Yellowstone, we are assured that it was even more than 75 per cent, and some outfits put their loss at 80 and 90 per cent. One concern running 30,000 head in Montana Wyoming have only been able to round-up 700 head, and we understand that there are some companies that are unable to find a brand. These statements are probably overdrawn, yet we are satisfied that the loss in some localities has been almost equal to total annihilation. But the severest losses have been with the new companies, as old-time cattlemen snuffed the danger from afar, and by rustling, got a fair portion of their herds through. The actual losses of the big companies, we are satisfied, are represented to be larger than they really were. The business having been carried on on the high-pressure principle with a business office in some of our railroad towns, with officers located there on salaries who never saw their herds, thousands of stock were represented to the stockholders to be tens of thousands, fictitious branding reported and all manner of swindles perpetrated. The winter being severe has given managers of the concerns an opportunity to even up their books, and an appalling loss is now shown up. This is, of course, bad for the industry, but as there is no interest manifested in having it perpetuated in the range form, the country will lose but little. But for the old-time grower who will make some preparations for winter, it matters not what the world thinks of the business, since he is not dependent upon the price of stock cattle for support. The cattle business is something that can be easily closed out by spaying

the heifers and letting them get fat for beef. Hence, the cattle growers need care nothing for anything save a good range and a fair
price for beef. And, since at present prices he can do reasonably
well, the wild stories of the losses of last winter will not effect him,
neither will the closing out of the large companies.

28

Vedalia Beetle or Ladybird Introduced to
Control Cottony-cushion Scale

Fluted or cottony-cushion scale, a small inactive insect that feeds on
the sap of the leaves and twigs of citrus trees, was apparently imported
into California about 1868 or 1869 on Australian acacia trees. Within
about 10 years, the insect was causing serious damage to citrus groves
in California. In another 10 years, many growers felt that the citrus
industry was doomed unless the scale could be brought under control.

Growers and their representatives in Congress appealed to the United
States Department of Agriculture, particularly to entomologist C. V.
Riley, for assistance. Riley sent two agents to California in the spring of
1886, and suggested in his annual report for that year that an expert be
sent to Australia to study the parasites of the fluted scale there and
send them to California. This could not be done readily, however, because of Congressional restrictions upon expenditures of funds for
travel abroad.

During the summer of 1887, small numbers of insects, including a
ladybird, that preyed upon the scale in Australia, were brought into
California from Australia. The numbers were so small, however, that
little could be learned regarding the possible usefulness of any of the
parasites. Riley felt that an agent should be sent to Australia to bring in
larger numbers of the parasites. Although Congress did not make the
needed appropriation, the Secretary of State, with the agreement of
Australian authorities concerned, agreed to use part of the fund appropriated for the United States representation at the Melbourne Exposition
to defray the expenses of an agent to conduct the investigation. Albert
Koebele, one of the agents sent to California by Riley in 1886, was sent
to Australia in the summer of 1888 and returned in the spring of 1889.

Koebele collected a great many of the numerous parasites of the scale and sent them to California, where they were permitted to increase and were then released. The immediate success of a ladybird, the cardinal vedalia, in eradicating cottony-cushion scale made Koebele's trip one of the most spectacularly successful in agricultural history.

Other parasites have been introduced to combat other pests, and varieties of plants less subject to attack for one reason or another have been developed. New insecticides and methods of applying them have been brought into use. The war against insects, however, has continued to engage the attention of many of America's leading scientists.

C. V. Riley Reports on the Importation of the Australian Ladybird

C. V. Riley, "Report of the Entomologist for the Year 1889," in U.S. Department of Agriculture, *Annual Report*, 1889, pp. 334-338 (Washington, Government Printing Office, 1890).

In our last annual report we gave an account of all recent observations upon this insect and brought the investigation down to January, 1889. Few additional points have been learned the present year, and the great practical success of the importation of the Australian insect enemies of the Scale has so relieved the minds of the citrus growers of the Pacific coast little attention has been paid by them to the subject of washes and gas treatment. In fact the Fluted or White Scale is practically no longer a factor to be considered in the cultivation of oranges and lemons in California. The history of the introduction of this pest; its spread for upward of twenty years, and the discouragement which resulted; the numerous experiments which were made to overcome the insect, and its final reduction to unimportant numbers by means of an apparently insignificant little beetle imported for the purpose from Australia, will always remain one of the most interesting stories in the records of practical entomology.

We may hardly hope, however, that the last chapter in the story is written. On the contrary, it is more than probable, and in fact we strongly anticipate, that the Icerya will partially recuperate; that the Vedalia will, after its first victorious spread, gradually decrease for lack of food, and that the remnants of the Fluted Scale will in the interim multiply and spread again. This contest between the plant-feeder and its deadliest enemy will go on with alternate fluctuations in the supremacy of either, varying from year to year according to locality or conditions; but there is no reason to doubt that the Vedalia will continue substantially victorious, and that the power for serious harm, such as the Icerya has done in the past, has been forever destroyed. We have learned, also, that it will always be easy to secure new colonizations of the Vedalia where such may prove necessary, or even new importations should these become desirable.

We shall give in this connection simply a summary of the closing phases of the interesting experiment, with such other facts as are worthy of being placed upon record.

IMPORTATION OF THE AUSTRALIAN INSECT ENEMIES.

In our report for 1888 we showed how Mr. Koebele was sent to Australia in August and gave an account of his early sendings of insect enemies, recording how his first shipment arrived in excellent condition and containing a very large number of healthy living specimens of the Dipterous parasite which at that time was known by the name of *Lestophonus iceryce*, together with ladybirds and lace-wing flies. We also showed how the ladybird larvae attacked the first Iceryas which they met upon being liberated from the packages. The next shipment, as we there indicated, was not so successful, some of the boxes having been smashed by the falling of ice in the ice-house on the steamer, and the contents of others molding. In January another small lot containing fifty Lestophoni and forty-eight Vedalias together with a few other insects was received. It was in the December shipment that a secondary parasite of the Lestophonus was found. Late in February Mr. Koebele left Australia and spent a large part of the month of March in New Zealand, pursuing there the same quest. Before leaving Australia he sent another quantity of Lestophonus and a large number of Ladybirds of four different species, all of which were alive upon arrival in Los Angeles. The Ladybirds made themselves perfectly at home and began at once to feed upon Icerya. In New Zealand he was unable to find any true parasites, with the possible exception of a single small two-winged fly, but he collected a large number of Ladybirds, among them the same species of Vedalia which he had previously found in Australia. Many of these were brought with him on his return to California in April.

The parasites had been received in California by Mr. Coquillett, and after the disasterous second shipment, which was further delayed in the custom-house in San Francisco, the Secretary of the Treasury, at our request, kindly issued an order to the collector of the port to allow the subsequent packages entry free of duty and to forward them at once to Mr. Coquillett. The manner in which Mr. Coquillett disposed of the Lestophonus was mentioned in our last report, and we there figured on Plate VIII the tent under which he endeavored to colonize them. Concerning his experience with the Vedalia and the details of its early distribution we have given an account in No. 3, Vol. II, INSECT LIFE, and as this bulletin reaches but a small share of the readers of this annual report we may briefly state that as fast as the ladybirds were received they were placed under a tent on an Icerya-infested orange tree at Los Angeles. Here they were allowed to breed unmolested, and early in April it was found that nearly all of the Iceryas on the tree had been destroyed. Accordingly, one side of the tent was removed and the Ladybirds were allowed to spread to the adjoining trees. At this time Mr. Coquillett began sending out colonies to various parts of the State with the assistance of Mr. J. W. Wolfskill and Mr. Alex. Craw, and by the 12th of June ten thousand five hundred and fifty-five specimens had been distributed to two hundred and eight different orchardists. This was the course taken with the first three consignments, one hundred and twenty-nine specimens in all.

The last two consignments, numbering one hundred and eighty-five, were colonized in the groves of Col. J. R. Dobbins, in San Gabriel, and Messrs. A. B. and A. Scott Chapman, in the San Gabriel Valley; Mr. Dobbins receiving eighty-five and the Chapmans one hundred. Mr. Coquillett, writing in August last, said of the distributions made by himself, Mr. Wolfskill, and Mr. Craw from the Los Angeles colony, that in nearly every instance of the two hundred and eight the colonizing of the ladybirds on infested trees in the open air proved successful. The orange and other trees, about seventy-five in number, and also the shrubs and plants growing in Mr. Wolfskill's yard, had been practically cleared of Icerya by the ladybirds, and the latter had of their own accord spread to the adjoining trees for a distance of three-quarters of a mile from the original tree. That, as we have said, was in August.

Concerning the later colonizations, Colonel Dobbins and the Messrs. Chapman have themselves reported. Colonel Dobbins, writing as early as July 2, made use of the following language:

The Vedalia has multiplied in numbers and spread so rapidly that ever one of my thirty-two hundred orchard trees is literally swarming with them. All of my ornamental trees, shrubs, and vines which were infested with White Scale are practically cleansed by this wonderful parasite. About one month since I made a public statement that my orchard would be free from "Icerya by November 1," but the work has gone on with such amazing speed and thoroughness that I am to-day confident that the pest will have been exterminated from my trees by the middle of August. People are coming here daily, and by placing infested branches upon the ground beneath my trees for two hours can secure colonies of thousands of the Vedalia, which are there in countless numbers seeking food. Over fifty thousand have been taken away to other orchards during the present week, and there are millions still remaining, and I have distributed a total of sixty-three thousand since June 1. I have a list of one hundred and thirty names of persons who have taken the colonies, and as they have been placed in orchards extending from South Pasadena to Azusa, over a belt of country 10 miles long and 6 or 7 in width, I feel positive from my own experience that the entire valley will be practically free from Icerya before the advent of the new year. You will be as much pleased to read this as I am to write it.

October 22, Colonel Dobbins wrote further as follows:

The Vedalia had practically freed my orchard of Icerya on the 31st of July. It was on that date that I was obliged to post a notice at the entrance to my place saying that I had no more Vedalias for distribution. The Scale and Ladybird had fought out the battle, and while the carcasses of the vanquished were everywhere present to tell of the slaughter, the victors had disappeared almost entirely from the field. I have 35 acres in orchard—some three thousand two hundred trees in all. I never colonized any Vedalias in my grove, excepting two consignments which you brought to me yourself—one box on February 22 and two boxes March 20. I noticed the first increase from lot No. 1 on the 15th of April, and from lot No. 2 on the 24th of the same month. On the 25th of April I found larvae upon several adjacent trees. These facts are from memoranda made at the time. I have a list of the names of fruit-growers, two hundred and twenty-six in number, to whom I personally distributed over one hundred and twenty thousand Vedalias in colonies of various sizes between May 31 and July 31.

Mr. A. Scott Chapman describes the result of the colonization upon his own place and that of his father in a letter dated October 18th as follows:

. . . The Vedalias that you brought to my place about the 20th of last March, and which we colonized on four large orange trees that were covered with Fluted Scale, have spread in all directions, although, to begin with, they followed the direction of the wind most readily. From those four trees they have multiplied so rapidly that in my orchard of three thousand trees it is seldom that we can now find a Fluted Scale. I find a few of them on some weeds in spots, but I can also find the beetles there. The trees have put on a new growth and look altogether different: even the black fungus on the old leaves has loosened its hold and begins to fall to the ground. Besides having cleaned my orchard they spread also to the orchard of my cousin and to my father's orchard; the latter was also re-enforced by colonies from Mr. J. W. Wolfskill and from Col. J. R. Dobbins. As my father has some ten thousand trees, and most all were more or less infested, the Vedalias had a grand feast ahead of them, and they have done their work most wonderfully. What I have said of my orchard applies to my father's also, and really to all our neighbors. When the Vedalias first began to multiply we took colonies of fifty or more in the pupa state and placed them in different portions of the orchard, and even had we not done so the Vedalia unaided would itself have reached there in almost the same time.

On the Chapman place the Vedalias have cleaned the Fluted Scales off of the 150 acres of land. They have taken more than an oppressive burden off the orange-grower's hands, and I for one very much thank the Division of Entomology for the *Vedalia cardinalis*, the insect that has worked a miracle.

In August Prof. W. A. Henry, director of the Wisconsin Agricultural Experiment Station, visited California in the interest of the Department of Agriculture and made personal observations upon the result of this importation of the Vedalia. His account we quote in brief

In studying this insect we first visited the place of Mr. William Niles, in Los Angeles, where the "Ladybird" (*Vedalia cardinalis*) was being propagated by the county insect commission for dissemination among the orange groves infested with the Cottony Cushion, or White Scale. We found five orange trees, standing about 18 feet high, inclosed by walls of cheap muslin supported by a light frame-work of wood. The orange trees inside this canvas covering had originally been covered with the White Scale, but the Vedalia which had been placed on these trees were rapidly consuming the last of the pests. Entering one of these canvas houses we found the Vedalia, both larvae and adults, busy consuming the Scale; here and there on the canvas were the beetles endeavoring to escape to other trees. These insectaries were in charge of Mr. Kircheval, one of the county insect commissioners, who kept a record of the distribution of the beetle. It was indeed a most interesting sight to see the people come—singly and in groups—with pill boxes, spool-cotton boxes, or some sort of receptacle, in which to place the Vedalias. On application they were allowed within the insectaries, and each was permitted to help himself to the beetles, which were placed in the boxes and carried away to be placed on trees and vines infested with the White Scale at their homes. Mr. Kircheval kept a record of the parties and the number of beetles carried off. The number coming for Vedalia was surprisingly large—scores in a day—and each secured at least a few of the helpful beetles. That the supply should hold out under such a drain was a great surprise, and speaks better than words of the rapidity with which the Vedalia multiplies when there are Scale insects enough to nurture the young.

We visited other points—Lamanda Park, Santa Anita, Sierra Madre Villa, Pasadena, etc. At the time of our visit to Sierra Madre Villa, August 23, the White Scale had already disappeared before the Vedalia. At Santa Anita, the ranch of Mr. E. J. Baldwin, we examined a 350-acre orange orchard, in which the White Scale had started a most destructive course. Mr. Baldwin began an equally vigorous defense, going personally into the orchard and superintending the work of fighting the White Scale. There was every sign, however, that the Scale was going to be the victor. Some of the trees were almost ruined by the severity of the application made. Happily, before the pest had gone far in its work, the Vedalia was heard from, and Mr. Baldwin secured a number, which were placed in the hands of one man specially detailed to look after its welfare. This individual spent six weeks colonizing the Vedalia in various parts of the orchard. After that time a careful examination showed the superintendent that the work of colonizing was so complete that further effort in that line was unprofitable. It was predicted at the time of our visit that a few weeks more would leave the orchard entirely free from the White Scale. At Chapman's we found the citrus orchard, formerly so famous, entering the death stages from the White Scale, which was now fortunately being so effectually checked. At Pasadena, on the grounds of Prof. Ezra Carr, we found that some of the shrubbery had been seriously injured by the White Scale, but thanks to the Vedalia not a single pest was alive at the time of our visit. Mrs. Jennie Carr pronounced the Vedalia "a miracle in entomology."

A word in relation to the grand work of the Department in the introduction of this one predaceous insect. Without doubt it is the best stroke ever made by the Agricultural Department at Washington. Doubtless other efforts have been productive of greater good, but they were such character that the people could not clearly see and appreciate the benefits, so that the Department did not receive the credit it deserved. Here is the finest illustration possible of the value of the Department to give people aid in time of distress. And the distress was very great indeed. Of all scale pests the White Scale seems the most difficult to cope with, and had no remedy been found it would probably have destroyed the citrus industry of the State, for its spreading to every grove would probably be only a matter of time. It was the Department of Agriculture at Washington which introduced the Washington Navel Orange into South California, and the Department has now given an effective remedy for the worst scale insect. The people will not soon forget these beneficial acts.

29

State Experiment Stations Provide the Basis for Scientific Agriculture

The establishment of the state colleges of agriculture after the passage of the Morrill Land Grant Act of 1862 had marked a notable step in the advancement of American agriculture. Nevertheless, agricultural courses of a college level had to await the development of experiment stations that would provide basic knowledge upon which courses could be built.

The idea for a nationwide system of agricultural experiment stations was expressed in 1845 by John Pitkin Norton. Norton, who was studying agricultural chemistry in Scotland, suggested in an article that stations be established in connection with agricultural colleges. His greatest influence, however, was upon one of his students a few years later. While Norton was teaching at Yale, Samuel William Johnson became one of his students and an advocate of agricultural experiment stations. In 1875, Johnson's efforts led to the establishment of the Connecticut Experiment Station, the first state supported agricultural experiment station in the United States. A number of other states established stations during the next decade.

Meanwhile, an organized movement to secure federal and state aid for the establishment of agricultural experiment stations was under way. A convention of 29 persons representing several of the land-grant colleges met in Chicago in August, 1871. The idea of establishing experiment stations was discussed. The convention passed a resolution, establishing a committee composed of one person from each state, to memorialize Congress and the state legislatures for the speedy establishment of stations. During the next several years, a number of organizations and conventions passed resolutions urging both federal and state governments to provide aid. In 1882 the first bills to grant federal aid were introduced into Congress. Finally, in 1887, the Hatch Act was approved by Congress and signed by the President.

The new law provided for a yearly grant to each state for the support of an agricultural experiment station. Within a year, every state had accepted the provisions of the act, and within a decade the stations were devoting themselves to the basic work of original research. As Earle D. Ross has said, "The stations brought system and gave direction to the land-grant colleges, and more than any other factor assured their continuation."

A Call for the Establishment of Experiment Stations

"Convention of Friends of Agricultural Education," in Illinois Industrial University, *Annual Report*, 1870-1, 4: 215, 238-239, 343 (Springfield, Illinois Journal Printing Office, 1872).

In accordance with the call of a circular issued after correspondence with persons interested in the Agricultural Colleges founded on the national grant of lands, a convention was held at Chicago, on the 24th and 25th of August, 1871. . . .

Dr. Gregory—The committee have taken it for granted, I suppose, that all the agricultural colleges and institutions, or institutions that are teaching agriculture, are conducting experiments. It is of course understood that the agricultural colleges were organized, not for the purpose of experimenting first and foremost, but for the purpose of teaching agriculture, or the branches of learning relating to agriculture, and it has not been uniformly accepted that the agricultural colleges are to be experiment stations. They are not necessarily experiment stations. One of the questions for us to settle is, how far they can be made experiment stations, how far their forces and funds can be diverted for this purpose and used for this purpose. In Europe the agricultural experiment stations are sometimes connected with the institutions, but not always. If I am rightly informed, there are some thirty-three different agricultural experiment stations in Europe, under the charge of some agricultural chemists, besides other parties assisting them. These experiment stations, some of them at least, are found connected with the institutions. Those that I saw myself were always connected with them, because I did not turn aside to visit any of those that were not; but many of them, like the celebrated experiment station of Lawes and Gilbert, are not connected with any of the institutions of learning. We know this, that the country is demanding of the institutions that they shall conduct experiments. The agricultural public expects us to conduct experiments. They are constantly calling, through the agriculture press, at agricultural conventions and otherwise, upon these colleges to help them to settle questions relating to agriculture. Whatever might have been claimed at the outset to be the duty of these colleges, I trust we shall fulfill a public demand and duty by instituting experimentation. At least it seems to be the judgment, I think, of the gentlemen present here, and all I have known in connection with the agricultural colleges, that experiments shall be prosecuted. What has been already said here will perhaps, sufficiently, lead us to infer the great difficulty attending these experiments. But we have been told long ago that there is no excellence anywhere without great labor. The truth does not lie on the surface always. It hides itself in the depths. It is to be sought for with great patience and with great care, and great study. When it is found at last, be it after ever so long a search, and after ever so great expense, it will richly reward the seeker. Now in the solution of the problems in agriculture, the discovery of laws in agriculture—for I suppose that is the object of the experiment, and not merely to gratify the curiosity of the experimenter, not merely to get at some half-way results, like weighing a thing by taking it first in one hand and then in another, and then giving a guess—it is possible to determine, somewhere approximately at least, what are the facts, and ultimately to reach a law. . . .

Mr. Flagg offered the following resolutions:

Resolved, That the very strong commendation that the agricultural experiment stations of Europe have received from such persons as Johnson and Liebig as a source of a large amount of agricultural science and practical progress, as well as our own examinations into the subject, make us believe the establishment of not less than one such station in each of the several States of the Union, would be eminently beneficial to the agricultural interests of the country.

Resolved, That a committee, consisting of one from each of the several States in which an institution founded on the national grant has been organized, be appointed by the President, whose duty it shall be to memorialize Congress and the several State Legislatures for the speedy establishment of such stations throughout the country.

The resolutions were adopted.

30

Tick Fever of Cattle Controlled

Tick fever has challenged the American cattle grower since colonial times. The disease, earlier called cattle fever and then Texas fever, particularly affected northern cattle when they were exposed to apparently healthy southern cattle.

After the Civil War, Texans began to ship and drive north some of the cattle that roamed in vast numbers over the Texas plains. Texas cattle shipped up the Mississippi River to Cairo and then by rail into Illinois and Indiana caused enormous losses of cattle in those states during the summer of 1868. Other Texas herds infected western cattle, many of which died during shipment east to market.

Investigations were undertaken by various authorities without finding either the cause of or a remedy for the disease. By the 1880's, D. E. Salmon of the United States Department of Agriculture had determined that much of the southern United States was permanently infected.

The Department's Bureau of Animal Industry in 1888 assigned Theobald Smith and F. L. Kilborne the task of discovering the nature of the disease and the means by which it was transmitted. The next year the two investigators, aided by others, found that the disease was caused by a micro-organism in the red corpuscles and that cattle ticks were necessary to the transmission of the disease. Further experiments confirmed these findings, which were announced in the annual reports of the Bureau of Animal Industry for 1889 and 1890. Smith concluded: "No ticks, no Texas fever." Smith and Kilborne published a complete report of their investigations in 1893, which was reprinted many years later, by a firm publishing medical books, as a "medical classic."

Smith and his fellow workers had shown that cattle fever could be eradicated by eradicating cattle ticks, which was virtually accomplished throughout the United States by 1954. However great the value of the discovery was in saving cattle, as much as 40 million dollars a year from $65,000 spent on research, its implications for human health were much greater. Other research men saw its possible application in investigating other diseases. The most spectacular result came when the mosquito was recognized as the carrier of yellow fever. Since then, many areas of the world have been cleared of this once dreaded disease, and the mysteries of malaria, typhus, bubonic plague, and Rocky Mountain spotted fever—all insect borne—have been solved.

Theobald Smith Reports on Texas Fever

Theobald Smith, "Investigations of the Infectious Diseases of Animals," United States Department of Agriculture, Bureau of Animal Industry, *Annual Report*, 1889 and 1890, pp. 93-98 (Washington, Government Printing Office, 1891).

The investigations into the nature and causes of Texas or southern cattle fever have been busily pushed during the summer of 1890, and some very important advances made which are destined to be of great practical importance.

During the summer of 1888 much time was spent in determining whether or not any specific bacteria are the cause of this disease as they are of a host of human and animal infectious diseases. This was the more necessary inasmuch as former observers have always described bacteria of one kind or another associated with it. But no bacteria could be found in the bodies of animals which had succumbed to Texas fever excepting those which quite invariably multiply in dead bodies after a time and have no significance whatever. At the same time the writer came to the conclusion that the disease was confined to the blood and consisted essentially in a breaking down of the red corpuscles.

During the summer of 1889 arrangements were made by which the disease could be studied near the laboratory in Washington, and, as reported, a parasite was found within the red corpuscles whose presence could only mean the breaking up of the corpuscle itself sooner or later. This discovery was adapted to explain satisfactorily the various lesions observed, as well as the great reduction in the number of corpuscles observed in those cases which died after prolonged disease or which ultimately survived. In some of these cases the blood is watery; it has in fact scarcely any color remaining. This condition was expressed mathematically by counting the number of blood corpuscles. Thus in most cases before death the number of corpuscles was but one-sixth of the number normally present in the body. When we contemplate the very important functions of these elements we need not be surprised at the serious effects resulting from loss to the body, within one or two weeks, of five-sixths of its corpuscles.

During the present year the disease was produced at the Experiment Station by the importation of North Carolina and Texas cattle and the investigations continued. The work was sufficiently extensive to occupy most of the time from July to December, while the examination of preparations and other work connected with this subject occupied much of the writer's time last winter and will of necessity require much additional labor this winter. . . .

While the investigations into the nature of this disease were going on other equally important work was being carried on at the Experiment Station on the external characters of the disease.

It is well known to those who have come in contact with southern cattle in summer that they are infested with the so-called cattle-tick, a pest belonging to the class *Arachnoidea* and to the family *Ixodidoe*. These ticks are carried north with cattle during the warm season of the year. When fully matured they drop off from the southern animals, lay their eggs on the ground, and perish. The young ticks are hatched within fifteen to thirty days after the eggs are laid and at once get upon the cattle, where they become mature within twenty to thirty days to again drop off, lay their eggs, and die. This process goes on continuously until the cold weather comes.

At various times and in different parts of the country it has been suggested that the ticks were the cause of Texas fever in northern cattle. This inference was undoubtedly suggested by the fact that nearly all cattle that die of Texas fever are observed to have these ticks of various sizes attached to the skin. Moreover the disease only makes its appearance after the young ticks have attached themselves to cattle. Though this was purely a *post hoc propter hoc* inference, it was nevertheless true, as the experiments to be recorded will amply prove.

During the summer of 1889 Dr. F. L. Kilborne, in arranging the various inclosures at the Experiment Station for the exposure of native cattle to the infection of Texas fever, conceived the happy idea of testing this popular theory of the relation of ticks to the disease. This he did by placing southern (North Carolina) cattle with native cattle in the same inclosure and picking the ticks from the southern stock as soon as they had grown large enough to be detected on the skin. This prevented any ticks from maturing and infecting the pasture with the eggs and hence prevented any ticks from infesting native cattle subsequently. At the same time, in another inclosure, the ticks were left on the southern cattle. The natives in the latter field died of Texas fever; those in the former did not show any signs of the disease.

Another experiment was made in September in the same manner by preparing three fields, one with southern cattle and ticks, a second with southern cattle from which the ticks were being removed, and a third over which only adult ticks had been scattered. The result was equally positive. In the first field no natives died, but careful examination of the blood by the writer showed Texas fever in an unmistakable manner. In the "tick" field one animal died of Texas fever, and the examination of the blood showed that most other natives in the field were sick. In the third field containing southern cattle without ticks no disease could be detected.

These two tests pointed directly to ticks as being in some way the cause of Texas fever. At the same time it was thought best to confirm these results by further experiments during the present year before other agencies could be eliminated. The immediate inference was that the ticks infect the pastures, and that in some unexplained manner the infection finds its way into the body of susceptible cattle. The preliminary conclusions deducible from the work of 1888 and 1889 can be formulated as follows:

(1) Texas fever is a disease not caused by bacteria. Its nature can not be understood by supposing a simple transfer of bacteria from southern cattle to pastures and from pastures to northern cattle.

(2) The cause is very probably a protozoon, with a more complex life history, living for a time within the red corpuscles of infected animals.

(3) Southern cattle without ticks can not infect a pasture.

(4) Ticks alone scattered on a pasture will produce the disease.

The work of 1890 was planned to confirm or refute these preliminary conclusions and to furnish additional information.

The fields were arranged as before. One contained North Carolina cattle with ticks, a second Texas cattle with ticks, a third North Carolina cattle without ticks, a fourth ticks only, and a fifth soil from the pastures of infected North Carolina farms. Other fields were also laid out to test questions which need not engage our attention in this brief survey.

The results confirmed those of last year. The first animal to die was in the "tick" field, containing no southern cattle. No disease appeared in the soil field. Unfortunately, owing to the limited space of ground at our disposal and its barren, rolling character, ticks or eggs were washed during the very heavy rains of the summer from the tick field into the field containing southern cattle without ticks, although a wide lane intervened. The natives in this field thereupon all died of Texas fever. At the autopsy of these cases ticks were found attached to their skin in abundance.

The disease caused by Texas cattle could not be distinguished in character from that which was produced by North Carolina cattle.

These results similarly pointed to ticks as the cause. The precise manner in which they caused the disease was by no means clear, however. The theory which seemed for a time most acceptable was that the adult ticks as they dropped off infected the pastures with germs which they had taken in with the blood of southern cattle, and that the germs were introduced into the body of of northern cattle with the food. At the same time no parasite could be detected in the blood of southern cattle examined at various times, on which fact I would lay no great stress, however. Of more importance is the peculiarity which is exhibited by this disease in its period of incubation, as it may be provisionally denominated, and which is opposed to this theory. Thus, when native and southern cattle are placed on the same pasture at the same time it will take from forty to sixty days for the disease to appear. After the disease has once shown itself fresh animals placed on the same pasture may die, according to our experience, within thirteen days after the beginning of the exposure. We might say that the virus has "to ripen" on the pasture, which takes nearly two months, depending on meteorological conditions. When once "ripened" this virus does its deadly work within two or three weeks. This explanation, however, would be merely formulating our ignorance concerning the true nature of the infectious principle.

To the writer there seemed but one inference to be drawn from the facts, and that is that the presence of young ticks is in some way directly associated with the appearance of the disease. It requires from forty to sixty days for the matured ticks to drop from the southern cattle and the eggs laid by them to develop into young ticks. After that period young ticks are present on the pastures until they are destroyed by the cold, or until the cold interferes with the development of the embryo in the egg. In other words, the period of incubation of the disease is explained without any difficulty by the life history of the tick.

The question was solved, experimentally, in the following manner: Eggs laid by ticks sent from North Carolina were placed on dried leaves in dishes partly filled with moist soil and kept in the laboratory until the young emerged from the egg. The period of incubation depends entirely upon the relative amount of heat, and has varied from fifteen days in midsummer to forty days in November, when the rooms of the laboratory became cold at night (50 degrees to 60 degrees F.). These young ticks were placed on four different animals of different ages, kept away from any infected inclosures. Two were placed in stalls, one of them on an adjoining farm, and two were allowed to stay in a patch of woodland with healthy cattle. Of these four two died of Texas fever, as determined by careful post-mortem examination. One of them was in the stall away from the station, the other in the patch of woodland. The other two became very ill. One of them never recovered, but had to be killed later on; the other recovered. In all of them the germs were observed in the blood. The disease possessed the same characters as those observed in cattle in the infected pastures during the summer. There was an elevation of temperature from nine to twelve days after the young ticks were placed on the animals, going as high as 107 degrees F. in one animal. Accompanying the fever a gradual reduction in the number of blood corpuscles was observed. . . .

These brief notes demonstrate that Texas fever can be produced by placing young ticks on cattle, and that the disease can not be due to any abstraction of blood, for the ticks were still quite small and had scarcely begun to draw blood on a large scale. Moreover the corpuscles perished *in the body* as is shown by the coloring matter in the urine, by the thick bile, and the presence of pigment in the liver and kidneys. No disease appeared among the other cattle in the same inclosure.

While the nature of Texas fever is by no means made clear as yet, we are able to affirm that ticks can produce it. Whether the disease can be transmitted by any other agency must be decided by future investigations. Meanwhile the evidence accumulated thus far seems to favor very strongly the dictum: No ticks, no Texas fever.

31

Babcock Butterfat Test Developed

The importance of dairying increased as American industry developed. Industrial activity led to the growth of cities, which, with increasing demands for milk, butter, and cheese, led in turn to the development of a highly specialized dairy business.

The period 1870-1890 was one of rapid development in the dairy industry. The number of cows doubled, while the number per 1,000 persons increased from 231 in 1870 to 262 in 1890. Dairy organizations were formed, while scientific methods were applied to all branches of dairying. Such methods and the adoption of new devices brought about great changes in the industry.

The use of the thermometer became general in making butter and cheese. The first American silo, which permitted better year-around feeding of dairy stock, was constructed in 1873. Refrigerator cars were first used for transporting perishable farm products about 1875. The centrifugal separator for separating cream from milk was invented in Sweden and brought to the United States in 1882. Finally, the Babcock test for measuring the quantity of fat in milk was invented in 1890.

Trained at Cornell and Goettingen University, Stephen M. Babcock was appointed professor of agricultural chemistry at the University of Wisconsin and chief chemist of the experiment station in 1888. Devising a simple, accurate test for determining the quantity of butterfat in milk was one of his first assignments. Babcock developed such a method, thoroughly tested it, and announced it in 1890. This outstanding invention encouraged emphasis upon improving special breeds of dairy cattle and permitted dairymen to sell their milk and cream upon a rational basis.

The Babcock test is still in use throughout the United States. Babcock stated in his introduction to the description of his test: "In the hope that it may benefit some who are striving to improve their stock and enable creameries to avoid the evils of the present system, the test is given to the public." Babcock's modest hope was realized beyond all possible expectation. He concluded his description by stating: "The test is not patented." This contribution to the dairy industry aided in developing confidence in the experiment stations at a time when their future was still uncertain.

Babcock Describes His Test

Stephen M. Babcock, "A New Method for the Estimation of Fat in Milk, Especially Adapted to Creameries and Cheese Factories," in Wisconsin Agricultural Experiment Station, *Annual Report,* 1890, pp. 98, 103-108, 113 (Madison, Wisconsin, Democrat Printing Co., 1890).

During the past few years a number of methods have been proposed by which the estimation of fat in milk may be accomplished without the delicate appliances of a chemical laboratory, and by persons unskilled in chemical manipulations. Although most of these methods have been found either too complicated or too expensive to meet the wants of the practical dairyman, a few of them are being used to a considerable extent by careful breeders of dairy stock to determine the quality of their cows, and by creameries for adjusting the price of milk between their patrons. The results already attained in this direction have been so satisfactory to the parties interested that the demand is rapidly growing, and there can be little doubt of the speedy adoption of some test in all creameries and factories where milk is pooled. The chief obstacle to this much desired end, at present, is the time required and the expense involved for apparatus and chemicals where a large number of tests must be made from day to day. Several of the tests now used have been shown repeatedly to be substantially correct, and little improvement can be expected except in simplicity and economy of both time and money. In the test described in this Bulletin, it is believed that some progress has been made in both of these directions, without sacrificing the accuracy of the results. Whether this test will find a place among those already introduced, time alone can decide. In the hope that it may benefit some who are striving to improve their stock and enable creameries to avoid the evils of the present system, the test is given to the public. . . .

MAKING THE TEST.

Sampling the Milk. Every precaution should be taken to have the sample represent as nearly as possible the whole lot of milk from which it is taken. Milk fresh from the cow, while still warm and before the cream has separated in a layer, may be thoroughly mixed by pouring three or four times from one vessel to another. Samples taken at once from milk mixed in this way are the most satisfactory of any. Milk that has stood until a layer of cream has formed should be poured more times, until the cream is thoroughly broken up and the whole appears homogeneous. No clots of cream should appear upon the surface when the milk is left quiet for a moment. With proper care any milk that has not coagulated, or that has not been exposed to the air until the surface of the cream has become dried, may be mixed so that a representative sample may be taken. Milk should not be poured more times than is necessary, as continual mixing in this way is liable to churn the cream, forming little granules of butter that quickly rise to the surface. When this occurs it is impossible to obtain a fair sample. Milk is sometimes churned by being transported long distances in vessels that are not full. When this occurs it is useless to make an examination.

It is impracticable to sample a large amount of sour milk but a small sample of a pint to a quart may be thoroughly mixed by adding five per cent. of strong ammonia water which will dissolve the curd and permit a uniform mixture being made. When ammonia is added, the final results should be increased by five per cent. Samples from sour milk are, however, never as satisfactory as those taken when the milk is in a proper condition.

Measuring the Milk. When the milk has been sufficiently mixed, the milk pipette is filled by placing its lower end in the milk and sucking at the upper end until the milk rises above the mark on the stem; then remove the pipette from the mouth and quickly close the tube at the upper end by firmly pressing the end of the index finger upon it to prevent access of air; so long as this is done the milk cannot flow from the pipette. Holding the pipette in a perpendicular position, with the mark on a level with the eye, carefully relieve the pressure on the finger so as to admit air slowly to the space above the milk. When the upper surface of the milk coincides with the mark upon the stem, the pressure should be renewed to stop the flow of milk. Next, place the point of the pipette in the mouth of one of the test bottles, held in slightly inclined position so that the milk will flow down the side of the tube leaving a space for the air to escape without clogging the neck, and remove the finger allowing the milk to flow into the bottle. After waiting a short time for the pipette to drain, blow into the upper end to expel the milk held by capillary attraction in the point. If the pipette is not dry when used it should be filled with the milk to be tested, and this thrown away before taking the test sample. If several samples of the same milk are taken for comparison, the milk should be poured once from one vessel to another after each sample is measured. Neglect of this precaution may make a perceptible difference in the results, through the separation of cream, especially when the milk examined is rich.

Persons who have had no experience in the use of a pipette will do well to practice a short time by measuring water into a test bottle before attempting to make an analysis. The manipulation is easily acquired, and with a little practice milk may be measured nearly as rapidly with a pipette as with a graduate, and with much greater accuracy.

Adding the Acid. When the milk has been measured into the test bottles the necessary amount of sulphuric acid may be added immediately, or the bottles may be left for a day or two without materially changing the results; samples that have remained in the test bottles more than a week have given the same amount of fat as samples tested immediately after being measured. If the milk has become coagulated, the curd should be broken up by shaking the test bottle before the acid is added.

The volume of commercial sulphuric acid required for a test is approximately the same as that of the milk, 17.5 c.c. for the ordinary test. If too little acid is added, the casein is not all held in solution throughout the test, and an imperfect separation of the fat results. If too much acid is used, the fat itself is attacked. The acid need not be measured with great accuracy, any quantity between 17 c.c. and 18 c.c. will answer the purpose.

Great care must be taken in handling the acid to avoid getting any of it upon the skin or clothing, as it is very corrosive. If by accident any is spilled upon the hands or clothes, it should be washed off immediately, using plenty of water. A prompt application of ammonia water to clothing upon which acid is spilled may prevent the destruction of the fabric, and restore the color.

When all of the samples of milk to be tested are measured ready for the test, the acid measure is filled to the 17.5 c.c. mark with sulphuric acid, and from this it is carefully poured into a test bottle, containing milk, that is held in a slightly inclined position for reasons given in directions for measuring the milk. The acid being much heavier than milk sinks directly to the bottom of the test bottle without mixing with the milk that floats upon it. The acid and milk should be thoroughly mixed together by gently shaking with a rotary motion. At first there is a precipitation of curd from the milk, but this rapidly dissolves. There is a large amount of heat evolved by the chemical action, and the solution, at first nearly colorless, soon changes to a very dark brown, owing to the charring of the milk sugar and perhaps some other constituents of the milk.

Upon standing a short time the fat begins to collect upon the surface, not in a clear layer, but having at first, the appearance of a dirty cream. The separation of fat by gravity alone is not complete even when the bottles are left standing for several hours; with the centrifuge, however, a perfect separation is accomplished in a few minutes.

Whirling the Bottles. The test bottles containing the mixture of milk and acid may be placed in the machine directly after the acid is added, or they may stand several hours without harm. An even number of bottles should be whirled at the same time, and they should be placed in the wheel in pairs opposite to each other, so that the equilibrium of the apparatus will not be disturbed. When all of the test bottles are placed in the apparatus, the cover is placed upon the copper jacket, and the machine is turned either by hand or by power at such a rate that the wheel carrying the bottles will make from 600 to 800 revolutions per minute, and this motion must be kept up for six or seven minutes. If this wheel is less than about twenty inches in diameter the speed should be greater, or else the whirling should be continued for a longer time.

When the bottles are placed in the machine directly after the acid is added, the separation may be affected without any extra heat, as that caused by the chemical action is sufficient to keep the fat liquid. If the bottles have stood after the acid is added until the contents are cooled below 100 degrees F., the water in the tank should be warmed to about 200 degrees F. before putting the bottles in the machine. The bottles should not be kept heated in the machine as high as the boiling point of water while the separation is being effected. The proper degree of heat may be obtained by lighting the burner or kerosine stove under the jacket when the machine is started; so much water having been poured into the jacket as will be just heated to boiling when the whirling is finished. In this way hot water is always available for filling the tubes at the proper time. In creameries, heat can be most easily supplied by steam connection with the boiler. If the machine is stopped after about six minutes, a layer of fat will be found upon the upper surface of the liquid in the tubes. This fat will not usually be clear;

this however, will make no difference in the result, as the subsequent treatment will clarify it.

As soon as the bottles have been sufficiently whirled, they should be filled to the neck with hot water. This is most conveniently done by placing a vessel containing boiling water above the machine, and by means of a syphon, made from a small rubber tube with a glass tip, run the water directly into the bottles without removing them from the wheel. The flow of water can be perfectly controlled by a pinch-cock upon the rubber tube. If only a few tests are to be made, the bottles may be easily filled with a pipette, or by pouring from a graduate. The cover should then be replaced and the machine turned for one or two minutes, after which more hot water is added, filling the tube to about the seven per cent. mark. The fat will slowly rise into the graduated tube, losing its cloudy appearance as it passes through the hot water. When all of the bottles are filled, the cover is put upon the tank, and the machine again turned for a short time. During this time the water in the tank should be kept hot, either by placing a lamp or kerosine stove beneath it, or by pouring in a quantity of boiling hot water before starting the machine. If the fat in some of the tubes still has a cloudy appearance, the cover should be placed upon the tank and heat applied for a few minutes, when the fat should become clear and in condition to be measured. The clearing may be hastened by whirling the tubes while hot. When the bottles are allowed to cool off to a point where the fat will crystallize and then warmed again, the fat will usually be much clearer than before, but as this does not materially change the volume of fat it is considered unnecessary. Even a slight cloudy appearance does no harm.

Measuring the Fat. The fat when measured should be warm enough to flow readily, so that the line between the acid liquid and the column of fat will quickly assume a horizontal position when the bottle is removed from the machine. Any temperature between 110 degrees F. and 150 degrees F. will answer, but the higher temperature is to be preferred. The slight difference in the volume of fat due to this difference in temperature is not sufficient to materially affect results. A difference in temperature of 40 degrees F. will make less than one-tenth per cent. difference in milk containing five per cent. of fat. To measure the fat, take a bottle from its socket, and holding it in a perpendicular position with the scale, on a level with the eye, observe the divisions which mark the highest and lowest limits of the fat. The difference between these gives the per cent. of fat directly. The reading can easily be taken to half divisions or to one-tenth per cent.

If the column of fat is less than about one division, as will sometimes happen with skimmilk, buttermilk or whey it may assume a globular form instead of a uniform layer across the tube; when this occurs the fat can usually be estimated with sufficient accuracy by simple inspection, but if an accurate reading is desired it may be obtained by taking four samples of the milk in four test bottles, and after treating them in the usual way, until the bottles are ready to be filled with water, adding water to three of them only, filling them as full as possible without running them over. After whirling them for a minute to bring the fat all into the neck, the fat may be poured off from these three tubes into the fourth. If any fat remains adhering to the sides of these tubes, they should be filled a second time with water and the remaining fat poured into the fourth bottle, which is then filled with water, whirled and the reading taken; this divided by four will give the per cent. of fat.

A better way would undoubtedly be to have a special test bottle, holding three or four times as much as the ordinary bottle, that could be used for skimmilk, buttermilk and whey. Three or four times the usual test sample could then be taken and by adding the proper quantity of acid, the test could be made without transferring the fat. . . .

HOW THE APPARATUS CAN BE OBTAINED.

At the solicitation of the Station, several manufacturers of dairy supplies have visited Madison to see the test and have signified their intention of putting the apparatus upon the market. Parties doing so will, no doubt, inform the public through the advertising columns of the dairy press.

The test is not patented.

32

Gasoline Tractor Invented

The new farm machines invented and improvements made in old, including plows, harvesters, seed drills, cultivators, threshers, hay rakes, and others, in the period 1820 to 1870 permitted farmers to substitute animal power for manpower. This substitution was accompanied by efforts to find a source of mechanical power. The demand for mechanical farm traction was greatest on western wheat farms, where operations were on such a scale that large machines could be utilized. Economies in operation meant large sums to such farmers.

The steam traction engine was the first answer to the problem of mechanical power. Portable steam engines, built especially for use with threshing machines, were produced in the United States as early as 1849. By 1870 a number of steam plows had been devised, and during the next ten years, successful steam-traction engines were placed in production. By 1900 more than 30 firms were manufacturing some 5,000 large steam-traction engines a year.

Although they were useful in threshing grain, steam tractors were not an answer to all farm power needs. They were so large that they could not be used for plowing and other work on any but the largest farms. Their weight packed the soil over which they passed, and sparks from smokestacks caused many fires. The internal combustion engine seemed to be the solution.

The internal combustion engine had been invented and improved in Europe, but by 1890 a number of American firms had begun to manufacture stationary engines. The early development of the tractor followed a pattern similar to the steam-traction engine. The stationary engine was mounted on wheels to make it portable. Later a drive was devised to make it self-propelled.

John Froelich of Froelich, Iowa, built the first gasoline tractor of record that was an operating success. In 1892 he mounted a gasoline engine, built by the Van Duzen Gas and Gasoline Engine Company of Cincinnati, on a running gear equipped with a traction arrangement of his own manufacture. The tractor completed a fifty-day threshing run. During this time, it powered the thresher and pulled it over difficult terrain, operating in temperatures from –3 degrees to 100 degrees F.

Several companies began manufacturing gasoline tractors after 1892. The first business in the United States devoted exclusively to the manufacture of tractors was established by C. W. Hart and C. H. Parr in Iowa City, Iowa, about 1903. Hart and Parr had started working on internal combustion engines after they met as students at the University of Wisconsin in 1893. Their first tractor was completed in 1901. Crude as it was, it remained in operation for nearly 20 years. The partners moved to Iowa City, built additional models, and then went into full factory production of the Hart-Parr tractor.

The change from animal to mechanical power came slowly. Many manufacturers made improvements in tractors which led more farmers to use them. But World War II gave great impetus to the transition, and in 1950 there were more tractors than horses on American farms.

First Description of the Froelich Tractor

"Another Gasoline Engine," *Farm Implement News*, 13(49):24-25. Dec. 8, 1892.

A few months ago we illustrated a portable gasoline engine and spoke of its many advantages. The cut accompanying this represents a gasoline traction engine, which, at this writing, has run fifty days and threshed over 62,000 bushels of grain and seeds this fall, near Langford, S. Dak., driving a 40x58 J. I. Case separator.

The engine proper was built by the Vanduzin Gasoline Engine Company, of Cincinnati, O., to order of John Froelich, of Froelich, Iowa, who built the traction for it and made some improvements in feeding the gasoline to the engine. The engine is of the vertical type, thereby overcoming the end motion caused by the piston of horizontal engines. Its cylinder is 12x14, and rates thirty h.p. indicated, or twenty actual h.p. Its weight is, complete, nearly 9,000 pounds, or about two-thirds the weight of a fourteen h.p. steam traction engine, when steamed up.

The gear is so arranged that with a single lever the traction is stopped, started, and reversed, and is more handy than a steam engine. The belt wheel is provided with a friction clutch, which can be thrown out or in while the engine is in motion, thereby stopping the machine without stopping the engine. The traction gear is protected with a similar device. In this way the engine need not be stopped or started when moving from one setting to another, and much time is saved. The gasoline is not carried above as is customary in all engines where the feed depends on the gravity of the gasoline. When jarred on the road it would be disturbed in its flow, causing irregularity in the explosions and power. In this engine the gasoline is in a tank, located on the bed of the engine and forced to the carburetter by means of an automatic pump, with an air cushion connected to the pipe near its exit to the engine, thereby securing an even flow of gas. The engine has pulled the separator over all kinds of ground, and in temperature varying from 100° above to 3° below zero. It is much easier understood than a steam engine, and runs with less than half the care and attention, entirely free from danger to life.

With a few improvements in the gear it will make the most complete and economic engine ever made for plowing. Carrying a supply of gasoline and water with it, it does away with hauling water and fuel, which makes the steam engine almost impractical in many parts of the west and northwest. The engine during the fifty days consumed 1,315 gallons of gasoline, or twenty-six gallons a day. About two barrels of water per day are necessary to keep it cool.

The following are a few of the superiorities of the gasoline engine over steam: There is no danger of fire or explosion, no leaky flues, no boiler repairs, no water team. The running expenses of a steam engine vary, of course, in different localities. Where this engine was at work it figures about as follows: About 1,500 pounds of coal are used, costing $7.50 per ton; with $1.50 added for hauling, are used by a sixteen h.p. engine, making it cost about $6.75 per day. The tank or water man, team and wagon, cost $5 per day. An average of $1 per day is figured for boiler repairs caused by alkali in the water. The engineer is paid $3.50 per day. In many places straw is used as fuel, but in that case it takes an extra man to fire, and the wear on the boiler is more than twice as hard as with coal, and many claim it is cheaper in the end to burn coal. Steam therefore costs about $15 per day. A gasoline engine would require an engineer at $3.50, and $3.15 worth of gasoline, or a total of $6.65, a saving of $8.60 a day. If the loss of property destroyed by fire could be estimated it might be safe to add another $2 for each day's work. Mr. Froelich has applied for patents, and is now figuring with several parties to manufacture the engines and put them on the market the coming season. He has spent seven seasons in the fields of Dakota with threshing machines of his own, and knows what is needed. He has experimented till he found the best, safest, and cheapest power for that purpose. His address is Froelich, Iowa, where he has been engaged for some years as a dealer.

33

Breeding Disease-Resistant Strains of Plants

The flowering of agricultural research in the last decades of the nineteenth century resulted in the establishment of principles that have affected every aspect of agricultural production and the welfare of the nation. Scientific knowledge, support for research, and the needs of commercial agriculture coincided in bringing about fundamental changes in American agriculture.

The commercial cotton farmers of the South were threatened at the turn of the century by cotton wilt. Wilt is a fungus disease that lives indefinitely in the soil and kills and damages plants by stopping up the root systems. In 1899 the task of investigating cotton wilt was assigned to William A. Orton, a young plant pathologist from Vermont. Orton first visited the islands off the coast of South Carolina, where long-staple cotton had particularly suffered from the disease, although wilt was spreading to upland cotton as well. There, Orton met a grower named Elias L. Rivers, who pointed out that a few plants often survived in a field attacked by wilt. Rivers had been saving seed from these resistant plants.

Orton encouraged Rivers to continue his work, and determined to attempt to develop wilt-resistant varieties of upland cotton. The work, undertaken near Dillon, South Carolina, was so successful that Orton reported on it in a bulletin published early in 1900.

The long-term control of cotton wilt by breeding disease-resistant strains was of tremendous importance to cotton growers. The theory of selective breeding for plants resistant to disease developed by Orton has since been applied to most of the major crops grown by the American farmer. In addition, the principle of selective breeding has been extended not only to resistance to disease but to resistance to insects and to drought, adaptation to differing climates, improved flavor, better marketing qualities, and increased food value.

Selective Breeding Controls Wilt Disease

W. A. Orton, *The Wilt Disease of Cotton and Its Control*, United States Department of Agriculture, Division of Vegetable Physiology and Pathology Bulletin 27, pp. 5-7, 11-15 (Washington, Government Printing Office, 1900).

The wilt disease is now known to occur on the coast of South Carolina, where it attacks the fine sea island cotton, and at Dillon, Salters, and other places in the same State, where it attacks upland cotton.

Prof. F. S. Earle, of the State experiment station, reports it to be widely distributed in Alabama, particularly in the southern part, and states that it is undoubtedly growing worse from year to year. It has been reported from many localities in Georgia, and is known to occur in Florida and Arkansas.

It is certain that this disease is widely distributed through the Southern States, and it is probable that it occurs in many places where it has not yet been distinguished from other troubles, such as "rust" and the effects of lightning.

EXTENT OF LOSS.

The annual loss from the wilt disease is very considerable. It is more keenly felt by the individual planters than most cotton troubles, because the disease remains in the soil and grows worse with each succeeding crop. On the sea islands of South Carolina alone a careful estimate indicates that nearly, if not quite, one-third of the land planted to high-grade cotton is affected by this disease, the larger portion of it so badly that it is no longer profitable to plant it in cotton. In many instances it has been necessary to abandon from 20 to 50 acres on a single plantation. Much of this land is tile-drained and in a high state of cultivation. No other crop has been so profitable as the sea island cotton, and the problem before these planters is a very serious one. The loss to the planters of upland cotton in areas affected by the disease has been proportionally great. On one farm in Dillon, S. C., where the Department has been conducting some experiments, 15 acres of fine land are already affected and the disease is spreading rapidly on this and adjoining plantations. . . . The loss to this community from the wilt disease the past season is estimated at several thousand dollars. In Alabama the loss from this disease is reported from many sources to be very large.

The importance of the disease, however, does not lie so much in the amount of the present loss as in the danger of its future increase, for it must ultimately spread so much as to entail far greater losses and possibly threaten the life of the industry unless the methods for its control are perfected.

DESCRIPTION OF THE DISEASE.

The wilt is very distinct from any other disease of cotton, so that there need be no difficulty in its identification. It usually makes its first appearance in the spring about the last of May, when the plants are 6 to 8 inches high. It appears in well-defined areas, which enlarge if cotton is planted on the same land again. The first outward indication of its presence is a dwarfed growth and unhealthy appearance of the plants. The leaves turn yellow between the veins, their margins shrivel up, and some plants wilt and die at once. In other plants the progress of the disease is often slow, and many of them live the entire summer and die late in the season. On cutting across the stem of a diseased plant, the woody part will be found to be stained brown wherever the disease is present. In the absence of microsopic examinations, this brown discoloration of the internal tissue is the best ocular evidence of the presence of the wilt disease.

Plants may partially recover from a severe attack of the wilt disease by the development of strong lateral branches near the ground. Such plants may be distinguished by their dwarfed and bushy appearance and by the tendency of their branches to lie prostrate on the ground.

CAUSE OF THE DISEASE.

The cause of the wilt disease of cotton is a fungus, *Neocosmospora vasinfecta* (Atk.) Erw. Sm., which attacks the plant from the soil. It first enters the smaller roots and subsequently grows from these into the taproot and stem, filling the water ducts with its mycelium. The result is that the supply of food and moisture carried up from the roots is greatly decreased and the symptoms described above are produced. . . .

The progress of the disease is always slow as compared with that of other plant diseases. The period of incubation, or the time elapsing after the young seedling is exposed to the attacks of the fungus and before the disease becomes manifest, is usually at least forty days and often much longer. Much depends on the individual plant itself. The conditions which favor the progress of the fungus through the plant are not fully understood, but from some observations that have been made it is believed that highly fertilized plants, growing vigorously, succumb more readily than those which have grown on poorer soil.

In the early history of the wilt disease the cause was supposed by the planters to be the excessive applications or injudicious use of commercial fertilizers, and many of the leading planters in the

Farmsteads

The log cabin introduced by the Swedes became the typical home of Americans on their way West.

As subsistence farming gave way to commercial agriculture, attractive and well-built homes dotted the landscape. Pictured here is the Minnesota home of Oliver H. Kelley, founder of the National Grange.

The High Plains of the West was the last part of the nation to be settled under the Homestead Act. This Montana ranch was established about 1905.

Accumulated wealth, expanded markets, increased technical knowledge, and mechanization made possible the development of substantial farmsteads.

In 1800, farm tools and equipment, such as the sickle and flail shown here, were nearly as primitive as those used in Biblical days.

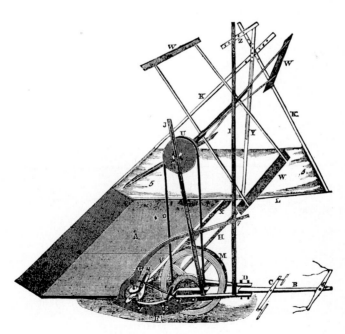

Horse-drawn mechanical grain reapers were patented in 1833 and 1834 by Obed Hussey and Cyrus H. McCormick. This is a drawing of McCormick's 1834 machine.

The reaper, after it was perfected, cut grain and tied it into bundles which were later threshed by a tractor operating a separator.

In the arid West large scale machines were developed for cutting and threshing the grain in one operation, thus eliminating the laborious task of shocking wheat and later getting it into the threshing machines.

The horse-drawn "combines" gave way to highly efficient tractor-powered machines.

Tools and Machinery: Plows and Power

The crude oxen-powered wooden plow of the colonial period was replaced on some farms by Jethro Wood's iron plow after 1814.

After the 1830's, when John Lane and John Deere invented steel plows, even the tough prairie sod could be broken.

Tractors pulling plows with several shares greatly speeded up the preparation of seed-beds. By 1955, there were more tractors than there were horses and mules on farms.

Throughout the colonial period and until after the Civil War, sailing ships carried nearly all of our agricultural exports.

Frontier agriculture was dependent on products of high value like corn whiskey that could be carried on a pack horse, or on livestock that could walk to market. Cattle trails on the Great Plains were long preceded by similar trails east of the Appalachian Mountains and in the Ohio country.

Freighting farm products such as bales of cotton on land was slow and expensive, and was usually limited to short hauls to water or, later, rail transportation.

Stage coach transportation, whether in the Concord stage or in such smaller vehicles as this one in western Nebraska, was limited to passengers, mail, and particularly valuable packages.

The railroad with steam locomotive was the all-important development in transportation. This Currier and Ives print contrasts the old with the new.

Modern truck markets such as this one at Benton Harbor, Michigan, developed during the 1950's.

The chain store and supermarket became widespread after World War I. By the 1960's, many supermarkets carried a wide assortment of food, dry goods, and hardware.

Community Life

On the frontier, farm homes were often isolated and the most frequent visitors were the doctor and circuit rider.

As land areas were opened to settlement, towns grew up rapidly.

The spread of education resulted in the construction of public schools in rural areas.

With the establishment of the Extension Service in 1914, county agents, home demonstration agents, and soil conservation people started work with young people to teach them the value of better methods.

The growth of agricultural colleges gave farm youth an opportunity to prepare themselves for community leadership and to learn modern agricultural methods.

Sea Islands made careful experiments with various modifications of their fertilizers, such as the use of marl, salt mud, kainit, and lime, and the increase or decrease of the proportions of phosphoric acid and potash. Mr. W. G. Hinson, of James Island, South Carolina, a very successful planter, has informed the writer that the result of all these trials has been to convince those who made them that the disease can not be controlled by any changes in their system of fertilizing.

The wilt disease occurs in so many widely separated localities and under such varied cultural conditions that it is not probable that any errors in the agricultural practice are the primary cause of the trouble, although the planting of cotton year after year on the same land and the common practice of plowing under the last year's stems in preparing the ground in the spring both tend to hasten the spread of the wilt fungus after it has once been introduced. . . .

SELECTION OF RESISTANT RACES.

The most encouraging results have come from the endeavor of the Department to find a race of cotton which can be grown on the infected lands. There are always some plants in every field which resist the disease to a greater or less extent, and it frequently happens that of two plants in the same hill, equally exposed to infection, one will die and the other live to the end of the season. All degrees of resistance may be found, from plants nearly killed by the wilt disease to those entirely healthy. The latter are comparatively uncommon, however.

Different races of cotton vary considerably in their susceptibility to the wilt disease. This was shown by an experiment carried out by the Department on the farm of Mr. H. L. Galloway, at Dillon, S. C. Twenty races, including the more prominent ones in cultivation, were planted in a field that was thoroughly infected with the wilt disease, and their comparative resistance determined in August by counting the number of plants remaining healthy, those partially diseased, and those killed.

None of the races tested were entirely resistant, but some showed great promise in this regard. The greatest resistance was shown by the Egyptian cottons, Mitafifi, Abbasi, and Jannovitch, which withstood the disease to a very marked extent. Very few plants were killed outright, although nearly all were considerably reduced in size and yield. . . . There were one or more plants in each race that entirely withstood the disease, and the seed from these has been saved with the intention of securing valuable resistant strains by cross-breeding them.

The ability of certain cotton plants to grow on infected land is due to the fact that the wilt fungus is unable to enter their principal root system and not to any lack of infection. This has been determined by microscopic examination. . . .

In this connection the most important question is whether this quality of resistance to disease is transmissible through the seed to succeeding generations. An experiment designed to settle this point proved a remarkable success. It was carried out by Mr. Elias L. Rivers, of James Island, S. C., who selected a healthy plant of sea island cotton that grew in a badly blighted field in 1899. The seed from this resistant plant was saved and planted in a single row through a field that had been infected with the wilt disease for several years. The adjoining rows were planted with seed from his main crop, grown on noninfected land. . . .The wilt disease made almost a clean sweep through the ordinary cotton, 95 percent of the plants being killed, while in the row planted with seed from the resistant plant *not a single plant was killed by the wilt disease.*

These plants were vigorous and productive. The dwarfing noted in Egyptian and upland cotton grown by the writer on infected land at Dillon, S. C., was not so marked here. The quality of lint was good, though not equal to the crop from which the selection was made. It is believed, however, that by continued cross breeding and selection in succeeding years the quality of the cotton may be improved without loss of resistance to the wilt disease. Work along this line has already been started in a small way by the Department, which it is hoped may be enlarged.

It has been shown that much can be accomplished in the control of the wilt disease of cotton by simply selecting seed from resistant plants. It is very probable that better results will be obtained by cross-breeding these resistant individuals, for in this way the resistant qualities of two plants will be combined and there will be added the increased vigor which usually comes from crossing. On the other hand, if the flowers of a resistant cotton plant should be fertilized by pollen brought by insects from a diseased plant, as may easily happen in the field, plants grown from the resulting seeds will very likely be less resistant than if they had been ferti-lized by pollen from another resistant plant. On this account, in the selection of resistant races, it will be desirable to cross by hand as many flowers as possible in order to increase the chances of success.

In connection with the work of the Department a large number of crosses between resistant plants have already been made. It has been our aim to secure resistant strains from our common races by cross-fertilizing plants of the same race, and at the same time to increase the productiveness and improve the quality of selecting the best plants of each sort for breeding.

The fact that the Egyptian cottons are resistant to the wilt disease has led to the attempt to produce a resistant long-staple upland cotton, by hybridizing resistant plants of the common upland races with the Egyptian cotton. It is very desirable that everyone who undertakes the breeding of resistant cotton should at the same time pay great attention to securing a more productive race and a finer quality of staple.

CONTROL OF OTHER WILT DISEASES BY SELECTION.

The indications are that other diseases similar to the cotton wilt may also be controlled by the selection of resistant races.

The wilt of the cowpea, which is a troublesome disease in many parts of the South, is caused by a fungus closely allied to that producing the cotton wilt (*Neocomospora vasinfecta* var. *trachei-phila*). In this case we already have a race, known as Little Iron, which will grow on infected land. A fine crop of this pea was grown during the past season by Mr. T. S. Williams, of Monetta, S. C., on fields where the whole crop was lost last year and where other races planted alongside it this year have been practically ruined.

Further investigations will probably result in the discovery of other races of cowpeas which may be so improved by selection that they may be planted on land infected by the wilt disease.

The wilt disease of watermelons, also allied to the two preceding, may prove amenable to the same treatment. The Department has under way some experiments to determine the possibility of finding a race of watermelon which may be grown on infected land. This would be exceedingly desirable, for this disease has made the grow-ing of melons for market impossible over large areas in the South which formerly produced them in great abundance.

CONCLUSIONS.

There is great promise of a successful remedy for the cotton-wilt disease in selection of seeds from healthy plants growing on infected soils and by continuing to select and cross-breed the most resistant plants in succeeding crops with a view both to resistance and quality of staple.

It would be well in the case of upland cotton to start with a race like the Jackson, which is already highly resistant, and improve and fix the quality by careful cross breeding and selection. In places where this cluster type of cotton is undesirable a resistant strain of the sorts commonly cultivated can probably be obtained by cross breeding and selection. It is hardly to be expected that this process will result in a perfectly immune race the first year. Even though much of the cotton become diseased, the selection should be continued each succeeding year until the quality of resistance is fixed.

In the case of the sea island cotton, where length and fine quality of staple are essential, the process of selection and breeding should be the same. Resistance to disease must be the primary requisite, and from the resistant plants those bearing the finest lint may be selected.

The Egyptian cottons will probably prove of the greatest value when crossed with our upland races so as to add the vigor and quality of the former to the productiveness of the latter. It is hoped that the Department will be able to extend its work along this promising line.

In addition to selection for resistance, all practicable preventive measures should be applied. Rotation of crops is even more important on these infected soils than on healthy ones, for the continual growing of cotton on these lands will increase the amount of disease and decrease the resistance of the cotton.

Prompt destruction of diseased plants is also very important. Every effort should be made to avoid the infection of healthy fields by animals, tools, wash water from diseased fields, diseased plants, infected compost, etc. As already stated, land once infected with this disease remains infected for an unknown period.

34

Rise of Dry Farming

Dry farming, that is, agriculture without irrigation in regions of scanty precipitation, has been widely practiced in the Great Plains area and in a few other parts of the western United States. It has been most important as a definite system of farming in areas where rainfall averages less than 20 inches a year. From 1875 to 1886, when settlers were first moving into the Great Plains, abundant rainfall occurred. Thereafter, the climate fluctuated between periods of drought, abundant rainfall, and scanty rainfall. These wide climatic fluctuations never seemed to be expected by the farmers of the region.

A definite system of dry farming was developed in the 1890's as a reaction to the scanty rainfall of the 1880's. The system can be attributed to the efforts of one man, Hardy Webster Campbell, a Vermonter who had homesteaded in Brown County, Dakota Territory. Campbell invented a subsoil packer about 1890, and then operated demonstration farms for railroads. In 1894 a dry-farming experiment station was established at Cheyenne Wells, Colorado. By the end of the century dry farming was hailed as the solution to the agricultural problems of the Great Plains.

Campbell published the first edition of his *Soil Culture Manual* in 1902, drawing for part of his theory upon the work of F. H. King, professor of agricultural physics at the University of Wisconsin. All dry-farming practices centered upon the aim of conserving the scant moisture supply by reducing or eliminating run-off and evaporation and by increasing the absorption and retention of moisture by the soil. Campbell emphasized that the subsoil should be packed, so that water would be attracted from the lower depths by capillarity. The surface of the soil should be protected against evaporation by a dust mulch, which must be renewed after each rainfall. These basic practices were supplemented by Campbell and others to include deep fall plowing, thorough cultivation both before and after seeding, light seeding, and alternating summer fallow with tillage. Some scientists, particularly those at the Montana Agricultural Experiment Station, urged that crops adapted to dry conditions be planted.

The United States Department of Agriculture concluded after experiments that no single system of dry farming was suitable for all conditions, that emphasis must be given to selecting plants suitable to dry climates, and that a balanced farm economy was necessary. A group of plant explorers, notably Nils E. Hansen and Mark Carleton, brought hardy crops from Russia, Siberia, China, and other parts of the world.

The work of the Department and many of the state experiment stations was not completed and publicized in time to prevent the dry-farming movement from becoming a promotional device. Campbell himself was professionally identified with various western railroads during most of his career, and had widespread support form other business leaders interested in promoting settlement in the region. The Dry Farming Congress, first held in Denver in 1907, was sponsored by the same groups interested in attracting new settlers. Over a period of years, dry farming as a system was modified in every particular. Its greatest importance lies not in the value of the system to farming, but in its promotional role in settlement of the semiarid region.

Campbell's System of Dry Farming

H. W. Campbell, *Campbell's 1902 Soil Culture Manual*, pp. 12, 22, 29, 34, 47. (Holdrege, Nebr., H. W. Campbell, 1902).

In outlining our general suggestions for securing the best possible crop results throughout this great plains country, we must of course begin with the preparation of the ground. Owing to the fact that in the settled portions the average farmer has already a sufficient area of ground under cultivation, we will start out with the preparation of ground that has been in crop the previous year. The first and all important work is the double discing of this ground in early spring, beginning as soon as the frost is out a fair depth and the surface sufficiently dry to allow of discing without having the soil adhere to the disc too much. It is not uncommon to see farmers double disc by first going over the ground one way and then cross disc it. This results in a series of ridges and trenches, leaving the surface very uneven. The trenches exposing solid soil to the surface allow of much evaporation. The proper manner of double discing is to lap half, which leaves the surface smooth and thoroughly pulverized. In the lapping of the half of the disc the last time over, the last discs revolve at right angles with the discs that precede. . . . The packing of the subsoil, or what may be properly termed the root-bed, aids us in these important points; increasing the water holding capacity of the soil facilitates the movement of the water from below up to this point when it is needed, is conducive to a much greater development of root growth; and still further, and quite as important, enables us to utilize the entire soil, having no waste ground caused by a loose or porous condition of the soil.

This is so important that it may be stated again plainly, so that no reader may misunderstand. The process of packing the under portion of furrow or plowed ground creates three conditions to aid in carrying the growing crop over long dry periods, namely:

1. More water in the soil.
2. A stronger capillary movement of water.
3. More prolific growth of roots.

Don't pack the surface; it increases the loss of moisture by evaporation.

Less seed is needed in packed soil than in loose soil for the same crop result.

Pack the lower portion of your plowing the same day you plow, to save the moisture. . . .

The proper time for cultivating a field is one that cannot be fixed without much thought, observation, and judgment by the farmer, especially if he would get the best results. Always cultivate immediately, or as soon after a rain as conditions will permit you on the field, and the soil is sufficiently dried so that it will not adhere to the cultivator teeth, or tools used. We do not mean by this that the soil should be absolutely dry on the surface. It is an error to wait for that time, for the moment the surface is apparently dry the crust begins to form. It is desirable to catch the ground just before this time when all the soil is simply moist and then there is a free and ready separation of all particles. In this condition the cultivator runs the easiest, the mulch made the finest and lies up light and loose. If the soil is a little too wet it settles, and not unfrequently forms absolute and perfect connection with the firm soil below, steadily carrying moisture to the surface. If too dry the cultivator produces an imperfect mulch that gives us but little protection.

Another and very important idea is that every moment's delay after the soil reaches the proper condition causes you to lose water very fast. It is at the rate of a quart or over per square foot per day providing it is clear sunny weather, and even more in case of heavy south winds. The more intense the heat the more frequent is it necessary to cultivate. A very good rule is to watch the condition of the firm soil just beneath the loose mulch or cultivated portion, and whenever the surface of this firm soil begins to show dryness it is high time to commence cultivating again. If the field is left too long during the extreme dry period the surface of the solid soil beneath the mulch will begin to form a crust, practically the same as is shown on the surface of the soil when uncultivated after a rain. . . .In treating the land as we would suggest we do not think the name summer fallow, applies. Therefore term it summer culture; beginning the work as early in the spring as the frost is sufficiently out of the ground and the surface dry enough to permit the use of the disc harrow without the soil adhering to the disc, going over the ground twice by lapping the disc one-half. This produces a mulch which prevents evaporation; also opens and loosens the surface, so that the later rains readily and quickly percolate into the soil, going over the ground after each subsequent rain with a harrow, or if the rain is too heavy so as to dissolve and pack the surface, a second discing may be necessary, especially so if the season is advanced far enough for weeds to start freely. Don't at all hazards permit the weeds to grow or the surface to become crusted, bearing in mind our main object is to *store* the water in the soil below. Plow in June or early July about seven inches deep. Do not leave the field at noon until that which has been plowed during the forenoon has been gone over with the sub-surface packer, if such a tool you have, if not, use the harrow. (If you have no packer borrow one) Then at night the same, and if you use the packer follow it with the Acme harrow at night, going over the entire day's plowing. . . .

With the fact that the moisture can be stored in the ground and there controlled and made available to the plant by the aid of capillary attraction, with such results as have been indicated, what are the possibilities of this great semi-arid belt? No one who has ever passed over this country, or remained in it for any length of time, has ever discovered any objections outside of this one fact, that crops and trees have not been successfully grown. All agree that the climate is most magnificent, the soil exceedingly fertile and very easy of tillage. The condition of the majority of the soil in the eastern states, that is, its composition and formation is such as to not be susceptible to the remarkable effects of capillary movements of moisture that are shown in the great semi-arid belt. . . .

Percolation, evaporation, and capillary attraction; they will be found more interesting the more the reader and investigator understands them, and when fully understood, the question of soil culture will be much better appreciated. You will then comprehend why the plowing should be reasonably deep and the under portion made fine and firm, while the top should be fine, but loose and dry.

35

Serum -Virus Treatment Against Hog Cholera

Progress in agriculture has been a many-sided development. New machines, new types of plants and animals, new methods, and new economic patterns have all contributed to this progress. The conquest of plant and animal diseases, a conquest that is never final, has been as marked a break with earlier experience as anything else that has contributed to present-day agriculture.

During the last part of the nineteenth century, hog cholera was causing farmers losses that in some years amounted to more than 65 million dollars. The Bureau of Animal Industry carried on research which indicated that a bacterium caused hog cholera and developed a serum from the bacteria. In 1894, the Bureau hired Marion Dorset to work on a preventative or cure for the disease. Dorset tested the serum in an outbreak of hog cholera in Iowa in the summer of 1897, but found that it did not protect the animals.

Back in Washington, Dorset, with the support of his immediate supervisor, E. A. de Schweinitz, undertook new investigations which proved that hog cholera was not caused by a bacterium but by a virus. He also proved that hogs that recovered from the disease were immune for life.

During another major outbreak in Iowa in 1903, Dorset, with the help of other investigators, found that injecting well hogs with blood from hogs that had recovered from the disease gave temporary immunity. Then Dorset developed the idea of using two injections. One was of blood from a hog that had survived both an attack and an injection of blood from an infected hog. The second injection was virus. This treatment, with slight modification, is still in use. Hog cholera has been brought under control.

The new theory regarding the cause of the disease and the treatment for immunizing hogs were first announced by de Schweinitz and Dorset in 1903. Both the theory and the treatment were subsequently refined, but the basic ideas were in the first announcement.

Serum-Virus Treatment Against Hog Cholera Announced

E. A. de Schweinitz and Marion Dorset, "New Fact Concerning the Etiology of Hog Cholera," U.S. Department of Agriculture, Bureau of Animal Industry, *Annual Report*, 1903, pp. 157-158, 160-162 (Washington, Government Printing Office, 1904).

During the course of the investigations concerning hog cholera which have been carried on by the Biochemic Division of the Bureau of Animal Industry, certain outbreaks of that disease were met with which apparently were not produced by the hog-cholera or the swine-plague bacilli. The disease was highly contagious and fatal to a large proportion of the hogs which were attacked. These observations, which were inexplicable previous to the researches herein recorded, together with the great variations in the physical symptoms and the postmortem lesions encountered in different outbreaks of so-called "hog cholera," have led us to institute experiments to determine, if possible, whether or not there are other infectious diseases among hogs in this country than those caused by the hog-cholera and swine-plague bacilli, and also to ascertain what was the etiological agent in those outbreaks of disease mentioned above, which apparently did not depend upon these bacilli for their existence. These experiments have not yet been completed, but have gone far enough to enable us to publish this preliminary information.

The outbreaks of disease which have furnished material for the study of the questions just outlined have all had their origin in southwestern Iowa, but, owing to the great distance of that point from Washington and the fact that it was not possible to establish a satisfactory laboratory in the field, it has been found necessary to expose a certain number of animals to infection in Iowa and then transport them by express to the Bureau Experiment Station near this city, where all the inoculations were made by the superintendent of the station. After once bringing the disease to Washington no trouble was, as a rule, experienced in perpetuating it by transferring from one animal to another.

The experiments have reached such a stage that we feel justified in stating that there is an infectious disease among hogs in this country which can not be distinguished clinically from hog cholera, and which may be reproduced by infecting with material which contains no hog cholera bacilli. It will be understood that at this time no estimate can be made as to the frequency with which this disease occurs, nor as to its distribution throughout the country.

Below is presented a brief outline of the facts which have been established in regard to this disease.

ETIOLOGY.

Nothing can be stated at present as to the cause of this disease. It has been demonstrated, however, that the primary cause is neither the hog-cholera bacillus nor the swine-plague bacillus. We have transferred the disease repeatedly from one hog to another by subcutaneous inoculation of certain body fluids, these fluids being always proved, by careful bacteriological examinations, by filtration through the finest porcelain filters, and by the inoculation of guinea pigs and rabbits, to be free from hog-cholera and swine-plague bacilli. We have used a system of checks upon the various inoculation experiments by means of which we have been able to exclude all chance of accidental pen infection or of infection through the syringes.

The disease is highly contagious, healthy pigs that were allowed to come in contact with sick animals almost invariably becoming sick within the usual period of incubation. So far we have been unable to communicate this disease to any other animal than hogs. Rabbits and guinea pigs are entirely insusceptible to inoculations that are of sufficient size to destroy pigs weighing from 30 to 40 pounds. . . .

The fact that this particular type of hemorrhagic hog cholera is so similar in both symptoms and lesions to the ordinary acute hog cholera supposed to be caused by the hog-cholera bacillus, and that, by our methods of inoculation, without the presence of the hog-cholera bacillus, we have never produced a case of *chronic* hog cholera, have led us to suspect that possibly in *all* outbreaks of *acute* hog cholera there is some other agent besides the hog-cholera bacillus at work, and that in those cases of acute disease where the hog-cholera bacillus is found we have to do, not with a pure infection, but with a mixed infection by hog-cholera bacilli and the organisms which are responsible for the disease which we have just described. In fact, virulent hog-cholera bacilli have been isolated from hogs in which the disease had been produced by inoculation with infective material in which the absence of the bacilli had been proved by filtration, by cultures, and by the inoculation of rabbits or guinea pigs.

If such supposition is well founded, it is quite evident what an important bearing it must have upon the prevention and treatment of hog cholera, and we hope to be able to decide this point positively when the experiments now under way shall have been completed.

Sufficient work has been done to show that this particular form of hog cholera may be prevented by those measures which have been found to be effective in dealing with the ordinary forms of that disease—the isolation of sick animals and disinfection of all infected lots with carbolic acid and lime being sufficient to prevent a spread of the disease.

METHODS OF PRODUCING IMMUNITY.

As experiments in this line and also in methods of producing immunity from this disease have been in progress for some years, it seems that, in view of the results, the important points of the investigations should be published, so that the State experiment stations and others, if they so desire, may make experiments on a large scale along the lines of work which have proved most successful.

On account of the often discordant results which were secured some years ago when the Bureau was treating diseased hogs with serum from animals which in their turn had received large and repeated doses of hog-cholera and swine plague cultures, it appeared that some other factor must be considered in the efforts to produce immunity. The first suggestion of de Schweinitz was that some parasite of the hog, such as the louse, should be studied. This was carefully done, but the results obtained were such as to make it appear that, while a louse might under certain conditions convey disease from a sick to a healthy animal, it was not the important agent in spreading so-called hog cholera.

A large number of specimens of blood from sick and healthy hogs were also examined and, while very small, peculiar, round bodies were found both inside and outside of the corpuscle, and sometimes bodies with distinct ameboid movement were noted, the relation, if any existed, of these bodies to the disease could not be determined satisfactorily. It was noted, however, that in cases of so-called hog cholera the disease could be readily conveyed from a sick animal to a healthy one by giving the latter a subcutaneous injection of the blood serum or defibrinated blood obtained from the former. It was found that a small fraction of a cubic centimeter would produce the disease, though we have in most of our experiments fixed 1 cubic centimeter as the most satisfactory dose for use. As has been indicated above, blood from a diseased animal which was passed through the finest Berkefeld or Chamberland filter produced in hogs the typical disease. This blood had been proved to be free from microorganisms detectable by the ordinary bacteriological methods or by the inoculation of small animals, such as the guinea pig or rabbit, which are known to be very susceptible to the ordinary hog-cholera bacillus. It appeared, therefore, that immunity could be produced by the use of blood in which the disease-producing property had been attenuated or partially neutralized. The experiments have well established the fact, which is also true of the so-called hog cholera, that animals once immunized against this disease will resist repeated large doses of disease-producing blood and also subsequent exposure to diseased hogs in the field.

The basis of the immunity experiments, therefore, has been the use of attenuated and disease-producing liquid or dried blood, or the use of this blood mixed with blood obtained from immune animals, in which animals the immunity has been increased by the injection of large doses of disease-producing blood obtained from hogs known to have the disease; or, in other words, disease-producing blood and antitoxic blood separate and combined have been successfully used.

In order to test the immunity of the treated animals, they were either exposed by inoculating them with known disease-producing blood or by placing them in the field or pen with sick animals.

The previous work of this Bureau has shown very clearly that animals immune from hog cholera are not necessarily immune from swine plague, or vice versa, and, furthermore, that many different diseases may at times be mistaken for hog cholera. In making practical exposure tests, therefore, it is absolutely necessary to prove the character of the disease by careful autopsies and by the use of a large number of checks, which checks should succumb to the disease in order to prove the positive virulence of the exposure.

Although we are still trying the experiments on a large scale and shall continue them during the coming summer before recommending the details of a plan for practical adoption, we feel that these results of the extensive and laborious experiments which have been carried on by the Bureau for a number of years should be presented now in this concrete form, as it will require a number of months to prepare the detailed reports of the experiments for publication.

The writers have had charge of the general plan of this work and proposed the use of blood from diseased and immunized animals. The practical inoculations and autopsies at the Experiment Station of the Bureau have been carried out under the supervision of Dr. E. C. Schroeder, who also made, at the request of the Chief of the Bureau, some immunity experiments with dried diseased blood. The work in Iowa has been in charge of Dr. W. B. Niles.

36

Farm Demonstrations to Combat Boll Weevil
Lead to County Agent System

The boll weevil crossed the Rio Grande River into the United States in 1892, and within ten years threatened to destroy the cotton industry. The Department of Agriculture began investigations in 1894. By 1897 the Division of Entomology had developed the "cultural" remedy, which has remained at the heart of boll weevil control.

The control plan, which was aimed basically at growing cotton in such a way that it would mature earlier, had been adopted by very few farmers by 1902. Damage to the Texas crop was so great in that year that a clamor arose for federal aid. Secretary of Agriculture James Wilson proposed a plan developed jointly by the Bureau of Plant Industry and the Bureau of Entomology, whereby attention would be given to ten distinct lines of work. One line, that of taking to cotton planters everywhere the latest results as to methods of meeting the emergency, was assigned to Seaman A. Knapp of the Bureau of Plant Industry.

Knapp, then seventy years old, had had wide experience in agriculture. He had been a farmer, professor of agriculture, and president of Iowa Agricultural College. He had then been in charge of developing a large tract of land in western Louisiana, where he introduced the successful production of rice. Later he served the Department of Agriculture as an agent in the Orient and in Puerto Rico.

Experience and observation had led Knapp to believe that farmers would not change their practices through observing work on demonstration farms operated at government expense, but could be convinced of the value of change through demonstrations carried on by the farmers themselves on their own farms and under ordinary farm conditions. Knapp decided to apply these observations on his new job.

Even before the new appropriation was available, Knapp had put his plan into effect on a farm near Terrell, Texas. A group of businessmen and farmers raised an indemnity fund to reimburse a volunteer farmer for any losses suffered through following the new methods. This experiment was so successful, in spite of bad weather and heavy boll weevil damage, that it gave much impetus to demonstration work carried on by farmers.

In establishing the work on a wider basis, Knapp solicited funds and cooperation from farmers, businessmen, railroads, and bankers. In 1906 the General Education Board of New York City agreed to supplement government funds for the employment of field agents under the direction of Dr. Knapp. The agents worked in districts which covered from ten to twenty counties.

On November 12, 1906, the first county agent, W. C. Stallings, was appointed in Smith County, Texas. The ravages of the boll weevil had been so severe that businessmen in the county offered to pay most of the expense involved in employing an agent to work full time with the farmers in the one county. The success of this experiment led to similar activities in a number of other counties. In 1910, demonstration work was carried on in 455 counties in 12 southern states by 450 agents. By that time, boys' and girls' club work and home demonstration work had become part of the program.

Demonstration or county agent work developed much more slowly and somewhat differently in the northern states. It was under the direction of the Office of Farm Management of the Bureau of Plant Industry. Several business groups and philanthropic organizations assisted in promoting and financing the movement, while the Office of Farm Management also cooperated closely with the state agricultural colleges.

In 1911 a "farm bureau" of the Binghamton, New York, Chamber of Commerce was established with a farm agent in charge. The bureau was to be financed jointly by the local railroad, the chamber of commerce, and the United States Department of Agriculture, with the state agricultural college aiding with advice and encouragement. This "farm bureau" gave the name to a movement which was to become most active in supporting the county agent program.

The usefulness of the county agents and the large number of organizations interested in the movement led to widespread agitation for federal aid. The agricultural college association drafted the first bill, which was introduced in 1908. Others followed. The Smith-Lever Act for cooperative extension work was approved May 8, 1914.

Knapp Discusses Demonstration Work

S. A. Knapp, "The Farmers' Cooperative Demonstration Work," in U.S. Department of Agriculture, *Yearbook,* 1909, pp. 153-160 (Washington, Government Printing Office, 1910).

PURPOSE OF THE WORK.

The aim of the Farmers' Cooperative Demonstration Work is to place a practical object lesson before the farm masses, illustrating the best and most profitable methods of producing the standard farm crops, and to secure such active participation in the demonstrations as to prove that the farmers can make a much larger average annual crop and secure a greater return for their toil.

This work shows also that there is no necessity for the general deterioration of farms and the too common poverty of the rural masses.

Briefly stated, the salient features of the rural lessons given by the farm demonstration work are as follows:

(1) Better drainage of the soil.

(2) A deeper and more thoroughly pulverized seed bed; deep fall breaking (plowing) with implements that will not bring the subsoil to the surface.

(3) The use of seed of the best variety, intelligently selected and carefully stored.

(4) In cultivated crop giving the rows and the plants in the rows a space suited to the plant, the soil, and the climate.

(5) Intensive tillage during the growing period of the crops.

(6) The importance of a high content of humus in the soil; the use of legumes, barnyard manure, farm refuse, and commercial fertilizers.

(7) The value of crop rotation and a winter cover crop on southern farms.

(8) The accomplishing of more work in a day by each laborer by using more horsepower and better implements.

(9) The importance of increasing the farm stock to the extent of utilizing all the waste products and idle lands of the farm.

(10) The production of all food required for the men and animals on the farm.

(11) The keeping of an account with each farm product, in order to know from which the gain or loss arises.

PLAN OF ORGANIZATION.

The Farmers' Cooperative Demonstration Work is conducted by a special agent in charge, who reports directly to the Chief of the Bureau of Plant Industry. There are five general assistants and a full office force; also a corps of field agents is employed, classified according to territory in charge, as state, district, and county agents. These agents are selected with special reference to a thorough knowledge of improved agriculture and practical experience in farming in the sections to which appointed. The county agents are appointed mainly on the advice of local committees of prominent business men and farmers conversant with the territory to be worked. Each agent has in charge the practical work in one or more counties, strictly under such general directions as may be issued from the central office at Washington D. C.; district agents are expected to have not only a knowledge of scientific agriculture, but to be practical farmers and to have had considerable experience in the demonstration work. State agents are strong and capable men, who have shown their ability to carry out successfully the instructions of the central office over a large territory, and they are especially qualified for the work by the possession of the tact necessary to influence men.

The term "demonstration farm" is used to designate a portion of land on a farm that is worked strictly according to our instructions. This is visited by an agent as often as once a month, if possible, to see that these instructions are carried out and to give any further advice necessary.

A "cooperator" is a farmer who agrees to work a part or all of his crop according to our instructions.

The Farmers' Cooperative Demonstration Work now covers portions of 12 States, employs 375 traveling agents, has many thousand demonstration farms, and potentially influences, through boys' corn clubs, field schools, and cooperators, a much larger number than are classed as demonstrators. At present it has close cooperation with six agricultural colleges and a large number of rural schools, assisting the latter to make field demonstrations. It also cooperates with state and county superintendents of public instruction in demonstrations for boys' corn clubs.

This work is supported by Congressional appropriation, by liberal contributions from the General Education Board, by county aid, and by donations from boards of trade and private individuals.

A REAL RURAL SCHOOL FOR THE MAN WITH THE PLOW.

The demonstration work may be regarded as a system of adult education given to the farmer upon his farm by means of object lessons in the soil, prepared under his observation and generally by his own hand.

The teaching by object lessons is more effective where it is simple, direct, and limited to a few common field crops, such as cotton, corn, cowpeas, and oats in the South, so that the comparisons may be evident and accepted at a glance. If general success can be secured with these standard crops, further diversification follows as a natural result.

The instruction given for the first year mainly refers to the method of making a larger and more profitable crop at a reduced cost of production, and consists of four lessons, called "the primary lessons:" (1) The best seed bed and how to make it; (2) the best seed of its variety and how to obtain it; (3) frequent and mainly shallow cultivation of the crop—how and why; (4) the use of better teams and tools to secure more economic production.

The principal defects in the seed bed for farm crops in the South are shallow breaking (plowing), failure to fully pulverize the soil before planting, insufficient humus in the soil, and defective drainage. Such a seed bed can never produce maximum crops. It carries insufficient moisture for periods of drought and has an excess under heavy precipitation. During most of the period of growth the plants are insufficiently nourished, either from inability to obtain sufficient food through lack of moisture, or a too diluted nourishment through excess of moisture. The result is a small crop.

The simple remedy is deeper breaking in the fall, thorough use of disk and harrow, plowing under of green crops at frequent periods, and an improvement of the drainage by ditches or tiles.

One cause of the general shallow breaking in the Southern States is the single mule used on many farms and the light mules where they are used double. . . .The one man with one mule is expected to break an acre a day 3 inches deep; one man with a disk plow and four large mules will average 3 acres a day 9 inches deep on rather stiff soil and do a better job.

SEED.

Prior to the commencement of the demonstration work the average farmer in the South gave little attention to seed selection. Corn was culled in the spring from the crib and cotton from the gin-run pile and planted without testing. The result was a poor stand—a condition that can rarely be remedied.

The demonstration work requires seed of a known type, carefully selected, graded, and stored for the first year's planting, and for each succeeding year the planting of a small field remote from any grain crop of the same type; this seed patch to be specially prepared, fertilized, and planted with the seed selected in the field the previous fall when the grain was ripe and afterwards stored in a dry place.

CULTIVATION.

Great use is made of the section harrow before and after planting and when the plants are quite small. Cultivation of cotton or corn in rows is at first deep, but shallow and frequent after the plants are 10 inches tall. This conserves the moisture.

In the practical application of these instructions it has been found that the best seed bed added 100 per cent to the average crop on similar lands with an average preparation; planting the best seed made a gain of 50 per cent, and shallow, frequent cultivation was equal to another 50 per cent, making a total gain of 200 per cent, or a crop three times the average. With better teams and implements this greater crop is made at less cost an acre. The profit increases faster than the yield. If the net profits on a crop of corn yielding 20 bushels an acre, valued at 75 cents a bushel, be $3, on a crop of 60 bushels the net profit would be $33 an acre; that is, the profit is tenfold where the gain in yield is threefold.

It generally requires from two to three years to thoroughly impress the farmer that this lesson of making a greater yield per acre is a practical method of farming applicable to his entire farm. The first year he rarely carries out the entire plan. He has not quite faith enough, or possibly the season is adverse, but he generally succeeds so much better than he expected that the second year's trial is more thorough, with a correspondingly increased gain.

The farmer is a natural doubter. When he has harvested the larger crop the second year, he is frequently inclined to attribute it to one thing, generally the seed, because this is most in evidence, instead of distributing the credit between the better seed bed, the better seed, and the intensive cultivation. Frequently his neighbors, full of the one-idea merit, offer $5 a bushel for the seed, thinking that the seed alone will make the crop. The third year the demonstration farmer is generally more of a convert and enlarges his trial area, frequently including his entire farm. In the meantime his neighbors have been observing and have commenced to inquire and follow his example.

It requires from three to five years to have the increased yield show a considerable average gain in the local markets. This depends, however, somewhat upon the number of demonstrations established in a county. Where one can be placed in each neighborhood the progress is rapid, because the interest soon becomes intense. If only one or two demonstration farms are established in a county, the work does not create interest enough to arouse public sentiment and produce at once a strong opinion in its favor.

As soon as the primary lessons, as above explained, have been accepted and tested by a farmer, a secondary series is commenced, which includes—

(1) Demonstrations in conserving and enriching the soil by the use of legumes and winter cover crops. These involve simple crop rotation and the turning under of green crops; also the prevention of soil waste by erosion.

(2) The value and uses of barnyard manures and commercial fertilizers, and how to apply them.

(3) Simple methods of farm drainage.

The third series of lessons relates to better pastures and meadows and how to secure them; the most economic grain crops for work animals or to produce flesh as a supplement to the pasture and meadow grasses. This line of instruction is necessary, because the economic production of farm crops depends in a great measure upon an economic support of the work teams.

The general method among the small farmers of the South was to depend mainly upon corn fodder and corn. Some had pastures, but rarely a good pasture. This method is expensive and causes a reduction in the number of animals kept for work to the smallest number possible and a corresponding substitution of hand labor. Modern methods of farming require considerable increase in the number and strength of teams. Profitable farming has become a team and implement problem. The improved pasture and cover-cured hay furnished foods of great economy and are sufficiently nutritious for the ordinary support of work stock. For heavy work a small addition of grain to the ration is required.

If it be necessary in the interests of economy to produce upon the farm the food for the work animals it is still more important to produce, as far as possible, the food required by all the laborers and their families. The family garden, the poultry, and the cow are great cash economizers and pocketbook conservers and may be classed with the better teams and tools as essential to better farm equipment.

FIELD SCHOOLS.

A very valuable method of instruction introduced by the demonstration work is the field school. Previous to the time the local agent of the work expects to visit a demonstrator he notifies all the cooperators in the vicinity to meet him there on a certain date at a given hour. Thus, a number of good farmers discuss the methods and, by comparison, place a value upon the work done. The same method is employed in the selection of seed corn. . . .

Such is the isolated situation of the average farmer that he may continue for years to believe he has the best seed of the several crops he produces unless he is brought into direct public comparison and competition with other farmers—not in a fair or exhibition where prizes are to be awarded and only the best specimens are brought, but in a mere exhibit of what the farmers expect to plant without any assorting. The farmers in the First Congressional District in North Carolina were invited to assemble in March, 1909, at central points and each bring about 50 ears of the seed corn they expected to plant. These ears were arranged on a long table in the public square, the owner's name being conspicuously attached to each pile. Expert judges were present to select and test. Some corn was brought that tested less than 45 per cent of fertile grains. At the close of the meeting over 90 per cent of the corn samples went for stock feed and was replaced by purchasing a better variety or quality.

BOYS' CORN CLUBS.

One of the greatest problems before the American people has been how to interest in rural life and attach to the farm the young man who has acquired a liberal education and displayed a capacity for leadership. The loss of rural leaders by emigration to the city has been one of the most serious retrogressive factors in our whole civilization. The Farmers' Cooperative Demonstration Work has solved the problem. These young men left the farm because they were repelled by the hardships, excessive toil, and meager gains on the farm and were allured by a seemingly greater opportunity to acquire wealth, influence, and position in the city. The demonstration work undertakes to create in the schoolboy a love of the farm and a new hope by showing the wonderful possibilities of the soil when properly managed and the ease with which wealth and distinction are achieved in rural life when science and art join hands. This is worked out by the cooperation of the demonstration workers, the county superintendent of public instruction, and the rural teachers.

The superintendent and teachers organize the schoolboys over 10 years of age into clubs; the demonstration work furnishes the plan of organization and the instructions (which the boys agree to observe); the respective parents furnish land, teams, and implements; the merchants and bankers provide the prizes, and the local papers give the publicity. Each boy must personally work 1 acre under the same regulations governing all other contestants. The result of 300 to 400 boys entering such a contest in a county arouses intense interest. The boy learns the best way to raise corn or cotton and his appreciation of the farm is greatly enhanced.

In 1909 the boys in the corn contest of one county in Mississippi averaged a production of 74 bushels of corn per acre, while the farmers averaged less than 20. In South Carolina one boy raised 152½ bushels on a measured acre, while the state average was less than 16.

INCIDENTAL TEACHING.

In addition to the demonstrations made to teach the best methods of securing the largest yields of field crops with the greatest economy, incidentally there is much instruction along the lines of rural improvement, the better home, its equipment and environment, the country roads, the school at the crossroads, rural society, etc. The average farmer takes it for granted that an agent of the Department of Agriculture is an authority upon all lines of husbandry, and innumerable inquiries are made of him about the dairy, the breeding and management of farm stock, horticulture, market gardening, insect pests, etc. All this incidental teaching is done without demonstration by referring the inquirers to the several bureaus in the United States Department of Agriculture, or request is made that bulletins covering the subject of inquiry be forwarded to them by mail.

In still another way the Farmers' Cooperative Demonstration Work is helpful. The many scientific divisions of the Bureau of Plant Industry are annually making discoveries of great value, and the problem has been how to get these to the farmers in a way so effective that they will adopt them. A bulletin does not do this with the average farmer. The agents of the Farmers' Cooperative Demonstration Work can place these improvements or discoveries in the hands of men who will utilize them to advantage because these agents are in touch with all the people. Thus the demonstration work is a means of disseminating information for all the bureaus of the Department that are close to rural life.

DEMONSTRATION WORK HELPFUL IN OTHER WAYS.

In the Southern States, where there are some white and many negro farmers who can not read, there is liable to sweep over a section a wave of depression amounting to a doubt about making a crop, which may cause a perceptible reduction in the acreage planted if the depression is felt prior to planting, or if later it may reduce the tillage of the crop or may result in its total abandonment. Nor is this wave of pessimism confined to the unlettered. Where crops are made on the advance system it may take such a hold of the merchant and the banker that they refuse to make the necessary advances, which forces the laborer and the tenant farmer to remove to territory where the advances can be obtained. In Harrison County, Tex., in 1907, about 500 tenants and laborers were preparing to abandon the farms after the cotton crop was up, through fear that they could not succeed in making it. The same cause enormously reduced the cotton acreage in Louisiana and Mississippi in 1909. The agents of the Farmers' Cooperative Demonstration Work have been exceedingly influential in restoring and maintaining confidence among all classes.

TWO VIEW POINTS.

The Farmers' Cooperative Demonstration Work may be regarded as a method of increasing farm crops and as logically the first step toward a true uplift, or it may be considered a system of rural education for boys and adults by which a readjustment of country life can be effected and placed upon a higher plane of profit, comfort, culture, influence, and power.

Because the first feature of this demonstration work is to show the farmer how he may more than double his crop at a reduced cost of production, it has been regarded by some solely as a method of increasing farm crops by applying scientific principles to the problem. This would be of great value to the world and would stand as a sufficient justification for the efforts put forth and the expenditures involved, but such a conception would fail to convey the broader purpose of this work.

There is much knowledge applicable and helpful to husbandry that is annually worked out and made available by the scientists in the United States Department of Agriculture and in the state experiment stations and by individual farmers upon their farms, which is sufficient to readjust agriculture and place it upon a basis of greater profit, to reconstruct the rural home, and give to country life an attraction, a dignity, and a potential influence it has never received. This body of knowledge can not be conveyed and delivered by a written message to the people in such a way that they will accept and adopt it. This can only be done by personal appeal and ocular demonstrations. This is the mission of the Farmers' Cooperative Demonstration Work, and it has justified its claims by the results.

It is noteworthy that the sciences adopted the demonstration method of instruction long since. The chemist and the physicist require their students to work out their problems in the laboratory, the doctor and surgeon must practice in the hospital, and the mechanical engineer must show efficiency in the shop to complete his education. The Farmers' Cooperative Demonstration Work seeks to apply the same scientific methods to farmers by requiring them to work out their problems in the soil and obtain the answer in the crib. The soil is the farmers' laboratory.

The demonstration method of reaching and influencing the men on the farms is destined ultimately to be adopted by most civilized nations as a part of a great system of rural education.

37

Country Life Commission

After discussing rural problems with a number of people and adopting an idea suggested by Gifford Pinchot, President Theodore Roosevelt on August 10, 1908, asked a group of farm leaders to serve on a country life commission that would report "upon the present condition of country life, upon what means are now available for supplying the deficiencies which exist, and upon the best methods of organized permanent effort in investigation and actual work along the lines I have indicated." Since the President wanted the report by the end of the year, he asked the commission to confine itself to a summary of what was already known, a statement of the problem, and the recommendation of measures tending toward its solution. The commission, under the leadership of Liberty Hyde Bailey, submitted its report to President Roosevelt on January 23, 1909.

The limitations upon the scope of the report make it particularly valuable as indicating recognized problems and solutions that had been previously proposed. The major proposed remedial measures had been suggested by others and had in some instances acquired considerable support. The Country Life Commission pointed out the need for consideration of the total picture and added its weight to the support already accorded several of the measures. However, Congress refused to give its approval to the work of the commission. Nevertheless, over the next few years the government took many of the actions recommended. The commission's effectiveness can also be measured by the recurrent emphasis upon the country life movement since that time and upon the urging during periods of farm distress that a new country life commission be appointed.

Country Life Commission Reports to President Roosevelt

U.S. Country Life Commission, *Report of the Country Life Commission*, 60th Congress, 2nd Session, Senate Document No. 705, pp. 13-20 (Washington, Government Printing Office, 1909).

The Commission finds that agriculture in the United States, taken altogether, is prosperous commercially, when measured by the conditions that have obtained in previous years, although there are some regions in which this is only partially true. The country people are producing vast quantities of supplies for food, shelter, clothing, and for use in the arts. The country homes are improving in comfort, attractiveness and healthfulness. Not only in the material wealth that they produce, but in the supply of independent and strong citizenship, the agricultural people constitute the very foundation of our national efficiency. As agriculture is the immediate basis of country life, so it follows that the general affairs of the open country, speaking broadly, are in a condition of improvement.

Many institutions, organizations, and movements are actively contributing to the increasing welfare of the open country. The most important of these are the United States Department of Agriculture, the colleges of agriculture and the experiment stations in the states, and the national farmers' organizations. These institutions and organizations are now properly assuming leadership in country life affairs, and consequently in many of the public questions of national bearing. With these agencies must be mentioned state departments of agriculture, agricultural societies and organizations of very many kinds, teachers in schools, workers in church and other religious associations, travelling libraries, and many other groups, all working with commendable zeal to further the welfare of the people of the open country.

The Most Prominent Deficiencies.

Yet it is true, notwithstanding all this progress as measured by historical standards, that agriculture is not commercially as profitable as it is entitled to be for the labor and energy that the farmer expends and the risks that he assumes, and that the social conditions in the open country are far short of their possibilities. We must measure our agricultural efficiency by its possibilities rather than by comparison with previous conditions. The farmer is almost necessarily handicapped in the development of his business because his capital is small, and the volume of his transactions limited; and he usually stands practically alone against organized interests. In general readjustment of modern life due to the great changes in manufactures and commerce, inequalities and discriminations have arisen, and naturally the separate man suffers most. The unattached man has problems that government should understand.

The reasons for the lack of a highly organized rural society are very many, as the full report explains. The leading specific causes are:

A lack of knowledge on the part of farmers of the exact agricultural conditions and possibilities of their regions;

Lack of good training for country life in the schools;

The disadvantage or handicap of the farmer as against the established business systems and interests, preventing him from securing adequate returns for his products, depriving him of the benefits that would result from unmonopolized rivers and the conservation of forests, and depriving the community, in many cases, of the good that would come from the use of great tracts of agricultural land that are now held for speculative purposes;

Lack of good highway facilities;

The widespread continuing depletion of soils, with the injurious effect on rural life;

A general need of new active leadership.

Other causes contributing to the general result are: Lack of any adequate system of agricultural credit, whereby the farmer may readily secure loans on fair terms; the shortage of labor, a condition that is often complicated by intemperance among workmen; lack of institutions and incentives that tie the laboring man to the soil; the burdens and the narrow life of farm women; lack of adequate supervision of public health.

The Nature of The Remedies.

Some of the remedies lie with the national Government, some of them with the States and communities in their corporate capacities, some with voluntary organizations, and some with individuals acting alone. From the great number of suggestions that have been made, covering every phase of country life, the Commission now enumerates those that seem to be most fundamental or most needed at the present time.

Congress can remove some of the handicaps of the farmer, and it can also set some kinds of work in motion, such as:

The encouragement of a system of thoroughgoing surveys of all agricultural regions in order to take stock and to collect local fact, with the idea of providing a basis on which to develop a scientifically and economically sound country life;

The encouragement of a system of extension work in rural communities through all the land-grant colleges with the people at their homes and on their farms;

A thoroughgoing investigation by experts of the middleman system of handling farm products, coupled with a general inquiry into the farmer's disadvantages in respect to taxation, transportation rates, cooperative organizations and credit, and the general business system;

An inquiry into the control and use of the streams of the United States with the object of protecting the people in their ownership and of saving to agricultural uses such benefits as should be reserved for these purposes;

The establishing of a highway engineering service, or equivalent organization, to be at the call of the states in working out effective and economical highway systems;

The establishing of a system of parcels posts and postal savings banks;

And providing some means or agency for the guidance of public opinion toward the development of a real rural society that shall rest directly on the land.

Other remedies recommended for consideration by Congress are:

The enlargement of the United States Bureau of Education, to enable it to stimulate and coordinate the educational work of the nation;

Careful attention to the farmers' interests in legislation on the tariff, on regulation of railroads, control of regulation of corporations and of speculation, legislation in respect to rivers, forests and the utilization of swamp lands;

Increasing the powers of the federal government in respect to the supervision and control of the public health;

Providing such regulations as will enable the states that do not permit the sale of liquors to protect themselves from traffic from adjoining states.

In setting all these forces in motion, the cooperation of the States will be necessary; and in many cases definite state laws may greatly aid the work.

Remedies of a more general nature are: A broad campaign of publicity, that must be undertaken until all the people are informed on the whole subject of rural life, and until there is an awakened appreciation of the necessity of giving this phase of our national development as much attention as has been given to other phases or interests; a quickened sense of responsibility in all country people, to the community and to the state in the conserving of soil fertility, and in the necessity for diversifying farming in order to conserve this fertility and to develop a better rural society, and also in the better safeguarding of the strength and happiness of the farm women; a more widespread conviction of the necessity for organization, not only for economic but for social purposes, this organization to be more or less cooperative, so that all the people may share equally in the benefits and have voice in the essential affairs of the community; a realization on the part of the farmer that he has a distinct natural responsibility toward the laborer in providing him with good living facilities and in helping him in every way to be a man among men; and a realization on the part of all the people of the obligation to protect and develop the natural scenery and attractiveness of the open country.

Certain remedies lie with voluntary organizations and institutions. All organized forces both in town and country should understand that there are country phases as well as city phases of our civilization, and that one phase needs help as much as the other. All these agencies should recognize their responsibility to society. Many existing organizations and institutions might become practically cooperative or mutual in spirit, as, for example, all agricultural societies, libraries, Young Men's Christian Associations and churches. All the organizations standing for rural progress should be federated, in states and nation.

The Underlying Problem of Country Life.

The mere enumeration of the foregoing deficiencies and remedies indicates that the problem of country life is one of reconstruction, and that temporary measures and defense work alone will not solve it. The underlying problem is to develop and maintain on our farms a civilization in full harmony with the best American ideals. To build up and retain this civilization means, first of all, that the business of agriculture must be made to yield a reasonable return to those who follow it intelligently; and life on the farm must be made permanently satisfying to intelligent, progressive people. The work before us, therefore, is nothing more or less than the gradual rebuilding of a new agriculture and new rural life. We regard it as absolutely essential that this great general work should be understood by all the people. Separate difficulties, important as they are, must be studied and worked out in the light of the greater fundamental problem.

The Commission has pointed out a number of remedies that are extremely important. But running through all of these remedies are several great forces, or principles, which must be utilized in the endeavor to solve the problems of country life. All the people should recognize what these fundamental forces and agencies are.

Knowledge.—To improve any situation, the underlying facts must be understood. The farmer must have exact knowledge of his business and of the particular conditions under which he works. The United States Department of Agriculture and the experiment stations and colleges are rapidly acquiring and distributing this knowledge; but the farmer may not be able to apply it to the best advantage because of lack of knowledge of his own soils, climate, animal and plant diseases, markets, and other local facts. The farmer is entitled to know what are the advantages and disadvantages of his conditions and environment. A thoroughgoing system of surveys in detail of the exact conditions underlying farming in every locality is now an indispensable need to complete and apply the work of the great agricultural institutions. As an occupation, agriculture is a means of developing our internal resources; we cannot develop these resources until we know exactly what they are.

Education.—There must be not only a fuller scheme of public education, but a new kind of education adapted to the real needs of the farming people. The country schools are to be so redirected that they shall educate their pupils in terms of the daily life. Opportunities for training toward agricultural callings are to be multiplied and made broadly effective. Every person on the land, old or young, in school or out of school, educated or illiterate, must have a chance to receive the information necessary for a successful business, and for a healthful, comfortable resourceful life, both in home and neighborhood. This means redoubled efforts for better country schools, and a vastly increased interest in the welfare of country boys and girls on the part of those who pay the school taxes. Education by means of agriculture is to be a part of our regular public school work. Special agricultural schools are to be organized. There is to be a well-developed plan of extension teaching conducted by the agricultural colleges, by means of the printed page, face-to-face talks, and demonstration or object lessons, designed to reach every farmer and his family, at or near their homes, with knowledge and stimulus in every department of country life.

Organization.—There must be a vast enlargement of voluntary organized effort among farmers themselves. It is indispensable that farmers shall work together for their common interests and for the national welfare. If they do not do this, no governmental activity, no legislation, not even better schools, will greatly avail. Much has been done. There is a multitude of clubs, and associations for social, educational and business purposes; and great national organizations are effective. But the farmers are nevertheless relatively unorganized. We have only begun to develop business cooperation in America. Farmers do not influence legislation as they should. They need a more fully organized social and recreative life.

Spiritual forces.—The forces and institutions that make for morality and spiritual ideas among rural people must be energized. We miss the heart of the problem if we neglect to foster personal character and neighborhood righteousness. The best way to preserve ideals for private conduct and public life is to build up the institutions of religion. The church has great power of leadership. The whole people should understand that it is vitally important to stand behind the rural church and to help it to become a great power in developing concrete country life ideals. It is especially important that the country church recognize that it has a social responsibility to the entire community as well as a religious responsibility to its own group of people.

RECOMMENDATIONS OF THE COMMISSION

The Commission recommends all the correctiv   that have been mentioned under the head of "The Nature of the Remedies." It does not wish to discriminate between important measures of relief for existing conditions. It has purposely avoided endorsing any particular bill now before Congress, no matter what its value or object.

There are, however, in the opinion of the Commission, two or three great movements of the utmost consequence that should be set under way at the earliest possible time because they are fundamental to the whole problem of ultimate permanent reconstruction; these call for special explanation.

1. *Taking stock of country life.*—There should be organized, as explained in the main Report, under government leadership, a comprehensive plan for an exhaustive study or survey of all the conditions that surround the business of farming and the people who live in the country, in order to take stock of our resources and to supply the farmer with local knowledge. Federal and state governments, agricultural colleges and other educational agencies, organizations of various types, and individual students of the problem, should be brought into cooperation for this great work of investigating with minute care all agricultural and country life conditions.

2. *Nationalized extension work.*—Each state college of agriculture should be empowered to organize as soon as practicable, a complete department of college extension, so managed as to reach every person on the land in its state, with both information and inspiration. The work should include such forms of extension teaching as lectures, bulletins, reading-courses, correspondence courses,

demonstration and other means of reaching the people at home and on their farms. It should be designed to forward not only the business of agriculture, but sanitation, education, home-making, and all interests of country life.

3. *A campaign for rural progress.*—We urge the holding of local, state and even national conferences on rural progress, designed to unite the interests of education, organization and religion into one forward movement for the rebuilding of country life. Rural teachers, librarians, clergymen, editors, physicians and others may well unite with farmers in studying and discussing the rural question in all its aspects. We must in some way unite all institutions, all organizations, all individuals, having any interest in country life into one great campaign for rural progress.

THE CALL FOR LEADERSHIP.

We must picture to ourselves a new rural social structure, developed from the strong resident forces of the open country; and then we must set at work all the agencies that will tend to bring this about. The entire people need to be roused to this avenue of usefulness. Most of the new leaders must be farmers who can find not only a satisfying business career on the farm, but who will throw themselves into the service of upbuilding the community. A new race of teachers is also to appear in the country. A new rural clergy is to be trained. These leaders will see the great underlying problem of country life, and together they will work, each in his own field, for the one goal of a new and permanent rural civilization. Upon the development of this distinctively rural civilization rests ultimately our ability, by methods of farming requiring the highest intelligence, to continue to feed and clothe the hungry nations; to supply the city and metropolis with fresh blood, clean bodies and clear brains that can endure the strain of modern urban life; and to preserve a race of men in the open country that, in the future as in the past, will be the stay and strength of the nation in time of war, and its guiding and controlling spirit in time of peace.

It is to be hoped that many young men and women, fresh from our schools and institutions of learning, and quick with ambition and trained intelligence, will feel a new and strong call to service.

PART V

World War I Stimulates Demand for Farm Products, 1914-1919

38

Farm Production Increases During World War I

The tremendous demand for farm products during World War I led to an eventual increase in agricultural production that reached a high point after the effective foreign demand for farm products declined. Before the war, agriculture had enjoyed a comparatively prosperous period in which it had attained something of a balance with other parts of the economy. The war accelerated agriculture's rate of growth, changed world trade channels, and led to a major agricultural depression.

The outbreak of hostilities in Europe during the late summer of 1914 led to a momentary halt in the export of the large American wheat and cotton crops. Exports resumed shortly, however, and prices, particularly of wheat, began to move upward. Farmers increased wheat acreages, and in 1915 produced the first billion-bushel wheat crop in the United States. Prices dropped, but reduced acreages and poor yields in 1916 again led to a price advance.

Cotton production and exports during the war years did not again match the 1914 figures, but the price rose gradually. Tobacco production and prices increased during the war years. Both the production and price of meat also increased.

After 1917 many farmers responded to patriotic appeals and to price inducements aimed at increasing farm output, although total output showed little change between 1917 and 1919, and a 10 per cent increase between 1913 and 1919. On August 10, 1917, the President signed the Food Production Act and the Food and Fuel Control Act. These provided encouragement to farmers to increase production and provided for government control of food supplies.

The Food Production Act was administered by the Secretary of Agriculture. It provided for aid in supplying seed, for activities that would facilitate the distribution of agricultural products, for further development of the Extension Service, and for other activities to encourage food production.

The Food and Fuel Control Act, also known as the Lever Act, gave the President power to control the entire food supply, guaranteed a minimum price of two dollars a bushel for the 1918 wheat crop, and authorized the President to fix such additional guaranteed prices for wheat as he found necessary. The President established the Food Administration, headed by a Food Administrator, to carry out the functions assigned by the Act.

The United States Grain Corporation was established by the Food Administration to purchase wheat and control its distribution. On August 30, 1917, the President fixed a minimum price of $2.20 a bushel for the 1917 wheat crop. On June 21, 1918, the price of wheat was raised to $2.26 a bushel. This price remained in effect for the 1919 crop.

The Food Administration announced on November 13, 1917, that it would attempt to keep the price of hogs in Chicago from going below $15.50 per hundredweight. The 1918 spring hog crop would be supported to return the farmer 13 times the cost per bushel of corn fed for each 100 pounds of hog sold. On September 25, 1918, the Food Administration modified its offer when it appeared that the support might be over $20.00 per hundredweight in relation to corn, and then fixed the minimum price at $18.00, which was not maintained. From November, 1918, to February, 1919, the price was maintained at $17.50.

The response to patriotic appeals, to government assistance, to price guarantees, and to other inducements resulted in an increase of 10 per cent in cropland used for crops between 1913 and 1919. Feed grain production increased 16 per cent from 1913 to 1919, and food grain production 26 per cent. The production of all livestock and livestock products increased 9 per cent in the same period.

Writing in 1918, Benjamin H. Hibbard, an agricultural economist, analyzed the effects of the war upon agriculture. Some of his data have been modified but his general analysis is still accepted.

A Wisconsin Economist Analyzes the Effect of World War I on Agriculture

Benjamin H. Hibbard, *Effects of the Great War Upon Agriculture in the United States and Great Britain*, Carnegie Endowment for International Peace, Preliminary Economic Studies of War No. 11, pp. 22-23, 49-50, 53-54, 74-75, 160-163 (New York, Oxford University Press, 1919).

From the time of the outbreak of the war in August, 1914, to the entrance of the United States into the war in 1917, there intervened two crop years. During these years there were, with few exceptions, sharp increases in prices, and increase in price is undoubtedly the most universally effective force in stimulating greater production. The most remarkable exception to the increase in prices in August, or almost immediately thereafter, was the opposite movement in cotton prices which almost immediately fell, the November price being but slightly over half that of the August price. While the governmental action for stimulating crop and animal production came only after the entrance of the United States into the war, there is so much continuity of influence of the war on agriculture from 1914 on that it seems best to deal with the whole war period as a unit, noting the modifications that occurred after April, 1917, in connection with each topic.

THE LEADING FOOD CROPS

At the outbreak of any war there is an immediate, abnormal demand for food crops and such feed grains as are of use in the army. It is much as though a new group of men and animals were brought within the market influence. Both men and horses do much additional work and therefore consume more. Much is destroyed, used lavishly, or perhaps captured by the enemy. At the same time the productive power of the belligerent nations is reduced in proportion as its man and horse power are withdrawn from peaceful pursuits and used in the armies. Moreover, where several countries which have previously traded among themselves are divided into two belligerent groups the course of trade must be changed to fit the new alignments. When the war broke out in Europe in 1914 all countries involved wanted to buy more supplies. It soon developed that a neutral country with vast stores of supplies for sale, but with few ships, could not go on trading in an undisturbed manner with all countries concerned. The shipping of the United States had been very largely in the hands of the belligerent nations and no sooner had the war begun than the German boats were interned and the English boats to a great extent withdrawn for service in connection with the war. Until the submarine became an important factor there were enough bottoms to carry the foodstuffs and munitions to the Allies. In fact the carrying power of the British merchant marine was increased so far as the United States was concerned, since many ships were withdrawn from the Pacific trade in order to take care of the more immediate needs on the Atlantic. This mobilizing of the shipping facilities between this country and the western Allies was a primary factor in the matter of price and exportation of American grain and cotton, and hence a stimulus to production. . . .

The total acreage of the fifteen principal crops of the United States for the years indicated were as follows:

1910	290,947,000 acres
1914	300,853,000 acres
1915	309,348,000 acres
1916	310,846,000 acres
1917	321,693,000 acres
1918	350,883,000 acres

The increase of these crops from 1910 to 1914 was but 3.4 per cent. From 1914 to 1917 the increase was 6.1 per cent, while from 1916 to 1917 alone it was 3.3 per cent, or almost as much as in four years just prior to the war. The Department of Agriculture estimates that the total area in crops in 1918 is 3.7 per cent greater than in 1917. Where did this increase of ten to fifteen million acres come from? It would be a difficult task to locate it. Undoubtedly it came quite largely from plowing up pastures, somewhat from the cropping of land which would normally have been left fallow. A little of it came from the natural expansion into the remaining wild lands. There is, however, one noticeable feature as to the expansion. It was somewhat greater in the South than in the North. The increase in the acreage of the fifteen crops above considered was greater in the South than in the North, but in addition to this fact there were four minor crops not included in the list of fifteen—sweet potatoes, peanuts, velvet beans and kaffir corn, which showed an aggregate increase of 4,876,000 acres in 1917 over the 1916 figures. Thus the South accounts for the larger part of the total increased crop acreage of the country.

Changes in the numbers of live stock are not made as readily as changes in the acreages of cultivated crops. There was, therefore, naturally a slower response to the price stimulus in the case of live stock than in plant products. However, the prices of bread grains, if not indeed of all grains, has a tendency to outrun live stock prices in time of war. Such is the case now, and the farmers are aware of it. The prices of wheat, rye, corn, and oats are so high that farmers hesitate to go more extensively into live stock, thinking that there is more profit in selling grain than in feeding it. This tendency has been for the most part overcome by the fixing of the hog-corn price ratio, by the fixing of milk prices, the virtual guarantee that beef prices will be steadied through government buying, and the regulation of wool prices. Why, it may be asked, should it be necessary to stabilize meat prices any more than to stabilize the prices of the corn, oats and hay used in animal production? The answer to this is that the process of production in the case of animals is a much longer one than in the case of crop production. The production of most animals not only requires a period of time running over several years, but it requires an investment which can not be shifted without considerable trouble and possible loss. As a result the producers of live stock are more apprehensive concerning future prices than

CROP ACREAGES, 1915-1918

	1910–14	1915	1916	1917	1918
Corn	105,239,000	106,197,000	105,296,000	119,775,000	113,835,000
Wheat	48,952,600	60,496,000	52,316,000	45,941,000	58,881,000
Hay	49,376,800	51,108,000	55,721,000	53,516,000	69,531,000
Oats	38,014,000	40,996,000	41,527,000	43,572,000	44,474,000
Cotton	35,330,000	31,412,000	34,985,000	33,634,000	37,073,000
Barley	7,592,000	7,149,000	7,757,000	8,835,000	9,108,000
Potatoes	3,685,400	3,734,000	3,565,000	4,390,000	4,113,000
Flax	2,402,200	1,387,000	1,474,000	1,809,000	1,967,000
Rye	2,305,200	3,120,000	3,213,000	4,102,000	5,435,000
Tobacco	1,209,000	1,370,000	1,413,000	1,446,600	1,453,000
Buckwheat	826,200	769,000	828,000	1,006,000	1,040,000
Beans			1,244,000	2,028,000	1,629,000
Rice	723,600	803,000	869,000	964,000	1,120,000
Sugar Beets	498,122	624,000	665,000	675,000	690,000
Sugar Cane	242,000	183,000			534,000
Total	296,405,122	309,348,000	310,873,000	321,693,000	350,883,000

are the grain farmers. If they start out to produce cattle, or sheep, for example, they can not abandon that line as readily as a wheat farmer can turn to something else, as barley and corn, and so divide his risks.

From the above argument, it might seem that under the circumstances which the war has brought about, stock raising must of necessity decline. This is what has happened in the countries more directly affected than are we by the war. There has been a very great reduction in the live stock of Europe. Since more people can be supported by the direct method of using the cereals, than by the indirect method of feeding the cereals to stock and then using the stock, it will no doubt continue to be the result that live stock will be kept in fewer and fewer numbers in times of such stress. However, in spite of the logic the fact remains that up to the present there has been an increase since the war began in the live stock kept in the United States. On the other hand there has not been enough, and is not enough, to supply the needs of the Allies for animal products, and the question of needs should, under the circumstances, be made paramount to the profits of the individual. To keep the individual producer fairly well satisfied and yet hold prices within reach of the consumer is the difficult task of a nation at war and this task involves more insight and foresight in the case of animals than of crops. . . . Increased prices were a great stimulus to production at the time the United States entered the war. Hence whatever has taken place by way of increased production in 1917 and 1918, is the resultant of two forces, price stimulus, and patriotism plus State effort. How much is to be attributed to the one and how much to the other is, in most instances, past finding out. Both have been strongly influential.

The work of increasing agricultural production has centered very largely in the Councils of Defense, on account of the authority given these bodies, although as stated above, a large number of agencies have had a part, and often the superior part in carrying out the plans. The extent to which acreages have been increased has already been discussed. The most tangible results have come from the wheat, potato, and "war garden" portions of the program. Likewise it is a clear case that hog production has been directly stimulated. Other products have been more or less influenced without a doubt, but it is also true that the greater part of the land now in use would have continued to produce some useful crop had no effort been made to stimulate or influence the farmers. The efforts of the Councils of Defence, Department of Agriculture, and allied organizations have been directed mainly in the line of encouragement through appeals to patriotism and self-interest; gathering of information as a basis of the organization of clubs, mainly among boys and girls; assistance in procuring seed, assistance with respect to labor, and in some instances control of labor prices. In a smaller number of cases help of a financial nature has been given in the form of loans; machinery, such as tractors, have been made available; and assistance in finding, reaching, and even creating markets has been afforded. These subjects will be discussed in order.

Patriotism and Self-interest. This campaign was begun at once, and is still in progress. Farmers are urged through almost numberless posters, newspapers, five minute speeches and bulletins, to produce every possible amount of food. It is shown that the Allies are dependent upon America for food, and that without sufficient food the war must of necessity be lost. The effect may be in doubt as to the total addition made by this means, but at all events there has been a great change in the particular products most needed, such as wheat and meat, and in a smaller way, in condensed milk and cheese, and potatoes. In the first two products the increase was induced to a great extent by a guaranteed price, while in the other cases no guarantees were made. . . . Reckoned in dollars the amount of exports of 1917 exceeded those of the year preceding the war by 164 per cent. In other words, where there was one dollar's worth of produce sold abroad in 1913, there were $2.64 worth sold in 1917. This is merely a criterion. The bulk of the farmers' sales are not to Europeans but to the non-farming population of the United States. Assuming that in this market the same amounts of produce all told were sold from year to year the receipts would vary with the price. Of the five leading cereals the increases in price from March 1, 1914, to March 1, 1918, ranged from 70 per cent for oats to 225 per cent for rye. Cotton rose 140 per cent; hay 50 per cent.

In the prices of animals and animal products, the increased prices were pronounced, but not so much so. Hogs rose almost 100 per cent; beef cattle 38.8 per cent; milch cows 34 per cent; sheep 130 per cent; wool 264 per cent. Horses, alone, show a slight decrease.

The total value of farm products for 1917 is estimated by the Department of Agriculture at $19,444,000,000. This value is reached twenty-one years in advance of the time when at the rate of increase of the period 1889-1909 such a sum would have been obtained. The value of farm products in 1915 rose a billion dollars over the value of the preceding year. This was looked upon as phenomenal. But the 1916 product outdid this increase nearly three times over, while the 1917 production exceeded that of 1916 by six billion dollars. The estimate for the 1910-1914 average product was $9,389,000,000. Thus the value of the 1917 product was more than double that of the prewar period.

It must not be supposed that the farmers received these sums as the income for the years designated. There are many duplications in the figures, particularly with respect to grain and live stock. However, the figures serve to show that the gross income of the farmers as a whole must have about doubled between 1914 and 1917. For those who sold cotton or grain the income more than doubled. For those who turned grain and hay into live stock, or live stock products, the gains, while great, were relatively less. . . .

Everything considered it is safe to say that the farmers are making money faster than they ever did before. How much faster is not a matter easy to determine. In the case of those who habitually pay out for living expenses about all of their income the situation has changed very little. They will still pay out most of the money taken in, since living expenses have advanced nearly as much as the prices of farm produce. However, for those who have had previously some margin with which to pay debts, or make investments, there is now an opportunity to pay debts or make investments at a rate much faster than before the war. In other words, the man who was able to pay a dollar of indebtedness, or invest a dollar, before the war can now use two dollars for such purposes. The man who just made a living before the war can just make a living now.

39

Federal Government Institutes Rural Credit Program

Throughout our colonial and national history the frontier farmer found it difficult to secure credit. Money was usually scarce, prices low, and both interest rates and risks high. The situation became acute after the Civil War. The Western farmer was of necessity a commercial farmer, while many Eastern farmers were making the change from subsistence to commercial farming. The establishment of a commercial farm and its continued existence depended in many cases upon the availability of credit. The Southern farmer, too, was in need of money to re-establish or establish himself in the production of cotton.

Farmers' needs were the more acute in that the federal government was aiding financial and business interests by reducing the amount of money per capita in circulation. Many farmers turned to the Greenback movement, the Populist party, or free silver as promising aid, but all failed in their attempts to get more money into circulation. Sensitive to the needs of the business community, the government was indifferent to the farmers' financial problems.

The first governmental recognition of the farmers' credit needs came in 1908 when President Theodore Roosevelt's Country Life Commission called attention in its report to the lack of any adequate system of agricultural credit. The commission commented upon the cooperative phases of mortgage credit and posed the entire problem as one needing solution.

The National Monetary Commission, appointed by President Roosevelt in 1909 to study general banking conditions, presented a detailed account of the German rural credit system. The American Bankers' Association carried on further studies. In the spring of 1912, the Southern Commercial Congress persuaded David Lubin, founder of the International Institute of Agriculture, to discuss the problem at the annual meeting of the Congress. With Lubin's encouragement, the Congress appointed an unofficial American Commission on Agricultural Credit and Cooperation to visit Europe in 1913 and study different agricultural credit systems.

Meanwhile, early in 1912, President Taft asked American diplomatic representatives abroad to gather material on European systems for a report. This report was sent to the state governors in the fall of 1912. In his transmittal letter, reproduced hereafter, the President outlined the problem and stated that the federal and state governments must assume responsibility for "economically and honestly conducted institutions."

Action seemed assured when, at their 1912 conventions, the Republican, Democratic, and Progressive parties pledged themselves to better credit facilities for the farmer. In the spring of 1913, President Wilson appointed an official United States Commission to cooperate with the American Commission on Agricultural Credit and Cooperation. The commissions issued their reports in the winter of 1913-1914, and legislation to effectuate their recommendations was introduced early in 1914.

Action on legislation was delayed by the need to reconcile three opposing views. One plan called for the establishment of privately owned farm mortgage banks under the supervision of the federal government. Another was for the organization of a system based on cooperative principles, while the third plan was for the federal government to make direct loans to farmers. It was not until July 17, 1916, that the Federal Farm Loan Act was passed and signed by the President. The compromise act permitted the establishment of both privately owned and cooperative farm mortgage banks, with certain financial assistance by the government. This law has been modified and, to some extent, replaced, particularly by the Farm Credit Act of 1933. However, it is of major importance historically as marking the acceptance of responsibility by the federal government for establishing and supervising a rural credit system.

President Taft Discusses Rural Credits

Preliminary Report on Land and Agricultural Credit in Europe, 62d Congress, 3d Session, Senate Document No. 967, pp. 3-7 (Washington, Government Printing Office, 1912).

For some months past, at my direction, the Department of State, through its diplomatic officers in Europe, has been engaged in an investigation of the agricultural credit systems in operation in certain of the European countries. Although the investigation is still under way, a preliminary report has been submitted, together with the recommendations of Ambassador Myron T. Herrick in connection with my proposal to adopt this system in the United States.

A study of these reports and of the recommendations of Ambassador Herrick, which I am sending you, convinces me of the adaptability to American conditions of the cooperative-credit plan as set forth in the organization of the Raiffeisen banks of Germany. The establishment and conduct of such banks, however, are matters for State control. I suggest, also, the establishment of land-mortgage banks under State charters and the formation of cooperative mortgage-bond societies along the lines of the Landschaften societies of Germany, provided that uniform State legislation can be secured to govern their organization and operation. As a later step I favor the enactment of laws by Congress permitting the organization of national land-mortgage banks, to be operated under strict Government supervision, with the power to guarantee and market the guaranteed debenture bonds of the State land-mortgage banks or cooperative societies. I recommend for your consideration the report and recommendations of Ambassador Herrick, now published by the Department of State for general distribution. This report should receive the attention of everyone interested in the problem of agricultural finance and, indeed, of all persons interested in the welfare of the American farmer.

The need for the establishment of an adequate financial system as an aid to the farmers of this country is now quite generally recognized. The governmental initiative, taken by the Department of State under instructions issued by my direction to the diplomatic officers in Europe on March 18 last, have been effectively supplemented by the American Bankers' Association, the Southern Commercial Congress, and by many other bodies by whom this question has been agitated, and valuable work has been done in studying and disseminating knowledge of those great instrumentalities which have been created in foreign lands to extend to their agriculturists credit facilities equal in benefits to those enjoyed by their industrial and commercial organizations. The handicap placed upon the American farmer through the lack of such a system and the loss sustained by the whole citizenship of the Nation because of this failure to assist the farmers to the utmost development of our agricultural resources is readily apparent.

The more than 6,000,000 farms in the United States add each year to the national wealth products with a gross value of between 8 and 9 billion dollars. The number of farm workers—including owners who work their own farms, tenants, hired laborers, and working members of the families of farmers—probably exceeds 12,000,000 people, and the farm population must approximate 35,000,000 people. The most recent statistics show that one-third of all farm owners who operate their own farms report mortgage indebtedness. Excluding farms operated by tenants and hired managers, the reports show that the value of the land and buildings for the farms of the more than 1,000,000 resident farm owners, for which both the fact of mortgage indebtedness and its amounts were reported, was $6,330,000,000. The amount of the debt was $1,726,000,000. On this sum they pay annually interest charges of nearly $150,000,000. Doubtless in addition, large numbers of farms operated by tenants and managers are mortgaged by their owners. Farmers also borrow hundreds of millions of dollars on chattel mortgages, growing crops, personal notes, and other securities. Counting commissions and renewal charges, the interest rate paid by the farmer of this country is averaged at 8½ per cent as compared to a rate of 4½ to 3½ per cent paid by the farmer, for instance, of France or Germany.

Again, the interest rate paid by the American farmer is considerably higher than that paid by our industrial corporations, railroads, or municipalities. Yet, I think, it will be admitted that the security offered by the farmer in his farm lands is quite as sound as that offered by industrial corporations. Why, then, will not the investor furnish the farmer with money at as advantageous rates as he is willing to supply it to the industrial corporations? Obviously, the advantage enjoyed by the industrial corporation lies in the financial machinery at its command, which permits it to place its offer before the investor in a more attractive and more readily negotiable form. The farmer lacks this machinery, and, lacking it, he suffers unreasonably. This is not theory. Through all the changing conditions of a century the soundness and practicability of such financial machinery, based upon the peculiar credit needs of the agriculturist, has been tried out, and so successful has been its operation that in Germany, in times of financial stress, money has been taken out of the commercial field and placed in the keeping of that Empire's agricultural cooperative banks for safety. The value of this assistance to the farmer receives unquestionable testimonial in the growth of the system in the countries of Europe. More specifically this advantage may be seen in the fact that through this machinery the German farmer has received money, at times, at rates lower than those current in commercial loans.

But the advantages to be gained by the adoption of this plan go beyond the direct saving in interest charges to the farmer. The great necessity which prompted the establishment and extension of this plan throughout Europe was that of checking the rapidly advancing increases in the cost of foodstuffs, brought about by the inevitable increase in consumption and the failure of the long-drained soil to afford a corresponding increase in production. That problem faces the people of this country today; not in so severe a form as it threatened the older countries of Europe, but still as a great and pressing economic problem.

In Europe this problem has been successfully met, first, by reducing the cost to the farmer of producing his crops, and, secondly, by increasing his production through the adoption of improved methods of cultivation. Both the Federal and State Governments in this country have done much to afford the farmers instruction in improved agricultural methods. But it still remains for us to reduce the cost of the farmer's production by affording him the necessary capital for the exploitation of his soil upon the most advantageous terms. He must be afforded the money necessary for him to adopt improved methods. It must be made profitable for him to place every acre of his ground under cultivation. This offers the consumer relief from the increasing cost of foodstuffs.

It is this portion of the task that still remains to be performed in this country, and it is in this task that I invite your cooperation.

The country enjoys to-day great prosperity. The factories are busy, the working men employed, and everywhere the wheels of industry hum. The farmer shares in this general prosperity. We have come to look upon the farmer of to-day as one of our most prosperous citizens. The proposal which I make is not to subsidize the American farmer. Fortunately for this country, he does not need it, nor would he accept it. What this plan offers is a means to secure to this country greater productivity, at less cost, from the farms that are now under cultivation, and, above all, to give us more farms and more farmers. It will make it profitable for the farmer to return to the cultivation of the abandoned farms of the East and to open up the vast areas of untilled land in the West.

All this can be done, and I am convinced that in this country it must be done, by the efforts of the farmer himself. It is natural that some of the European Governments should have extended a paternal protection over the systems of agricultural finance and to have given them financial as well as legal assistance. This, however, must be guarded against in this country. We must establish a credit system of, for, and by the farmers of the United States. It were better, otherwise, not to consider the matter at all. It is an interesting commentary on the value of paternalistic governmental support to note that this plan of agricultural cooperative credit has thrived best—in fact, has enjoyed a substantial development only—in those countries where the movement has grown up from the farmers and where the Government has to the greatest degree refrained from attempts artificially to nurture the plan by subsidy, and has restrained its interference to the proper field of imposing restrictional legislation for the purpose of preventing speculation.

The entire field of agricultural cooperative credit is properly divisible into two parts: First, the cooperative societies of farmers, formed for the purpose of obtaining personal credit, and secondly, the societies or private corporations formed to create a sound security in land mortgages for the purpose of gaining a national or international market for bonds based upon farm-land mortgages. Both of these forms of cooperative credit may be found in many of the European countries under varying forms of organization. The general principles, however, are very much the same.

It is not practicable here to go into the details of the organization followed in European countries in the formation of these cooperative societies. A very good law has been enacted by the State of Massachusetts allowing the incorporation of credit unions, which should furnish an excellent example for other States. Their establishment is generally a matter for State legislation and encouragement, their organization and management are wonderfully simple, and the experience of the European countries shows that their success is practically inevitable where the environment is congenial to their growth and where proper laws are passed for their conduct. Although undoubtedly the organization followed in the European countries could not be adopted in its entirety in this country, I would advocate the general principles followed by the so-called Raiffeisen banks of Germany. These smaller societies should restrict their loans to personal credit. They are not intended to make large loans on land mortgages, although, indirectly, the lands of all the members form the security. Above all, the cardinal principle should be followed that all money loaned should be for a strictly creative purpose. No loan for the purchase of anything merely for consumption should be tolerated.

The business of furnishing money on loans on real estate is the proper province of the cooperative societies or private corporations, which I have placed in the second class. In Germany this is done through cooperative societies known as Landschaften and through mortgage banks. In France it is done through the Credit Foncier.

The chief advantages brought to farmers through such institutions are lower interest rates and easy amortization, whereby the borrowing farmer may repay his loan bit by bit, extending these payments over a long number of years. Thus, his obligations are made proportionate to his annual receipts from the exploitation of his soil, and the danger of foreclosure is vastly reduced. To appreciate what this amortization plan would mean to the farmers of this country, it is only necessary to consider the foreclosure records of some of our States.

It is not my purpose here to lay down any one plan as necessarily the one most suitable for adoption in the United States. From the reports of our ambassadors and ministers in Europe and from the recommendations of Ambassador Herrick, to whom was given the task of compiling from these the general report, I am inclined to suggest the suitability of organizations similar to the German land-mortgage banks for incorporation under State charters in this country. It will be most desirable, if not, indeed, essential, that the laws creating and governing such institutions should be uniform throughout the States, in order that they might be well understood by the investor, and their debentures should be given character both at home and abroad. As a later step it may prove advisable to urge the enactment by Congress of laws permitting the creation of national land-mortgage banks similar to those of Germany and France, with limited privileges, and surrounded and guarded by strict supervision, but with sufficient appeal to American initiative and opportunity, with the power to guarantee and market a guaranteed debenture bond of the State mortgage bank or cooperative society. Securities issued by such national institutions would probably find a ready market in Europe at low rates of interest, since they are a favorite and familiar form of investment in those countries by the conservative investor.

The most essential point to bear in mind is the need for the assumption by the Federal and State Government of the responsibility for economically and honestly conducted institutions. Such assumption is the essential precedent for obtaining the confidence of the American as well as the European investing public. In this field, as in all others, there is room for harmful exploitation for personal gain. That must be guarded against. Therefore, I invite you to make this matter the subject of earnest study and exchange of views between the State executives, and I now extend to you, with the governors of the other States, a cordial invitation to confer with me in Washington, on the occasion of the next annual conference of governors, in order to consider means for the adoption of an agricultural credit system as a benefit to the American farmer. I understand that the congress of governors is to occur in December. Were not the interval so short, my conviction of the importance of this subject would impel me to invite you to a special conference at a still earlier date.

Renewing my request for your hearty cooperation in a work of such nation-wide benefit to the farmer, the consumer, and, indeed, to the Nation at large.

40

Modern Hybrid Seed Corn Developed

The theories of two great European scientists, Charles Darwin and Gregor Mendel, led to the development of modern hybrid seed corn. Darwin, in a book on cross- and self-fertilization of plants published in 1876, pointed out that inbreeding usually reduced plant vigor and cross-breeding restored it. Mendel had published in 1866 a study on plant hybridization in which he developed the basic laws of inheritance of specific characteristics. It was not until about 1900, however, that the importance of Mendel's work was recognized.

Darwin's influence upon American corn breeding was most notable in the work of William James Beal, an able botanist who was familiar with and admired Darwin's work. In 1876, at Michigan Agricultural College where he was professor of botany, Beal made the first controlled crosses between varieties of corn for the sole purpose of increasing yields through hybrid vigor.

The full utilization of Beal's conclusions could come only after the development of the science of genetics. Mendel's work had pointed the way and others added to his experiments. In 1904, George Shull, a botanist working at the experiment station at Cold Spring Harbor on Long Island, began to study the effects of self-fertilization and cross-fertilization on particular characteristics of corn. He concluded from his experiments that self-fertilization tended to separate and purify strains while weakening the plants, but that vigor could be restored by crossbreeding the inbred strains. He did not, however, apply the knowledge to agriculture.

At about the same time that Shull was conducting his experiments, Edward Murray East was also experimenting, first at the University of Illinois, then at the Connecticut Experiment Station. East used corn as one of his tools in adding to genetic knowledge through study of the comparative effects of inbreeding and outbreeding. His conclusions were similar to those reached by Shull, and, like Shull, East did not at that time appreciate the practical usefulness of his work.

When East left the Connecticut Station in 1910, he was succeeded by H. K. Hayes, who was followed shortly by Donald F. Jones. Jones had studied with East at Harvard, which led to his appointment to the Connecticut post in 1914. He found at Connecticut that considerable inbreeding work had been done with corn, and that several hybrid combinations had been made. The hybrids were vigorous but the inbred varieties were unproductive and unattractive. Jones immediately devoted himself to developing a method for making hybrid corn practical. Within three years he had developed the technique of double-crossing, using four inbred lines instead of two. This was the important step that made scientific theory applicable to the development of hybrid corn, one of the greatest agricultural accomplishments of modern times.

Theory of Breeding Hybrid Seed Corn

Edward M. East and Donald F. Jones, *Inbreeding and Outbreeding*, pp. 215-218, 219, 221-225 (Philadelphia, J. B. Lippincott Company, 1919).

The value of inbreeding in plant and animal improvement in the past may be summed up in the statement that it is the greatest single agency in bringing about uniformity and the concentration of desired qualities. So valuable have been the results, particularly with animals, that it has often been continued even though concentration of characters which made for lessened constitutional vigor and fertility accompanied the accumulation of desirable features, for the good outweighed the evil. To overcome anticipated calamities, animal breeders have from time to time introduced fresh stock. In doing this they certainly were wise, since a rather high probability always exists that such a procedure will introduce the dominant complements of the detrimental characters. But even granting the good sense at the base of both practices, it may be doubted whether inbreeding and crossbreeding have been used in the best possible manner as means of improvement. There are precise uses to which each may be put which hitherto have not been considered.

Experiments with maize show that undesirable qualities are brought to light by self-fertilization which either eliminate themselves or can be rejected by selection. The final result is a number of distinct types which are constant and uniform and able to persist indefinitely. They have gone through a process of purification such that only those individuals which possess much of the best that was in the variety at the beginning can survive. Although these result-ant, purified types have little value in themselves, they have possi-bilities. The characters which they have can now be estimated more nearly at their true worth. By crossing, the best qualities which have been distributed to the several inbred strains can be gathered to-gether again and a new variety re-created. Size, vigor and fertility can be fully restored with the advantage of real improvement through the elimination of certain undesirable characters.

At present, this application of inbreeding to the improvement of cross-bred animals and plants is somewhat of an unknown quantity. It has not been as thoroughly tested as might be desired, but the basic principle is sound. Although it is a drastic procedure, it is merely utilizing to the fullest extent what practical breeders have recognized as one of the most valuable benefits of close mating. Accepting the doctrine that consanguinity in itself is not in any way injurious and that good or evil results from it solely through the inheritance received, we can attack the century-old problem of inbreeding with a clarity of vision heretofore impossible. Breeds of animals, and naturally crossed varieties of plants, which are neces-sarily more or less heterogeneous in their hereditary constitution, can be split up into their component parts by this means. The pure types obtained can then be selected with far more surety than is ever possible with organisms in a continuously hybrid condition, thereby presenting basic stock of tested value for further hybridiza-tion and recombination.

With plants the application of this method would be simpler than with animals. Most naturally crossed plants can be artificially self-fertilized and constancy and uniformity reached in about eight generations if there are no complicating factors such as self-sterility. The expense would not be prohibitive, although many pure lines must be tested in order to have a high probability of obtaining all that is best in a variety. After the most desirable combinations are isolated, their recombination into a new and better variety, which could be maintained by seed propagation, would be a comparatively easy undertaking. . . .

While the full value of inbreeding in plant and animal improve-ment has not as yet been fully recognized, the advantages derived from outbreeding are more generally known. Outbreeding as a means of improvement may be considered under two heads: First, the immediate value to be derived from crossing related types and thus securing the maximum benefit from hybrid vigor; second, the more complex problem of crossing radically different forms to create variability out of which new breeds or new varieties may be constructed by a process of selection. . . .

Maize is the plant which is most suitable for use in this way, a notable fact since it is the most valuable farm crop in the Western Hemisphere. The reason it merits this statement is because it is easily crossed on a large scale by sowing the two types to be crossed in alternate rows in an isolated plot and detasseling all of one kind before pollen is shed. As early as 1876 Beal reported that corn could be increased in yield in this way. Since that time numerous tests have been made and the fact is established that crosses between varieties of corn of somewhat different type may be expected to outyield either parent in many cases, and when the parental varieties differ in time of maturing may be expected to ripen earlier than the later parent. Thus out of fifty first generation crosses between varieties of corn grown in Connecticut, eighty-eight per cent. yielded more than the average, and sixty-six per cent. yielded more than either parent. The average increase in all the crosses above the average of their parents was about ten per cent., including the crosses which gave no indication of hybrid vigor. The greatest increases occurred in the crosses between flint and dent varieties, and often there was a really noteworthy hastening of the time of ripening, which is of considerable importance in those regions where early fall frosts are a limiting factor.

The greatest improvement to be made in this way comes from crossing varieties which have previously been put through a process of self-pollination. When certain inbred strains are crossed the increase in growth is remarkable, as previously noted. This comes partly from the fact that following inbreeding the maximum effect of hybrid vigor is obtained while in ordinary varieties segregation brings about partial homozygosity in many plants. It is also due to the elimination of many undesirable characters during the process of inbreeding. The crossed plants are remarkably uniform. One plant is a replica of another. Given proper conditions they all produce good ears which form a remarkable contrast to ordinary varieties in their similarity to each other. There are no barren stalks, and the abnormalities and monstrosities which commonly occur in every field of corn are almost entirely absent. In those cases in

which one or both of the parent strains is resistant to parasitic infection, such as smut, the cross is also resistant and this is a factor
for greater production.

There are, on the other hand, certain serious disadvantages in the
practical utilization of first generation crosses between inbred
strains. In the first place the yields of the inbred plants are low,
which makes the cost of the crossed seed high. What is more serious,
the seeds produced on inbred plants are small and less well developed than seeds of ordinary corn, and the seedlings coming from
these seeds are less vigorous and are thereby greatly handicapped at
the start. The plants at first are smaller and have a less healthy color
than plants of ordinary varieties, and although they usually overcome this handicap, they may not always do so if the conditions
in the earlier part of the season are particularly unfavorable.

A method which overcomes these objections is now being tested
at the Connecticut Agricultural Experiment Station, and promises
excellent results. This method is as follows: Four inbred strains are
selected which when tested by crossing in all the six different combinations give an increased yield. Two of these strains are crossed
to make one first generation hybrid and the other two are crossed
to give another. These two different crosses, which are large vigorous plants, are again crossed and the seed obtained used for general field planting. . . .

In this way large yields of well-developed seed are obtained, and
the young plants are not handicapped in any way. The beautiful
uniformity of the first cross is sacrificed, but the advantages gained
promise to counterbalance any loss in this respect. Theoretically
there is little reduction in heterozygosity and presumably little reduction in the incentive towards increased size and productiveness.
A great many different possibilities are involved in such double
crossing and they have not been sufficiently tested to warrant extravagant claims, but judging by their appearance such doubly-
crossed plants are clearly the finest specimen of corn so far obtained
under the conditions in which they have been tested.

The first impression probably gained from the outline of this
method of crossing corn is that it is a rather complex proposition.
It is somewhat involved, but it is more simple than it seems at first
sight. It is not a method that will interest most farmers, but it is
something that may easily be taken up by seedsmen; in fact, it is
the first time in agricultural history that a seedsman is enabled to

gain the full benefit from a desirable origination of his own or something that he has purchased. The man who originates devices to open our boxes of shoe polish or to autograph our camera negatives, is able to patent his product and gain the full reward for his inventiveness. The man who originates a new plant which may be of incalculable benefit to the whole country gets nothing—not even fame—for his pains, as the plants can be propagated by anyone. There is correspondingly less incentive for the production of improved types. The utilization of first generation hybrids enables the originator to keep the parental types and give out only the crossed seeds, which are less valuable for continued propagation.

The second phase of the subject of outbreeding in its relation to plant and animal improvement—that of wide crossing between distinct varieties, species or even genera—is so large a topic it cannot be more than touched upon here. Each particular cross presents technical problems of its own. All one can say as a generality is that the principle in every case is the same. Crossing brings together germ plasms having various attributes. These attributes, the hereditary factors, recombine with regularity and precision. They Mendelize. From Mendelian segregation and recombination come the possibilities of new and improved races. Except in those rare instances when new variations previously unknown to the species occur, nothing can come out of the cross that did not go in. But the number of combinations possible when the two parents differ by many hereditary factors is so great that practically speaking many character complexes may appear which have never before had the chance of showing their merits or defects. In them lie our hopes.

It was noted earlier that many species crosses are partially sterile, that there is often a degeneration of many of the germ cells and embryos, and that certain extreme types are thereby produced more frequently than is usually to be expected. The extreme variability induced by such wide crossing offers the best field in which to look for the beginnings of new and valuable types of animals and plants. This is not a theory; it is a general fact born of long experience, for when we look into the origin of many of our most valuable domesticated animals and plants we find unmistakable evidence of their hybrid ancestry.

PART VI

Return to Normalcy and Agricultural
Depression, 1920-1932

41

Farm Bloc Organized in Congress

The collapse of agricultural prices in 1920, particularly while the rigidity of nonagricultural prices and wages was creating a new and alarming disparity between farm income and costs, caused distress in many parts of the farm economy and focused attention on possible governmental assistance to farmers. The Farm Bloc, an organization of senators and congressmen, mostly from the Midwest and South, who were determined to support agricultural legislation and oppose legislation unfavorable to farmers, regardless of party lines, was formally organized in 1921. Its membership was almost equally divided between Republicans and Democrats. The Farm Bloc, during its formal existence from 1921 to 1923, worked closely with the American Farm Bureau Federation. Its activities established a precedent for a bipartisan approach to agricultural legislation, and the term has frequently been applied to legislators who have put farm interests above party lines.

Senator Capper Describes the Farm Bloc

Arthur Capper, *The Agricultural Bloc*, pp. 3-4, 9-12, 146-148, 159, 161 (New York, Harcourt, Brace and Company, c. 1922).

The Agricultural Bloc is that group of Members of Congress who have recognized that an economic upheaval threatens the Nation if the foundations of our prosperity are weakened.

They recognize that the American welfare depends upon the land and upon a permanent and prosperous agriculture.

They recognize that the American farmer not only feeds and clothes us but that he is also the best customer of our industries.

They recognize that the American farmer supports commerce, foreign and domestic, by producing over half of our exports; pays over half of the annual cost of transportation and maintains more than half of our public institutions.

They recognize that national prosperity is dependant primarily upon agricultural prosperity and that unless that third of our population who live upon the farms prospers the Nation cannot have a continued growth and development.

They recognize that we have passed into a new era in our national history in which we cannot allow the balance of real production which comes only from the land to get out of balance with the dependent manufacturing industries, commerce, banking and government.

They recognize as just the claim of the man on the land for an equal voice in national affairs with those who live by trade, banking and manufactures which deal only with advancing stages of the raw product provided by the land. . . .

The agricultural group, later named the "Bloc" by popular writers, was formed at a meeting called by Senator Kenyon, May 9, 1921, held at the Washington office of the American Farm Bureau Federation, at which twelve Senators met to decide on a program for immediate attention. It included an equal number of representatives of the two leading political parties, principally Senators from the Middle West and South, our great agricultural sections, where the situation was most acute. Those present were Senators W. S. Kenyon, of Iowa; Arthur Capper, of Kansas; G. W. Norris, of Nebraska; F. R. Gooding, of Idaho; E. F. Ladd, of North Dakota; Robert M. La Follette, of Wisconsin; E. D. Smith, of South Carolina; J. B. Kendrick, of Wyoming; Duncan U. Fletcher, of Florida; Joseph E. Ransdell, of Louisiana; J. T. Heflin, of Alabama, and Morris Sheppard, of Texas.

At this meeting also there were present representatives of government departments, asked in to act as advisers on the program that should be adopted. There were representatives of the farmers who were asked to tell what farmers felt was their outstanding needs. The declaration of purpose by Senator W. S. Kenyon, of Iowa, was that this group give thorough and earnest consideration to the outstanding proposals to the end of securing action by Congress. Four Committees were appointed on the following subjects: Transportation, Federal Reserve Act, Commodity Financing and miscellaneous agricultural bills.

From the very beginning this movement was non-partisan and a recognition of the economic crisis; an endeavor to outline a plan for an economic re-adjustment rather than a scheme to gain partisan advantage. It declared *for* things rather than *against* them; for harmonizing views, not for creating discord; for cooperation, not antagonism; and for all citizens, not for farmers alone.

The outstanding reason that brought this group together was the fact that the general public and the majority of Congress had not realized that the nation had passed into a new economic era in which the balance between agriculture and other industries must be more carefully safeguarded. From this beginning in May, 1921, the group was enlarged to include some 22 Senators and meetings were held from time to time at the office of Senator Kenyon.

From the very first Senator Kenyon was recognized as the leader of the group and it was chiefly due to his sincere interest in agriculture and vigorous leadership that the Bloc became effective.

The following Senators joined the group: Charles L. McNary, of Oregon; Peter Norbeck, of South Dakota; John W. Harreld, of Oklahoma; A. A. Jones, of New Mexico; William J. Harris, of Georgia; H. F. Ashurst, of Arizona; Pat Harrison, of Mississippi; Wesley L. Jones, of Washington; Robert N. Stanfield, of Oregon; Frank B. Kellogg, of Minnesota; Charles A. Rawson, of Iowa; and Claude A. Swanson, of Virginia.

A similar movement was started in the House and a group of Representatives with the same purpose and non-partisan objective was organized to represent the leading agricultural districts. The group has not been so thoroughly established as in the Senate, however, nor has it functioned in such an effective manner. Agricultural matters have usually received more attention in the House than in the Senate.

The Agricultural Bloc was the result of the conviction forced upon the more thoughtful representatives of the farmers that they must unite on a simple and direct program in order to bring the nation to see the needs in the emergency and to act before it was too late. . . .

From the very first meeting the Agricultural Bloc was favored with the constructive advice of leaders who were familiar with the agricultural situation as well as numbers of other men prominent in national affairs, business and industry, who realized that the improvement of agricultural conditions was the first step toward the revival of prosperity.

In this group must be named Secretary of Agriculture Wallace, Secretary of Commerce Hoover, James R. Howard, President of the American Farm Bureau Federation; Charles S. Barrett, President of the Farmers' Union; S. J. Lowell, Master of the National Grange; Fred H. Bixby, President of the American National Live Stock Association; Gifford Pinchot, Barney Baruch, Eugene Meyer, Smith Brookhart, Aaron Sapiro, and Thomas A. Edison.

Most of these men appeared before meetings of the Bloc upon

invitation to discuss specific measures. Many of them conferred with members frequently in respect to legislation.

Supplementing the advice of these leaders the members of the Bloc were in constant touch with the representatives of farm organizations located at Washington, prominent among whom may be named Gray Silver, of the American Farm Bureau Federation; Dr. T. C. Atkeson, of the National Grange; Charles A. Lyman, of tht National Board of Farm Organizations; Charles Holman, of the National Milk Producers' Federation and many others. At the very outset, Senator Kenyon, the Bloc leader, requested the support and advice of all who were in close touch with farmers' needs.

A long list of proposals of various sorts by various individuals in Congress were attributed to the Bloc which in reality were never discussed or considered by the group at all. Any agricultural measure that received favorable comment was likely to be called a product of the Bloc even though it was proposed by some one in no wise connected with the group. In many instances group action which bore no relation whatever to the program of the agricultural group was pointed out as a part of its program in the press. From the very outset there were certain questions which the Agricultural Bloc regarded as distinctly partisan and outside the scope of a bi-partisan organization.   . . .

A list of measures relating to agriculture, enacted since the Agricultural Bloc was organized is as follows:

Amendment to the Farm Loan Act, increasing the Capital $25,000,000.

Amendment increasing Farm Loan Bond Interest Rate to 5½ per cent.

The Future Trading Act.

The Packer Control Act.

War Finance Corporation Amendment.

The Cooperative Marketing Bill.

Amendment to Include Representative for Agriculture on Federal Reserve Board. . . .

The Bloc has undoubtedly speeded the progress of the movement toward better marketing and more justice in the distribution of the consumer's price between the producer and distributor. We still have far to go but we are on the way.

42

Agricultural Crisis of 1920 - 1923 and the McNary - Haugen Plan

Agricultural prices dropped sharply and unexpectedly in the summer of 1920. A general expectation had prevailed after World War I that an enormous demand for American farm products would follow the removal of restrictions on consumption in the European nations. However, when the United States curtailed its loans abroad, foreign countries had no way to pay for the products in the face of American tariffs and they were forced to cut their imports. The European nations encouraged increased production at home and made their foreign purchases from nations which would accept industrial goods in payment.

During the war, the government had guaranteed hog and wheat prices at specified levels. The hog price guarantees were discontinued early in 1919 and the supports for wheat with the marketing of the 1919 crop. Thus, there were no government supports to halt the collapse in prices. All segments of the economy were affected by this depression, but agricultural prices were the most seriously disturbed. As a result, prices farmers received compared with the prices they had to pay for non-agricultural commodities were much lower in terms of purchasing power, than in the war or prewar years.

The decline in farm purchasing power had a depressing effect upon the industrial segment of the economy, particularly upon those units directly dependent upon farm trade. Thus the Moline Plow Company, managed by George N. Peek and Hugh S. Johnson, was thrown into insolvency. Peek and Johnson, who had served on the War Industries Board and believed that government action could promote economic stability, decided that farm prosperity must be restored before the farm machinery industry could prosper.

Late in 1921, Peek and Johnson presented a plan for the solution of the farm problem to the American Farm Bureau Federation. The plan proposed machinery for selling products for domestic consumption at a fair exchange value and surplus agricultural products at a world price. Later the plan was published under the title *Equality for Agriculture.* It was discussed with officials of farm organizations and of the federal government and many others. The plan was introduced into Congress in January, 1924, by Senator Charles L. McNary, of Oregon, and Representative Gilbert N. Haugen, of Iowa, and, with modifications from time to time, was known thereafter as the McNary-Haugen bill or plan.

The bills as first introduced into Congress provided for: the segregation of the surplus, which was to be sold abroad at world prices; the distribution of operating costs and losses among the growers by an equalization fee; a scrip device to collect the equalization fee; and a price-ratio provision to determine fair prices. The provisions were to apply to eight "basic" agricultural commodities, wheat, corn, cotton, wool, cattle, sheep, swine, and rice. A board to determine fair prices was to be established, as was a government corporation to sell the surplus abroad.

Modified McNary-Haugen bills were passed by both houses of Congress in 1927 and 1928, and were vetoed by the President. This marked the high point of the basic two-price system as proposed by Peek and Johnson.

While the plan was defeated, it had served during the 1920's as a rallying point for farmers, farm organizations, and farm leaders. Pressure for farm relief continued until by 1929 the federal government was committed to the idea of accepting some responsibility for farm prices.

Peek and Johnson Advocate a Two-Price Plan

[George N. Peek and Hugh S. Johnson], *Equality for Agriculture*, 1st ed., pp. 5-7, 11, 14-19, 22-25, 27-31, 37, 40 (Moline, Illinois, H. W. Harrington, 1922).

GENERAL STATMENT OF PLAN

This is a plan to improve marketing of farm products, to insure a fair return from farm operations, to stabilize farm securities, to facilitate farm finance, and to secure equality for agriculture in the benefits of the protective tariff, by the following means:

Establish each year the fair exchange value on the domestic market of each principal crop, by computing a price which bears the same relation to the general price index as the average price of such crop for ten pre-war years bore to average general price index for the same period. Protect this fair exchange value from world price by a tariff fluctuating with it and with world price.

Organize under federal legislative charter a private corporation to maintain this value by buying carry-over from any such crop from farmers or associations of farmers at such value. Such corporation may sell for export exportable surplus at the world price, even if less than domestic price, and to sell for domestic consumption, any of its carry-over at not less than the exchange value. The process will result in little, if any, material interference with existing mechanism for supplying domestic consumption.

Purchases and losses by reason of sales to export or of downward fluctuations in such fair exchange value to be financed, viz:

From worst experienced years of price, production, and surplus, determine an empirical formula, which when applied to any future year, will compute a percentage of price per-bushel or per-pound, large enough to absorb any probable loss. This differential to be computed and announced in ample time before planting season to enable farmers to plan croppage with reference to existing supply.

By authority of a federal statute, collect this percentage as a differential loan assessment on each pound or bushel when and as sold by the farmers. Issue scrip for such receipts, bearing interest on a retirable value to be fixed and announced when losses and expenses are determined.

Pass unabsorbed amounts in such fund to a Farm-Loan Fund for reloan to appropriate banks and associations of farmers, at moderate interest, and on farmers' notes, for one, two, or three years, given for purchase of reproductive facilities.

In the first year, after a sufficient fund has accumulated to take care of annual agricultural loan requirements, the installment of scrip issued in the first year's operations is retired, and so on for each succeeding year's installment.

Wheat, cotton, corn and oats are tentatively proposed for the operation of this plan.

I

Agricultural tariffs, unless modified as herein proposed, cannot protect agriculture. World price fixes domestic price of every crop of which we export a surplus. Industrial tariffs can and do protect prices of articles for which crop is exchanged. The fair exchange value of the crop is thus reduced in proportion to the protection afforded industry. The protective principle is operated for the benefit of industry to the detriment of agriculture which can no longer afford to bear the burden. . . .

II

In world depressions, the rapid spread between crop price (which collapses at once with world price) and protected prices (which do not) destroys farm buying power, demoralizes domestic commerce, and deprives our people of necessities. It finally stultifies the principle of protection by forcing industry to equalize with crop price which is world price. . . .

III

The doctrine of protection must be revised to insure agriculture a fair exchange value on the domestic market or the protective principle must perish.

It can be so revised only as follows:

    (a) Establish a method to ascertain a fair exchange value for crop on the domestic market and protect such value by a tariff fluctuating with it.

    (b) Organize and finance agriculture to equalize supply with demand on the domestic market, at not to exceed this value, and to divert surplus to export and sell it at world price.

(a) The doctrine of protection must be revised to insure agriculture a fair exchange value for crop or the protective principle must perish.

Fair exchange value is cost of production plus a profit. No industry can live on less. It was never supposed by the authors of protection that agriculture could. They found a way to compensate agriculture for the fact that it could not be protected by tariffs, as then conceived, and for the further and more startling fact, that, although unprotected, agriculture must pay industry half the benefit of protection. That way is gone. One of three things must happen. Either agriculture must die, or protection must die, or a way must be found so to revise protection as to insure agriculture a fair exchange value for its crop.

Agriculture will not die. But protection will die, politically, unless the principles necessary to secure a fair exchange value for agriculture are added to the doctrine. America could make no greater blunder at this crisis than to abandon protection.

(b) To retain protection and also secure a fair exchange value for crop, agriculture must be organized and financed to equalize supply with demand on the domestic market and, for this purpose, to withhold crop for fair exchange value and for no higher value, and to divert surplus to export and there sell it at world price.

1 Withholding crop.

Agricultural production is harvested in a few weeks. If entire domestic consumption is thrown on the market when harvested, there is a seasonal surplus and price loses its relation to exchange value. Only by finance and organization can this avoided. But organization must be restricted because power to withhold supply for a fair price would be power to withhold it for a greater price. Therefore, the power must be limited to hold for fair exchange value and for no greater value.

2 Sale of surplus to export.

Only by diverting surplus from the domestic market, can the protective principle protect agriculture, and world price be prevented from establishing domestic price for the entire crop.

3 Surplus must be sold at world price.

In a protected country, world price may be lower than fair exchange value on domestic markets. Selfish industrial interests may complain that this prejudices them in export. 5% to 10% of total trade is export—half of that is agricultural. Less than 5% of total trade asks the other 95% to suffer seasons such as this, and sacrifice domestic commerce; asks America to stultify the principle of protection and renounce living standards; asks a languishing agriculture to bear a crushing and absurd burden to the end that it may prosper. The request ought to shame itself to silence. There is only one way in which America can retain the principle of protection, and also engage in industrial export trade, without demoralizing domestic commerce, and that has just been proposed. Domestic commerce is too large a proportion of all to be sacrificed for export trade when there is a better way.

We must have export trade and our need for it will increase with every year. The reasons why the plan proposed is a better way are:

First. Under the plan, we shall get (and competing countries must pay) a much higher price for our farm products than is the case to-day. There is every evidence of pooled foreign buying in our markets. We hear of clever manipulation of world crop news and of very skilful buying. Under the plan we shall oppose pooled foreign buying by pooled export selling. Our exports of the crops considered are so great a proportion of the world's imports that a single seller can influence price. Also, the automatic effect of the per-unit loan is a much more direct and effective control of production than we now have, and this also will tend to raise the price that our foreign industrial competitors must pay for our agricultural products.

Second. We can engage in export trade, under the plan, to the full of our requirements and with scientific minimum of interference with living standards and domestic commerce. When, due to lack of world markets for our high-cost goods, and in response to our economic necessity for world trade, the price of industrial products falls, then the price and protection of agriculture falls, automatically and in precise relation, with the price of other products, and to a point where our industrial products can compete abroad. But a fair exchange value of the crop remains, our domestic market is preserved, and our living standards are retained. In other words, industry will share the concessions necessary to be made for export trade equally with agriculture. To attempt to export at the sole expense of agriculture is not only unjust, as has just been shown, it is absurd.

IV

A practical organization is a corporation to guarantee to buy carry-over from each year's crop at fair exchange value and to conduct export selling. Its charter must insure the following results:

1 No "government in business."
2 No class-preference or subsidy for agriculture.
3 Complete assumption of risk by agriculture.
4 Financial solvency under all conditions.
5 Simplicity of operation.
6 Minimum of interference with existing institutions.

Explanation of operations:

(i) Maintaining fair exchange value.

Fair exchange value can be maintained on domestic market, either by buying the whole crop or by buying carry-over. Since it is desired to maintain existing facilities with the minimum of interference with existing methods, the latter is the obvious course. For the sake of brevity, call the corporation K. Its method is as follows:

(ii) Fair exchange value.

Fair exchange value is computed and announced by K. just before harvest on average general price index number for twelve months immediately preceding.

(iii) Buying.

Beginning about the time of harvest of the new crop. K is required to buy from farmers only, unsold quantities of the crop immediately preceding, at not less than computed fair exchange value on such old crop.

K is also required so to buy from associations of farmers quantities of such crop produced by farmers, members of such associations, which have not been traded in except by the original sale from any such farmer to such association.

(iv) Selling.

Domestic Market.

K will not retain from the domestic market, for a price higher than current fair exchange value any quantities for which there is a demand at such value, or above, except that K may, in its discretion, so retain not to exceed $\frac{1}{10}$ of the annual domestic consumption, computed by multiplying average per capita consumption for four preceding years by current census estimate of population. K will sell at a loss in the domestic market, only when fair exchange value has been reduced by a new computation, as provided in Paragraph (ii), and then not below such value.

Export Market.

Sales to export not by, or with consent of K are invalid. Sales to export must immediately be exported, or bonded for export, and must not again come on domestic market. K will sell or permit sales for export at such prices, at such times, and in such quantities, as in K's judgment will best serve American agricultural interests. K will not sell or permit sales at less than fair exchange value in export unless "carry-over," in K's hands, from preceding crop, exceeds domestic consumption, viz: wheat, two months; cotton, four months; corn and oats, one month. Regardless of current exchange value, K will not sell in domestic trade, or sell or permit sales in export trade, at prices which would compute a loss on quantities in K's hands, purchased from farmers or associations of farmers, from a crop in respect of which the total guaranty fund has been absorbed by losses, expenses, and reserves.

V

A fair exchange value for any crop is one which bears the same ratio to current general price index as a ten-year, pre-war, average, crop price bore to average general price index, for the same period. It is mathematically correct, economically sound and operates to the fair advantage of agriculture, industry and America at large.

Explanation.

Average general price index number 1906-1915	97
Average wheat price, Chicago, 1906-1915	$1.02
Present general price index number	152
Corresponding wheat price	$1.60

The fair exchange value is computed, each year, on the average general price index number for the months of production, and is announced just before harvest. It is maintained and administered as explained under Point IV hereof. It is protected by a tariff fluctuating with it.

(a) It is mathematically correct.

Cost of farm production cannot be compiled. It can be computed, with no other variance from accuracy, than the profit experienced in production and sale of crop. It is too well established to require argument that, in the pre-war years, 1906-1915, such profit was less than in any other major enterprise. In terms of industrial accounting, and as explained under Point I, there was no profit, and fair exchange values were reduced by 40% to 60% of the protection afforded industry by the tariff. Therefore, he who objects that the relation proposed favors the farmer will find no comfort in the mathematics of the case. He who complains that it prejudices the farmer is answered in subdivision (c) under this Point. The relation proposed is, fair exchange value of the crop MINUS fair exchange value of profit. Since the farmer has no recent experience with profit, we must look to sub-division (c) for a study of future profit.

It is true that the expedient accepts, as a criterion, the relation between crop price and general index in the period 1906-1915, with a result that, if the cost of crop production, relative to the cost of general production, decreases, the benefit will go to the farmer. If it increases, the farmer will be prejudiced. But this is fair. Because if this relative cost decreases, it will be solely because of savings achieved by the farmer in production, finance or marketing and, since he starts with no profit, he is entitled to all savings. If the relative cost increases, it will be because of extravagance and waste and the country cannot countenance these. It is important to note that the above discussion refers only to relative increases or decreases in cost of crop production in comparison with the cost of general production. Increases or decreases due to the rise or fall of wages or prices are, of course, compensated for with precise equity by the effect of the formula to cause crop price to fluctuate in precise proportion with increases or decreases in the general price index. Speaking generally, and with sufficient accuracy, any considerable reduction in a major element of crop cost, as for instance, freight or the price of implements, simply means that the general price index has fallen, and with it, under the plan, the crop price. This is true because freight rates and implement costs are governed directly by the general price index.

Similarly the general index, and not some special index of articles used in production of a particular crop, is the correct criterion; first, because what we are seeking is an exchange value. Crop is exchanged for what the farmer buys and, being a class universal in dissemination and type, he buys everything; second, because it is an economic fact that the difference between a composite index of many commodities and one of a moderate number makes no material difference in result—manifestly because the elements of all are reflected to greater or less extent in each. For the latter reason, it is immaterial that some things he does not buy are included in the general index and some elements of crop cost are not.

(b) It is economically sound.

In normal economic process, basic utility fixes the value of an article in terms of articles for which it is exchanged. Such is the law of barter which would be the law of trade, were it not for the artificial expedient of money as a medium of exchange. Money, being itself subject to fluctuations of quantity, effect and utility, imposes such incongruous fluctuations as we now suffer and is to that extent itself a violation of economic law, occasionally imposing the destructive effect of all artificial invasions of natural processes. Any sound expedient that tends to stabilize relative values is an improvement on the monetary system and an approach to economic perfection.

(1) No price fixing.

Price fixing is an attempt by human discretion to establish values which are fixed by fundamental economic forces over which it has no control. Examples are the Brazilian coffee valorizations and war price fixing. Such attempts are always unsound. The proposed plan has nothing whatever in common with such schemes. The formula for computing fair exchange value is merely a means for expressing a pure economic relation of values and for preserving it from, and offsetting, the subversive and disturbing interference of such artificial invasions of economic law, as the tariff, money, industrial and commercial combinations, and the like. The absolute necessity for such an offset from the effect of the tariff is fully demonstrated in Points I and II. The controlling formula is fixed by statute and is thus completely removed from human or partisan control. It is as a harp of the winds, exposed to the free play of every economic influence and guarded at every point from human touch. Its effect is only to bind together some of the most important of values which money measures and thus to cause them to rise and fall together rather than in paralyzing confusion.

(2) No inflation.

Inflation in the price of a particular product occurs when it is above fair exchange value. Inflation in general prices occurs when they are above their fair exchange value in money. The effect of this plan would never be to inflate prices of farm products because it only brings them toward fair exchange value and never above it. Moreover there can be no boom in the sense of run-away upward markets because the effect of the plan on price is measured and certain and subject to no doubt. Therefore the plan is a positive insurance against inflation in the price of farm products and he who complains of the slight increase in general prices that will be caused by giving agriculture a fair price, says (though, of course, he does not mean) that he wants to have lower general prices by taking crops away from farmers without paying for them.

The effect of the plan will be a slight increase in the general price index. Irving Fisher says that a 20% increase in price of wheat raises the general index 1%. Some prices other than farm prices are now abortively below their proper place and the restoration of commerce will bring these into line. Agriculture is at the base of such an important segment of all commerce, that the effect of a formula insuring fair exchange value for farm products will be very powerful in equalizing prices throughout the whole structure. . . .

(c) It is fair to the farmer.

First prices computed and announced under the plan would result in such increases from the present depression that the farmer, who has been able to produce a crop by going without everything, may be disposed to accept the result with unquestioning glee. As shown in section (a) under this Point, he is being given only a chance to help himself. Yet he ought to accept the plan for the following reasons:

(1) As long as America retains the protective principle (and she must retain it for many years to come) there is no other way by which the farmer can make a profit when world price is lower than domestic price. He is justified in asking for a relation higher than that in 1906-1915 but computation of the increased amount involves guess work and he could not get it. By accepting this relation, he places himself in a position of unassailable fairness upon which he is sure to prevail.

(2) The establishment of that relation, insures to the farmer every dollar of saving that he can achieve by better methods. This is a point of tremendous importance because, however much he may economize and increase his efficiency, without this expedient, he has no certain assurance that the benefit of such savings will not be taken away from him and appropriated to others by a lower price. Especially is this true when world price is higher than domestic price. For example:

(i) The plan makes cooperative marketing, with all its manifest advantages and savings immediately practicable, and insures every dollar benefit to the farmer, but without the plan, such savings may simply result in a domestic price reduced by the amount of his savings.

(ii) Similarly the plan results in very great savings in cost of farm finance and insures the benefit of all such savings to the farmer. In the absence of the plan there is no such saving and even if it could be otherwise achieved the farmer has no assurance of retaining it.

(3) The plan controls export selling for his benefit and so protects him from the strength and wiles of pooled foreign buying in the domestic market. Of cotton and wheat, America exports so great a proportion of the world's imports that when she sells as a unit, she ought to exercise a powerful upward control on world price. The plan insures to the farmer all the benefit of this.

(4) Finally, so long as world prices are below fair exchange value on the domestic market, the plan insures the farmer a fair

price. In the absence of the plan he will receive a price as much less than cost of production as the protected American general index is above the world general index. Even when world price is equal to or greater than fair exchange value on the home market, the plan insures him against destructive down-swing, assures financing, economizes cost, and secures him the maximum attainable price for his sales to export.

(d) It is fair to industry.

The plan preserves industry's domestic market and therefore ninety to ninety-five per cent of our total commerce. As long as world price is on the downward swing and the American doctrine of protection is retained, these domestic markets can be preserved in no other way. The subject is fully discussed under Points I and II. All discussion reduces to this: If industry favors and desires protection it favors and desires this plan. For, in such periods of world depression as we now suffer and without this plan, there can be no protection from world price either for agriculture or for industry. Industry is as effectively disadvantaged in domestic markets as though it were crowded out by cheap German goods with the additional disadvantage that the power of agriculture to buy goods of any make—foreign or domestic—is greatly restricted.

(e) It is fair to the country as a whole.

If the farmer accepts the pre-war relation, he is saying to the rest of America, "I served you without profit for years. We both agree that neither you nor I can afford to have me do so any longer, but I am willing to retain the old exchange relation between your product and mine and win my profit by saving it out of waste and lost motion." It would certainly be a shabby America that would refuse so fair a challenge.

It would also be a fatuous America.

Upon these principles alone can agriculture operate at a profit. The alternative is discussed under Points I and II. It is an America whose industries are starved at their source, whose rural population is being rapidly forced to impoverished tenantry and eventually to peasantry—an America whose living standards are rapidly dropping toward those of an unhappy and dissatisfied world. Such is the natural result of an internal policy of injustice. The principle of protection operated fairly enough at its inception but, under present conditions, it will become a policy of gross inequity.

VI

Finance is procurable by a statutory loan assessment per pound or bushel on entire crop, collected when and as crop is first sold. It must be ample to absorb expenses, losses in sales to export, and losses from annual fluctuations in guaranteed price. . . .

VII

Agricultural requirements for financing the purchase of reproductive facilities are not served. They can be adequately provided, viz:

(a) Issue to farmers interest-bearing scrip, salable on the investment market, for their share of the unabsorbed balances of the guaranty fund.

(b) Pass such balance to a Farm Loan Fund available at moderate interest to appropriate banks or associations of farmers on farmers notes for one, two or three years given for the purchase of reproductive facilities and bearing interest at not to exceed a stated reasonable rate. . . .

VIII

If we are to retain the doctrine of protection, we can equalize our price structure and preserve our domestic markets only by application of the principles stated in Point III. No plan yet proposed recognizes this.

The prime cause of the present depression in our domestic market is organic. Its effect will remain with us as long as that cause persists and until cause is eradicated it is futile to hope for orderly domestic prosperity. That cause is a protected price for industry, a world price for agriculture and the impossibility of equalizing them by the tariff alone.

There are only two ways to equalize price. One is Free Trade; the other is to segregate agricultural surplus from the domestic market and sell it in export. Free Trade is unthinkable. There remains only the method advocated by this brief. . . .

43

Master Farmer Movement Begins

The Master Farmer movement was started in 1925 by Clifford V. Gregory, editor of the *Prairie Farmer*, as a means of dignifying agriculture, honoring outstandingly successful farmers, and providing examples for farm boys and girls. A carefully drafted score card was published in the *Prairie Farmer* and nominations for the title of Master Farmer were invited in June, 1925. After extended investigation with reference to the score card, twenty-three farmers were awarded gold medals at a banquet attended by notables in Chicago. Other farm journals soon joined the *Prairie Farmer* in designating Master Farmers. During the first ten years of the movement, about 1400 Master Farmers were named. The movement represented a successful effort to dignify agriculture and honor those engaged in it at a time when many farmers felt that they were at an economic and social disadvantage.

Master Farmers Awards Are Announced

"Who Are the Best All-Around Farmers? Prairie Farmer Will Award the Degree of Master Farmer to 20 of Them," *Prairie Farmer*, 97(25):3. June 20, 1925.

Who is the best all-around farmer and citizen in your community? Prairie Farmer is looking for the 20 best farmers in our territory. When we find them, we will award them the degree of Master Farmer. An attractive gold watch fob and a certificate of merit, suitable for framing will be awarded to each one.

Only men whose sole business is farming can qualify for the degree of Master Farmer. Even being a good farmer will not be enough. The winners must be good citizens as well, and good husbands and fathers.

These Master Farmers will be selected in accordance with the scale of points in our Farmer's Score Card, which was printed in our issue of January 17 and which is reproduced on this page. Before the score card can be properly filled out, it will be necessary to read the detailed directions for scoring which were printed January 17. If you did not keep this copy of Prairie Farmer, write us and we will send you a reprint of the directions for scoring.

Nominations for Master Farmers may be made by any friend or neighbor, or by the man himself or some member of his family. A score card, properly filled out, must accompany the nomination, together with the name and address of the person making the nomination. All this information will be regarded as confidential by us. Names of persons nominated will not be printed; only the names of those to whom the degrees are finally awarded.

In filling out the score card, be as accurate and fair as possible. We will verify and correct the score in a number of ways. In doing this, if we find that any serious misrepresentation or error in judgment has been made in the original score, the name will be dropped from consideration. When the scores have finally been revised and corrected to the point where we feel that they are as accurate as they can be made, the degree of Master Farmer will be awarded to the 20 farmers having the highest score.

Final decision and awards will be made by the following committee:

Dr. W. L. Burlison, University of Illinois

S. H. Thompson, Illinois Agricultural Association

C. V. Gregory, Editor Prairie Farmer.

Our reason for offering these awards is that we feel that real farmers, who have made an outstanding success in their chosen field, deserve some public recognition. Various attempts have been made to do this. Farmers' halls of fame have been established. Biographical sketches of famous farmers have been published. But the outcome is usually the same. The men who get the recognition are not farmers, but professors or scientists or inventors or something else which, while related to farming, is not farming. Thus the whole purpose is defeated.

For that reason we are limiting our awards to real farmers who live on and operate their farms and who have no other business. We believe that these awards will accomplish great good. They will furnish farmers with an additional incentive. They will attract the attention of the business and professional world to the real business of farming and farm life, rather than to the show front of men who spend money playing at farming.

Our Farmer's Score Card has attracted nation-wide comment and favorable mention. It furnishes an accurate basis of analysis and comparison that makes possible such a contest as we are now launching.

We hope our readers will cooperate with us in making nominations for these Master Farmer degrees. We want the 20 men finally selected to be the 20 best all-around farmers in our territory. The only way to assure this is to have several hundred nominations made, including the best farmers in each community.

Failure to win an award at the first attempt should not be cause for discouragement. A comparison of your score with that of the winner's will indicate on what points you have fallen short, and how much, and will make possible improvements that may give you a place in the list of winners later.

Nominations must reach us by July 15. Awards will be announced as soon thereafter as possible, probably about September 1.

PRAIRIE FARMER'S SCORE CARD FOR FARMERS

(Copyright, 1925, by Prairie Farmer Publishing Company)

	Full Score	Score
I. Operation and Organization of Farm	260	
1. Maintenance of soil fertility................	65	....
2. Crop Rotation	30	....
3. Efficient Use of Man and Horse Labor.......	30	....
4. Crop Yields	30	....
5. Seed	10	....
6. Feeding and Care of Livestock..............	30	....
7. Quality of Livestock	20	....
8. Adequate Tools, Machinery and Equipment, Well Housed and Repaired..............	15	....
9. Large and uniform sized fields..............	15	....
10. Convenient farmstead arrangement..........	15	....
II. Business Methods and Ability	200	....
1. Relation of Income to Expenses.............	100	....
2. Accounting Methods	50	....
3. Business Reputation	50	....
III. General Farm Appearance and Upkeep..........	90	....
1. Repair and Upkeep of Buildings............	25	....
2. Condition of Fields	25	....
3. Maintenance of Fences, Ditches and Roads...	20	....
4. Freedom From Weeds and Rubbish.........	20	....
IV. Home Life	300	....
1. Convenient House	50	....
2. Labor-Saving Equipment in Home..........	75	....

    3. Character as a Husband and Father.......... 100   ....
    4. Education and Training of Children......... 75   ....

V. Citizenship   150   ....

    1. Neighborliness 50   ....
    2. Interest in School and Churches............ 40   ....
    3. Interest in Other Community Enterprises.... 30   ....
    4. Interest in Local, State and National Govern-
       ment 30   ....
                       Total   1000 ....

Name of person scored.....................................
Address ....
Name of Scorer ....
Address ....
Date ....

44

Hybrid Seed Corn Commercially Available in the Corn Belt

Corn, the life-saving crop adopted from the Indians by the first settlers in Jamestown and Plymouth, and variously known as maize, Indian corn, and corn, pointed the way to a second revolution in American agriculture. Its evolution at the hands of such practical men as John Lorain and such scientists as William James Beal, George Harrison Shull, and Edward M. East, has been traced. Finally, in the mid-1920's, hybrid seed corn became available to farmers, largely through the efforts of Henry A. Wallace. Early in 1926, farm journals carried advertisements of "Copper Cross—The only cross of inbred strains for sale in the cornbelt." At the end of 1926, the first advertisements of Henry A. Wallace's Hi-Bred Corn Company, later the Pioneer Hi-Bred Corn Company, appeared. This hybrid seed brought about a revolution in corn production that, as Henry A. Wallace forecast in 1925, affected the lives of every person in the Corn Belt, changed systems of farm management, and influenced both domestic and foreign policies of the American government.

Wallace Discusses the Revolution in Corn Breeding

Henry A. Wallace, "The Revolution in Corn Breeding," *Prairie Farmer*, 79 (12): 3, 15 (Mar. 21, 1925).

The revolution in corn breeding began back in 1905, when E. M. East, an Illinois boy, began inbreeding some Leaming corn at the Connecticut station. Perhaps East became interested in corn originally by associating with Hopkins and Smith at the Illinois station. At any rate, when he got a job at the Connecticut station, he evidently decided to forget all about ear-row breeding and other methods which were so popular in the corn belt at the time. He was a scientist, and therefore he struck out boldly into a new field. He bagged the silks and tassels of his corn and by hand put the pollen of a plant on the silk of the same plant. He not only did this one year, but for several years.

Within a few years the inbred corn became discouragingly weak, and some of the strains were so very bad that they died out entirely. The best of them yielded less than half as much as ordinary corn. East then crossed these inbred strains and found that the original vigor and yielding power came back, and more, too. This was announced to the scientific world in 1910, and created something of a stir, but nothing came of it directly. George H. Shull, of the Carnegie Institution, did the same kind of work as East, beginning in 1905, and also announced his results, which were the same as East's, in 1910. East's work is of more interest because his inbred strains are still in existence and have given combinations of high productive value when crossed.

East went into purely scientific work at Harvard and a young fellow by the name of Hayes took up the task of continuing the inbred strains which East had started. After a few years Hayes was called to head the plant-breeding work of the Minnesota station, and a Kansas boy named Jones came in charge. Jones thought that if breeding two inbreds together was good, that maybe it would be still better to breed four.

This double crossing, as he called it gave astonishing yields. Double-crossed strains yielded 100 to 120 bushels per acre on the same soil where standard Connecticut varieties were yielding 80 or 90 and the inbred parents less than 40 bushels. Jones fairly bubbled over with enthusiam and wrote a number of interesting bulletins and articles during 1918-22.

At the same time other scientific men, notably those at the

Nebraska station and in the United States Department of Agriculture, began to take a vivid interest in inbreeding work. For a number of years these men had done inbreeding work, but apparently with no great hope of a practical outcome. All of this suddenly changed, and by 1923 every experiment station in the corn belt was actively at work on the new idea.

No seed company, or farmer, or experiment station, has any inbred seed or cross of inbred seed for sale today. The revolution has not come yet, but I am certain that it will come within 10 or 15 years. A foretaste of it was in the south-central section of the Iowa corn yield contest last year, when a cross of three inbreds outyielded the nearest strain of Reid corn by 30 percent. It is safe to say that if this cross had been planted in the Reid Yellow Dent Territory of Iowa last year that the average farmer would have had 500 bushels more corn and the state total would have been increased by fully 50,000,000 bushels.

The story of this particular cross is interesting. Holbert, working for the United States Department of Agriculture, on the root-rot problem in corn, started inbreeding work with Funk Yellow Dent about six years ago, finding two vigorous strains which he called his A and B strains. Holbert found that a cross of these two strains yielded unusually well in Central Illinois. Jenkins, who worked with Holbert at Bloomington, went to the Iowa station at Ames in 1922, taking with him seed of this cross. In the meantime, at Des Moines, I had been inbreeding Burnett's Iodent, which is the Iowa station strain of Reid. To hasten matters along I produced two generations a year by using a greenhouse in the winter. This particular inbred was unusually bad, producing some plants with striped leaves, some with rolled tops which wouldn't let the tassel come out normally, some with zig-zag stalks, and many plants seriously affected with root-rot. It was early, however, and produced ears with nice, horny kernels. One of the graduate students at Ames wanted to experiment with some inbred strains of corn, so I sent this up to him.

Burnett tells me that Holbert's A by B cross was crossed on this inbred Iodent and part of the resulting seed was planted in the Ames plot of the Iowa corn yield contest in 1923. It outyielded the nearest strain of Reid by eight bushels to the acre, and so in 1924 the rest of the seed was entered in all the plots of South Central Iowa in the regular way, and this time the cross had a lead of more than 10 bushels per acre over the nearest strain of Reid. Moreover, it contained only 14 percent moisture, as compared with 19 for the typical Reid strain.

Next to this particular inbred cross in the 1924 Iowa corn yield contest was a red inbred cross which yielded 11 bushels per acre more than the average of the 32 Reid strains entered. This sort is of particular interest because on its dam's side it is one of the inbred Leaming strains started by East back in 1905. The sire is a Bloody Butcher originally from China, inbred one year by Richey of the United States Department of Agriculture, and then by myself for two or three years, one generation being in the greenhouse during the winter. The inbred dam which was de-tasseled in 1923 was seriously attacked by diplodia and the seed which was planted in the corn yield contest was the poorest looking seed corn that was ever planted in Iowa. Nevertheless, the punch was there, because it outyielded 32 strains of Reid corn, including such well-tested strains as the Krug, Black, Steen, and McCulloch.

The problem now is to find the very best inbred strains of corn. So far, the strains used have been more or less makeshifts, and I am certain from studying the work of Hoffer at the Indiana station that they can be greatly improved upon. Just the same there are 10 or 15 strains in existence today that combine sufficiently well that if we used nothing but them, I am certain that the corn yield of the corn belt could be increased at least 100,000,000 bushels annually. The extra cost of producing seed by this method is perhaps $1.50 a bushel, which would add roughly 25 cents an acre to the cost of seeding. The average farmer, however, will not care to go to the bother of producing seed of this sort himself, but will doubtless prefer to buy it each year from seedsmen or local seed corn "cranks" at a total outlay of perhaps 50 cents or even $1 per acre for the improved seed.

This investment must be made afresh each year, because this cross of inbred seed will give its unusual yield only the one year. Of course a return of five or 10 bushels is very good for an outlay of 50 cents or a dollar, but it will doubtless take a lot of educational work before many farmers will care to buy the new type of seed corn fresh each year.

When the revolution gets well under way, a number of new things will develop. Types of corn will be put out which will not blow down in any ordinary windstorm, but at the same time yield well. High-yielding 90-day sort will be especially adapted to corn picking machinery, with strong shanked ears which will not drop off until pulled off by the machine. Certain sorts will excel our present-day strains in the fattening of hogs and cattle. Others will be specially adapted to seeding clover or wheat in the corn.

The average bushel of corn as produced in the corn belt now requires, in a favorable season, the expenditure of 35 minutes of man labor, 75 minutes of horse labor, and 35 cents' worth of land, machinery and seed corn. With the improved seed corn which I know can be produced by the method of crossing inbred strains, it will be possible under similar soil and climatic conditions to produce a bushel of corn at an outlay of 28 minutes of man labor, 60 minutes of horse labor and 32 cents' worth of land, machinery and seed corn. With this improved seed corn the average corn belt farmer will be able to produce as much corn as he now produces on 80 or 85 per cent as much land, which means a saving in man labor of over 100 hours a year and a saving in horse labor of more than 200 hours. Of course all of this is assuming that the ravages of the European corn-borer do not ultimately offset the gain from a more productive type of corn.

All of the corn belt stations are now in possession of hundreds of inbred strains of corn and will soon be in the process of trying out thousands of combinations to discover just which sorts "nick" best. Within five or 10 years they will have good inbred strains for general distribution. The men who will send for these strains at that time will probably be chiefly seedsmen and seed corn cranks. The stations will presumably have to set up a sort of certification bureau so as to prevent unscrupulous people from selling common seed corn under the name of a certain definite cross of inbreds. It will be a difficult matter to work out, but the prospect of larger corn yields is so great that a satisfactory scheme is sure to be found.

A revolution in corn breeding is coming which will affect directly or indirectly every man, woman and child in the corn belt within 20 years. Our systems of farm management will be changed somewhat and it is even possible that both domestic policies and the foreign relations of the United States will be somewhat influenced.

45

Domestic Allotment Plan Proposed

The domestic allotment plan for farm relief was first presented in 1926 by Harry N. Owen in his journal, *Farm, Stock and Home*. The plan drew upon ideas supplied by W. J. Spillman of the United States Department of Agriculture, who developed the plan further in a book, *Balancing the Farm Output*, published in January, 1927. It was a modification of and an alternative to the McNary-Haugen proposal. The plan was later modified and publicized by Beardsley Ruml of the Laura Spelman Rockefeller Memorial Foundation, John D. Black of Harvard University and M. L. Wilson of Montana State College.

The essential principle of the domestic allotment plan was to pay producers a free trade price plus the tariff duty for the part of their crop consumed in the United States, and the free trade price only for that part of the crop exported. This was to be carried out by making specific allotments to individual producers of rights to sell on the domestic market their proportionate shares of production needed by that market. The rights were to be transferable. Production not covered by allotment rights might be sold at the world price or used for feed.

The basic idea of the domestic allotment plan was endorsed by both political parties in 1932, although both were careful not to call it by that name.

In the fall of 1932 the plan was modified in two respects: the group promoting it emphasized that participation would be voluntary, and it was definitely tied to production control.

It was included in the Agricultural Adjustment Act of 1933 as one of the means authorized for attacking the farm problem and was immediately applied to wheat. In 1936 the idea was embodied by name in the Soil Conservation and Domestic Allotment Act, passed after the Supreme Court invalidated major parts of the Agricultural Adjustment Act of 1933.

The Domestic Allotment Plan is Proposed

Harry N. Owen, "Getting Tariff to the Farmer," *Farm, Stock and Home*, 42: 84-86. February 1, 1926.

How can farmers get the full benefit of the tariff on agricultural products without the same time increasing production and making their future situation worse than the present?

Can any plan be devised for taking care of the surplus without putting the government into business; without bringing about international complications on account of dumping our products on the world market and without disrupting all or part of present distributive agencies?

Is it possible to make any plan that will be economically sound and constitutional?

The writer was, we think, the first to suggest in the fall of 1920 the formation of an export corporation to segregate the estimated exportable surplus of wheat by purchase at market prices during the months of heavy marketing, merchandise it abroad at the best advantage and assess the loss if any, back to the producers.

The McNary-Haugen bill was a blundering, uneconomic, cumbersome attempt to do this. More mature thought and study show the export corporation idea is open to the following objections: It puts the Government into the grain business. It also presents many difficulties in the matter of assessing losses back to the producer, and we think absolutely falls down when an attempt is made to apply the idea to meats and meat products. It would also completely destroy the business of grain exporters.

The Dickinson Bill, now pending, removes the first objection, but leaves the others untouched. In removing the objection, it raises the question whether our cooperatives have yet reached the necessary development to permit them to function successfully in handling the surplus.

We have thus frankly acknowledged the shortcomings of the export corporation idea, because we believe we can now present an economic, workable and effective plan to get the full benefit of the tariff protection. . . .

The Plan

While the following plan, can, we think, apply to all agricultural products of which we have regularly or may have occasionally an exportable surplus, for the sake of simplicity, we will use wheat as an illustration.

Let us start with the initial transaction, the purchase and sale of a load of wheat at a country elevator. For easy figuring, we will start with a hundred bushels. Assume that it has previously been estimated that the probable exportable surplus of wheat is fifteen percent of the crop and previous year's carry-over.

The elevator man will be required to pay 42 cents a bushel over the station price for the hundred bushels, but the farmer will get this 42 cents on but 85 bushels and the market price for the other 15.

Right here is where you lose interest. Who is going to pay this? The same fellow that pays the tariff on everything else—Mr. U. Consumer.

When the wheat is sold, the elevator man adds this 42 cents to his price.

That price then automatically becomes the market price at terminals. The station, or local market, price will be figured at 42 cents, plus freight, lower than the terminal price, but that is a mere matter of establishing the basis. When the farmer sells, he gets the 42 cents added to the local price.

How Exporters Are Protected

This leaves the elevator man with 42 cents a bushel on 15 bushels. What does he do with it? He will be required by law and be under bonds to send this money to a Finance Board, which will be discussed later. This Board, in turn, will pay the wheat exporter 42 cents a bushel over the price he is compelled to sell the wheat for in competition with the world.

The miller exporting flour would be paid on the same basis as the exporter. This would probably be about a cent a pound for flour exported. It is necessary to do this otherwise it would be impossible to export any wheat or flour. It is plain that no exporter could sell wheat that he had been compelled to pay 42 cents a bushel over the world market.

It may be argued that this is open to the same objection made to the Noyes export bounty plan. That an exporter would give away a part of his 42 cents to get business and would depress the world market by forcing competitors down. The cases are not parallel. Under this plan, the exporter is buying wheat at the domestic price, plus 42 cents. He has not any 42 cents handed him to do with as he pleases. If he offers this wheat below what he paid for it, the loss is his, and there is nothing in the way of a gift to help him out.

What It Does to Production

This plan automatically encourages the farmers to produce up to domestic requirements. In the case of wheat, it will crack him 42 cents a bushel on every bushel he produces over those requirements, which is as it should be.

Benefit Is Direct

Unlike the Noyes export bounty plan, the benefit goes directly to the producer. There is no complicated equalization fee provisions leaving the farmer with the certainty of the tax and the mere hope of benefit.

It disposes at once of the complicated levying of equalization fees. The transaction is completed as far as the farmer is concerned when he delivers his wheat.

As it is impossible to estimate, with mathematical exactness, the amount of wheat that will be exported, it would be advisable for the first year of operation at least to make the estimate liberal. If any material fund is left over in the hands of the Finance Board, after rebating to exporters, millers and paying the cost of operation, this surplus money could be taken into consideration when making the following year's estimate of the exportable, and a slight under-estimate could be made.

This would not, of course, be a hundred per cent perfect, as far as individuals are concerned, but its simplicity and workability is so much greater than any equalization fee and refund provision that could be established that in actual practice the cost of operating this plan would, we think, cost the individual producers so little that it would never be noticed. An over-estimate one year might be corrected the next.

What Must Be Set Up

First it will be necessary to form a Finance Board to receive and administer the funds sent in by the wheat buyers and hire all clerical and executive help required to carry on the business of the Board. This Board should be small, not over five, with salaries large enough to pay good men to devote their entire time to the work. The salaries and expense of carrying on the work should be paid out of the funds collected. All employees should be under civil service.

The only connection the Government would have with the Board is the appointment of the members, which I think should be made by the President, subject to senatorial confirmation, and supervision of operations to prevent misuse of funds. Length of term of Board members and salaries is a detail to be taken up if we ever get that far.

The only duties of this Board would be to receive funds and paying out money to exporters and checking the grain buyers.

The estimating of exportable surplus at beginning of the crop year to be made either by the Department of Agriculture, the Department of Commerce, or preferably both working jointly.

How Financed

This Board's expenses could, and we think should be, financed just as payments to exporters and export millers are. It could be done in this way. Budget the expenses of the Board for the ensuing crop year. If it appears they will be $100,000.00, it is plain that retaining 42 cents a bushel on 238,095 bushels of wheat will meet the budget. Simply add this much wheat to the estimated exportable surplus on which 42 cents would have to be paid the exporters.

It would not be necessary even to have a loan to finance the first year's operation of the Board. It would begin to get its money as soon as the crop started moving.

Effect on the Grain Trade

How will it affect the grain trade and cooperatives? Practically not at all. It will be necessary to require that all initial purchasers of grain file a bond with the Finance Board to insure the forwarding of all moneys collected on the estimated exportable surplus. Require all such dealers to keep accurate and careful records, so that inspectors can easily check them from time to time. It might be possible for the Board to arrange to have national bank examiners do this checking.

We believe the foregoing meets every objection that has been raised to the McNary-Haugen Bill, the Noyes Export Bounty Plan and the pending Dickinson Bill.

It does not meet the President's statement that he is against price fixing direct or indirect. This plan does not contemplate any price fixing. The market price remains subject to all the vicissitudes that it at present undergoes.

Indirect price fixing it is, of course, but as it is impossible to afford farmers any relief except through higher prices for his produce, and as the President has said he would favor any sound, economic plan for the relief of agriculture, we believe, or at least hope, he will modify his position as to indirect price fixing, after he, or his advisors, have given consideration to this plan.

46

Federal Farm Board Established

President Hoover's approval of the Agricultural Marketing Act on June 15, 1929, marked the assumption by the federal government of responsibility for aiding farmers in marketing their products in order that they might attempt to attain economic equality with other industries. Governmental aid in regularizing the marketing of farm products had been endorsed by Herbert Hoover as early as October, 1920. During the 1920's he repeatedly proposed the creation of an independent board that would be charged with this responsibility. His advocacy was, in part, an attempt to offset the McNary-Haugen bills.

The Federal Farm Board, established by the Agricultural Marketing Act, aided farmers in organizing cooperative marketing associations and made loans to such associations. It also made loans to wheat and cotton stabilization corporations set up by the cooperatives for the purpose of controlling price-depressing surpluses. A revolving fund of 500 million dollars was provided for carrying out these functions.

The great depression of 1929 and subsequent years doomed the Farm Board to failure. It had neither the authority nor the funds to deal with the catastrophe. The net cost of the experiment has been estimated at 305 million dollars; its value as an experiment in economic assistance cannot be measured.

The Farm Board Reports on its Failure to Stabilize Farm Prices

U.S. Federal Farm Board, *Third Annual Report*, 1932, pp. 1, 2, 62, 85 (Washington, U.S. Government Printing Office, 1932).

Since its inauguration, the Federal Farm Board has devoted the major share of its efforts to aiding producers to develop a strong cooperative marketing system, under the mandate of the agricultural marketing act. If agriculture is ever to attain a position of economic equality with other industries in our highly organized society, producers of each type of product must establish their own cooperative organization and develop it to a high point of effectiveness. Recent experience has shown that in those fields where cooperative agencies are best developed, farmers have been most able to resist the disastrous effects of the economic depression. Effective organization will be equally important in strengthening their position during the subsequent period of advancing prices and business activity. . . .

Stabilization purchases had been suspended before the beginning of the past year. Stabilization sales programs during the year were carried on in such a way as not to depress domestic prices, but instead to support them as far as possible. The results of this policy were particularly successful in the case of wheat. Over half the accumulated stabilization supplies were disposed of, here or abroad, yet farm prices for the 1931 crop were maintained well above their usual relation to prices on world markets. . . .

Experience with stabilization thus demonstrates that no measure for improving the price of farm products other than increasing the demand of consumers can be effective over a period of years unless it provides a more definite control of production than has been achieved so far. In a few limited and specialized lines, co-operative associations have made progress toward such control. For the great staple products, however, the problem still remains for future solution. . . .

The present low prices of farm products must be ascribed to other causes than heavy surpluses, except in the case of a few commodities, where the effect of drastically reduced demand has been aggravated by the accumulation of unsold supplies from earlier years. Two sets of influences are largely responsible for the extremely low levels of prices and farm income which now prevail—the inability of many of our domestic consumers to buy, as a result of reduced incomes and widespread unemployment; and the inability of foreign customers to purchase our products to the usual extent, due to the disorganization of international trade, and the accompanying heavy unemployment and reduced incomes abroad.

In view of the present situation a program for restoration of farm incomes must, therefore, include the following lines of activity: (a) Hastening business recovery in the United States, thereby increasing returns from products sold in the domestic market; (b) steps to initiate recovery in international trade, thereby strengthening foreign demand for export products; (c) readjustment of taxes, interest, and principal payments, freight rates, and other fixed charges which enter into the farmer's expenses and now abnormally depress the share which he receives of the final retail price; (d) further strengthening and expanding of cooperative organization to reduce the expenses of marketing and increase the producer's share of the consumer's dollar; and (e) efforts, through cooperative marketing associations or in other ways, to secure a better adjustment between the quantities produced and the needs of the market.

PART VII

The New Deal, 1933-1939

47

Congress Authorizes Program to Control Production and Marketing

The inadequacies of the Federal Farm Board programs, the steadily worsening economic position of agriculture, the determination of farm leaders that something must be done, and a change in administration resulted in the Agricultural Adjustment Act of May 12, 1933. Congress declared its policy was "to establish and maintain such balance between the production and consumption of agricultural commodities, and such marketing conditions therefor, as will reestablish prices to farmers at a level that will give agricultural commodities a purchasing power with respect to articles that farmers buy, equivalent to the purchasing power of agricultural commodities in the base period."

The Secretary of Agriculture was given broad powers to effectuate the act, reflecting in part the diverse remedies that had been advocated by farm organizations since the 1920's. He was empowered to reduce acreage or production for market through voluntary agreements which might include rental or benefit payments, to enter into marketing agreements with processors and others for the purpose of controlling prices paid producers, and to issue licenses permitting processors and others to engage in handling agricultural commodities with the aim of eliminating unfair practices or charges. The act provided for processing taxes, the proceeds of which were to be made available for rental and benefit payments, expansion of markets, removal of surplus agricultural products, and other expenses.

From 1933 through 1935, benefit payments were provided for farmers who voluntarily contracted with the Secretary to reduce production and who complied with their contracts. Marketing agreement and order programs were first considered as an alternative to production controls for basic commodities, and in 1933 and 1934 were used for wheat, tobacco, peanuts, and rice. Later, while still used for tobacco, marketing agreement and order programs were used primarily for milk, fruits, and vegetables, which were not subject to production control.

The production control provisions of the act were invalidated on January 6, 1936, by the Hoosac Mills decision of the Supreme Court. It was replaced in part by the Soil Conservation and Domestic Allotment Act of February 29, 1936, which attempted to secure reduced production of surplus crops through payments for improved land use and conservation practices. While the marketing agreement and order provisions of the Act of 1933 were not invalidated, they were re-enacted by the Agricultural Marketing Agreement Act of 1937.

Economic Advisor to the Secretary of Agriculture
Discusses the Agricultural Adjustment Act

Mordecai Ezekiel, *Government and Agriculture*, U.S. Department of Agriculture, press release, July 13, 1934, pp. 6-8.

The Agricultural Adjustment Act went one step further [than the Farm Board]. The combination of benefit payments and processing taxes provided substantial rewards to those who participated in production adjustment, and insured that those who refused to participate would not share the gains. For the first time on any large scale, this provided a definite mechanism through which farmers could work together to really insure production control.

The AAA has succeeded in its first emergency task of controlling production. By the time the 1934 crops have been disposed of, the heavy excess supplies will have been greatly reduced, in the case of cotton, tobacco, and rice, and completely eliminated, in the case of wheat, corn, and hogs.

Now that the first emergency phase of eliminating the piled up excessive surpluses is drawing to a close, the future progress may be toward the evolution of methods for the continuous adjustment of production to demand. Such a continuous adjustment would provide for expansion of production in lines where increasing domestic buying power or reopening world markets was expanding demand; and for maintaining production where production was in line with demand. In each case the effort would be to expand production in line with, but not in advance of, the expansion in demand.

As a long-time program, the extent to which demand for our farm products will increase will depend very largely upon how far foreign markets can be reopened. As Secretary Wallace has pointed out so forcibly in "America Must Choose," we face the alternatives of withdrawing 40 million acres of land from cultivation, or of restoring the sale of our farm products to other countries through being willing to purchase their industrial products in return. But leveling the world trade barriers and restoring international trade will be an arduous, and long-drawn-out process, with the progress discouragingly slow, at least in the beginning.

Part of the necessary shrinkage of production may be secured through the purchase of submarginal land and its diversion to other uses, such as for forestry, recreation, or wild-life restoration. Part of the adjustment may be secured through continued organization of farmers for the rational adjustment of production so as to prevent a reappearance of the hog cycles, sheep cycles, cotton cycles, and potato cycles, which played such havoc with stability of prices and incomes in the past.

Regardless of how far we depend on withdrawal of land, or how far on regulation and control of the use of the land actually in farms, we will continue to face the need of shifting farmers from agriculture to other types of work. Temporarily, while city unemployment is large and relief loads are heavy, the tide is running country-ward. Some portion of the subsistence homesteads and rural rehabilitation projects may take permanent roots in a new and decentralized industrial life. By and large, though, most of the surplus population which recently has moved to farms—numbering over two million at the present time—will be perfectly satisfied to move back into industry as soon as satisfactory jobs develop for them there. And, for the reasons indicated earlier, the more those workers are absorbed in non-agricultural work, the higher our general productivity and standards of living will be. If we carry on vigorously the program of submarginal land withdrawal, that will add still more men to the number available to be absorbed in non-agricultural pursuits; and the more nearly nationalistic a foreign trade policy we follow, the more this number will have to be.

In the very long run, we may come to realize that real farm prosperity depends upon reducing the number of workers in agriculture as rapidly as productivity per worker rises.

48

Cross-Breeding Produces Meat-Type Hogs

The science of genetics, which deals with the manner in which characteristics are passed on from generation to generation, has made many contributions to agriculture. The most spectacular is hybrid corn, which has served as an example for all scientific breeding. The development of meat-type hogs is one such endeavor that has been carried out since the success of hybrid corn.

The development of a meat-type hog was related to market needs. Lard became less important as a source of fat with the greater use of cheaper vegetable oils, and meat packers called for a hog that would yield more lean meat and less fat, and thus more nearly meet market demands, even though they had not by 1960 yet made it profitable for farmers to generally produce such hogs.

American breeders over the years had devoted themselves to improving hogs within the pure breeds. Much emphasis had been given weight, and breeders had developed notable lard-type strains. Many producers found it impossible to find breeding stock that would fully meet the new market demands. Scientists in the state experiment stations and the Department of Agriculture turned to the experience of the Danes, Poles, and other Europeans, who were cross-breeding hogs to obtain lean meat and vigorous animals. The importation in 1934 of Danish Landrace hogs for breeding studies was the first step to adapt European experience to American needs through the science of genetics. Cross-breeding was undertaken at the Department's Beltsville station; at the Swine Breeding Laboratory in Ames, Iowa, established in 1936; and at several state experiment stations. The object of the cross-breeding experiments was to develop a streamlined hog with less fat and more total weight in the choice cuts.

The meat-type hog was not an overnight development. It took a number of years to obtain commercially valuable results. However, the breeding experiments eventually resulted in producing more lean meat and less fat, as well as larger litters and bigger pigs. The hopes expressed in 1935 by the authors of the following article were realized, even though twenty-five years later it was not profitable for most farmers to grow meat-type hogs. Similar work has resulted in notable improvements in other livestock and in plants.

Landrace Hogs Imported

O. G. Hankins and J. H. Zeller, "Hogs of Danish Origin Imported for Breeding Studies in this Country," U.S. Department of Agriculture, *Yearbook, 1935,* pp. 231-233 (Washington, U.S. Government Printing Office, 1935).

Science is constantly exploring new opportunities of aiding the producer of agricultural commodities to conduct his business more efficiently and to meet the needs of a changing economy. In this connection animal and plant breeders are putting forth their efforts toward making available new types and strains or varieties that are superior in important characteristics. These efforts have included importations and subsequent studies with respect to adaptability, merit in comparison with present varieties and strains, breed improvement, and possible advantages from crossbreeding.

For a number of years the Department of Agriculture has recognized the advantages of selecting breeding animals of the meat-producing species on the basis of performance records. It was with the needs of the industry in mind, especially for a more effective method of selecting breeding stock, that the Department together with the Iowa Agricultural Experiment Station, recently became interested in studying Danish hogs and methods under American conditions.

Since the beginning of the present century the swine industry of Denmark has shown remarkable development. That country has shown the world the striking improvement that can be accomplished by well-planned, systematic testing methods, associated with good feeding and management. Denmark's valuable background of performance records in both economy of production and quality of product caused the Department and the Iowa station to obtain a number of Danish pigs, carefully selected, for such research purposes.

The most important influence in the development of the swine industry in Denmark has been the selection of breeding animals based on detailed breeding-center, testing-station, and bacon-factory records. This method of selection, supported by good methods of feeding and management, has resulted in the very efficient production of high-quality bacon of the type known commercially as Wiltshire sides.

The breeds through which this has been accomplished in Denmark are the Landrace and Yorkshire, with the former of much the greater importance. This breed originally consisted of 15 different families, the progeny of which have been studied through the years and only the more efficient ones maintained. Today, on this basis of actual performance, only 4 of the original families are regarded as of particular importance, 2 of these, the B family and the F family, meeting with most favor.

Early in 1934 a swine specialist of the Department, representing also the Iowa station, selected in Denmark 8 boars and 16 gilts of the Landrace breed and 2 boars and 4 gilts of the Yorkshire breed. Six of the Landrace pigs, 2 boars and 4 gilts, were from the Stabil line of breeding, Stabil being a highly regarded boar of the B family. Another group, 2 boars and 4 gilts, was from the most popular line (Stendys Mariendal) of the F family. The remaining 12 Landrace pigs were selected to represent varied lines of good breeding. The Yorkshire pigs likewise represented some of the best breeding in the country.

The 30 pigs were assembled at Copenhagen and shipped to St. Croix, Virgin Islands, where they were held in quarantine to comply with the livestock sanitary laws of the United States. The importation was made into the United States in May 1934. After a further quarantine period of 7 days the pigs were shipped to the United States Animal Husbandry Experiment Station, Beltsville, Md., and 6 of the Landrace pigs, 2 boars, and 4 gilts, were sent on from there to the Iowa station at Ames.

Each of the pigs in the importation has a known background of prolificacy, feed-lot efficiency, and quality of product. In the investigations with these pigs, now in progress, one of the first considerations is whether the Danish lines of breeding will produce results in this country, comparable with the records under Danish conditions. In addition the studies outlined provide for comparisons with representative lines of breeding in leading breeds commonly raised in the United States. A further phase of the program is the study of certain modifications of the Danish testing methods to determine their value for use in swine-improvement work in this country. Crossbreeding with one or more leading domestic breeds constitutes another important phase of the program. This will be done to determine the possibilities of combining the better characteristics of the foreign and domestic breeds, as they may be found to occur.

The importation was made with no thought of minimizing the merits of the American hog, but to compare these merits with those of selected strains of known efficiency from Denmark and also to combine superior qualities through crossbreeding. In view of the nature and scope of this study a number of years will be required to carry it to completion, although it is likely that it will yield interesting and helpful results in the near future.

49

Soil Conservation Encouraged and
Aided by the Federal Government

The need for preserving the soil and its fertility has engaged the attention of agricultural reformers since colonial days. Yet, in spite of exhortations by farm journalists, leaders of farm organizations, governmental officials, and others, many farmers did not conserve their land because they did not have immediate monetary incentives.

Renters and owners interested in immediate income and profit often found the use of soil-wasting practices and methods more convenient and profitable. Too, in many cases, farmers were under economic pressure to obtain immediate cash returns to meet payments on land, machinery, and livestock. Conserving resources for a future generation was a luxury such farmers could not afford.

The general conservation movement of the late 1880's and early 1900's stimulated interest in soil conservation, but the problem was regarded as one for the individual farmer. By the 1920's, however, farm leaders were concerned over the increasing physical loss of soil as well as of soil fertility, partly because there were no new western lands left to be opened for agriculture. The waste caused by soil erosion and the extent of the problem was brought strongly to public attention by a circular issued by the United States Department of Agriculture in 1928, entitled *Soil Erosion A National Menace*. This publication has been regarded as a turning point in the fight to secure recognition of the problem as one facing the entire nation.

Congress appropriated funds to the Secretary of Agriculture in 1929 for soil erosion investigations and regional soil erosion experiment stations. The depression led to the establishment of erosion control work as a means of unemployment relief in 1933, and to the establishment of the Soil Erosion Service in the Department of the Interior. Demonstration projects were carried out by Civilian Conservation Corps personnel on public lands and, to a limited extent, on private lands.

The Soil Erosion Service was transferred to the Department of Agriculture in 1935. Later in the same year, Congress specifically established the Soil Conservation Service in the Department of Agriculture to develop and conduct a long-time program of soil and water conservation. By 1937 the Service began to shift from government-financed demonstration work to the provision of technical assistance to farmers organized in soil conservation districts.

Between 1936 and 1943, the long-range soil conservation program was supplemented, and to some extent overshadowed, by conservation payments authorized by the Soil Conservation and Domestic Allotment Act. This act provided direct payments to farmers for complying with acreage and, in some cases, marketing restrictions on certain "soil-depleting" crops, and for carrying out specified soil-conserving practices on their farms. Payments since 1943 under this act have been restricted to those for soil-conserving practices.

Hugh H. Bennett Discusses the Menace of Soil Erosion

H. H. Bennett and W. R. Chapline, *Soil Erosion A National Menace*, U.S. Department of Agriculture, Circular No. 33, pp. 2-3 (Washington, U.S. Government Printing Office, 1928).

Not less than 126,000,000,000 pounds of plant-food material is removed from the fields and pastures of the United States every year. Most of this loss is from cultivated and abandoned fields and over-grazed pastures and ranges. The value of the plant-food elements (considering only phosphorus, potash, and nitrogen) in this waste, as estimated on the basis of the chemical analyses of 389 samples of surface soil, collected throughout the United States, and the recent selling prices of the cheapest forms of fertilizer materials containing these plant nutrients, exceeds $2,000,000,000 annually. Of this amount there is evidence to indicate that at least $200,000,000 can be charged up as a tangible yearly loss to the farmers of the Nation. These calculations do not take into account the losses of lime, magnesia, and sulphur.

In this connection it must be considered that rainwash removes not only the plant-food elements but also the soil itself. The plant-food elements removed by crops (the crops do not take away the soil, but extract nutrients from it) can be restored in the form of fertilizers, manures, and soil-improving crops turned under; but the soil that is washed out of fields can not be restored, except by those exceedingly slow natural processes of soil building that require, in many instances, centuries to develop a comparatively thin layer. It would be entirely impracticable to replace even a small part of the eroded matter, which might be recoverable from stranded material not yet swept into the rivers.

A very considerable part of the wastage of erosion is obviously an immediate loss to the farmer, who in countless instances is in no economic position to stand the loss. Much of the wastage that perhaps might not be classed as an immediate farm loss is nevertheless a loss to posterity, and there are indications that our increasing population may feel acutely the evil effects of this scourge of the land, now largely unrestrained. A considerable part of the erosional debris goes to clog stream channels, to cover fertile alluvium with comparatively infertile sand and other coarse materials assorted from flood water, and to cause productive stream bottoms to become swampy and much less valuable. When the mellow topsoil is gone with its valuable humus and nitrogen, less productive, less permeable, less absorptive, and more intractable material is exposed in its place. As a rule this exposed material is the "raw" subsoil, which must be loosened, aerated, and supplied with the needed humus to put it into the condition best suited to plant growth. This rebuilding of the surface soil requires time, work, and money. In most places, this exposed material is heavier than the original soil, is stiffer, more difficult to plow, less penetrable to plant roots, less absorptive of rainfall and less retentive of that which is absorbed, and apparently its plant-food elements frequently have not been converted into available plant nutrients to anything like the degree that obtains in the displaced surface soil. This comparative inertness of the freshly exposed material is comparable to the lessened productivity brought about in some soils by suddenly plowing large quantities of the subsoil material to the surface. Such raw material must be given more intensive tillage in order to unlock its contained plant food, and on much of it lime and organic manures will be needed in order to reduce its stiffness sufficiently to make it amenable to efficient cultivation, to the establishment of a desirable seed-bed tilth. It bakes easier and, as a consequence, crops growing on it are less resistant to dry seasons, because of rapid evaporation from the hardened surface, and the many cracks that form deep into the subsoil to enlarge the area exposed to direct evaporation. Crops also suffer more in wet seasons because the material becomes more soggy or water-logged than did the original soil. On much of it both fertilizer and lime will be required for satisfactory yields. . . .

While these difficulties of tillage and the lowered productivity are being attended to by the farmer in those fields not yet abandoned, the unprotected fields continue to wash. Unfortunately the farmers in many localities are doing little or nothing to stop the wastage and much to accentuate it. In many instances the farmer does not know just what to do to slow down erosion. In many other cases he does not even suspect that the waning productivity of his fields results from any cause other than natural reduction of the plant-food supply by the crops removed. He does not recognize the fact that gradual erosion working unceasingly and more or less equally at all points, is the principal thief of the fertility of his soil until spots of subsoil clay or rock begin to appear over the sloping areas.

50

Artificial Breeding Changes Dairy Industry

In 1947 one of the nation's leading dairy husbandmen stated: "It would be possible to raise our national level of dairy production from four thousand five hundred-odd pounds of milk a year to 7,500 or more and from 185 pounds of butterfat to at least 300. The ways and means of doing it are at hand, but there is reason to believe that little measurable progress in breeding better dairy cattle has occurred in the past decade." In 1937 the average dairy cow produced 4,366 pounds of milk and 172 pounds of butterfat; in 1947, 5,007 pounds of milk and 199 pounds of butterfat; and in 1957, 6,160 pounds of milk and 235 pounds of butterfat.

The changes in the twenty-year period are due to many factors, such as the influence of markets, prices of milk and feeds, better knowledge of feeding, and the breeding of better cows. Available statistics do not permit a comprehensive breakdown of the importance of the various factors, but most dairymen agree that the use of sires that have proven their ability to get high-producing offspring could be a major factor in future improvement.

The supply of good dairy sires has always been limited. However, artificial breeding can revolutionize the use of meritorious bulls. A bull can service 30 to 50 cows a year; using artificial insemination, 2,000 cows a year may be impregnated from the same bull. Artificial insemination is useful primarily to speed up the rate of livestock improvement, even though there are other money-saving advantages to individual farmers.

An Italian scientist experimented successfully with artificial insemination in 1780, but its practical usefulness was not demonstrated until the twentieth century. A Russian scientist, Elie Ivanov, established the Central Experimental Breeding Station in Moscow in 1919, to continue work that had been under way for twenty years. In 1936 more than six million cattle and sheep were artificially inseminated in the Soviet Union.

Scientists in many nations, including the United States, experimented with artificial breeding after the Russians reported their successes. Denmark established such work on a cooperative basis in the 1930's. In 1937 a New Jersey state dairy specialist studied the Danish program and was so impressed that he took the lead in promoting an artificial breeding cooperative in New Jersey. This first group, launched in May, 1938, included about 125 cooperators who entered 1,050 cows in the project.

By January 1, 1939, 7 local cooperative artificial-breeding associations were serving 646 herds totaling 7,539 cows. In 1947, 1,184,000 cows in the United States were bred artificially, which was 4.6 per cent of the nation's total. Ten years later, in 1957, 6,056,000 cows were bred artificially, or 26.3 per cent of the total.

In 1943 the Department of Agriculture began collecting statistics through the artificial breeding associations to show the milk and butterfat production of proved sires' daughters. In 1943 such cows produced 10,155 pounds of milk and 419 pounds of butterfat; in 1947, 10,580 and 430; and in 1957, 11,304 and 477. These figures show that it would be possible to substantially increase the production of dairy products in the United States without increasing the number of milk cows.

First Artificial Breeding Cooperative is Organized

W. A. Haffert, "New Jersey Launches First Unit in Artificial Breeding," *New Jersey Farm and Garden,* 9 (6): 5, 18. June, 1938.

History was made at the farm of Peter P. Van Nuys, Bellemead, Somerset County, a few days ago. It was here that the first dairy cattle artificial breeding project in America was launched on May 25, attended by newspaper men, veterinarians, officials of breed organizations, and the officers and directors of the New Jersey Holstein-Friesian Association, the sponsoring organization.

Dr. J. A. Henderson, a well qualified young veterinarian, is in charge of the project, formally known as Artificial Breeding Unit No. 1. He is a graduate of Toronto Veterinary College, Canada, practiced a year in Michigan and has just completed his Master's Degree at Cornell. Assisting him for the first two months is Dr. K. A. F. Larsen, Danish veterinarian who has been in charge of cooperative artificial breeding work in Denmark.

It all started when Prof. E. J. Perry, state dairy specialist and active secretary of the Holstein-Friesian Association, was touring the dairy sections of Europe last year and spent several weeks with Dr. Larsen. Perry carefully studied the technique of artificial insemination, sounded out the sentiment of members of the Danish society and returned to America thrilled with the possibilities of this method of multiplying the productiveness of outstanding bulls and ushering in a new era of dairy cattle breeding.

After conferring with Dr. J. W. Bartlett, head of the Dairy Department at the College; County Agent Dwight Babbitt, of Hunterdon County; Clifford A. Snyder, of Pittstown, and Peter P. Van Nuys, of Bellemead, it was decided to sound out sentiment generally, and if favorable, then the state association would sponsor such a project. The subject of artificial breeding was given a prominent place on the program for the annual meeting of the association held on January 14 in New Brunswick. Prof. Stanley Brownell, of Cornell University, was invited to put on a demonstration, using a cow and a bull at the New Jersey College Farm. A crowd of 225 people attended this meeting, and it was at this same meeting that the officers were directed to reorganize and incorporate the state association into an artificial breeding society.

President Peter P. Van Nuys soon after called leading dairymen together, when definite plans were made. From then on, the scene shifted to Flemington, Hunterdon County, where County Agent Babbitt, with the cooperation of County Agents John Raab, of Warren, and Robert Gardner, of Somerset, staged the remaining three meetings, which brought the society into being.

Already 1,050 Holstein cows are entered in the project, the maximum limit agreed upon by the managing committee.

Thus has Perry's ambition been realized and thus has his trip to Denmark brought new fame to New Jersey and new opportunities for its dairymen. So rapidly has the word spread of the New Jersey project that similar projects are already being organized in Arizona, Connecticut and Ohio.

In artificial breeding, the semen is collected from the bull and is artificially placed in the cervix of the cow. Only a small portion is needed to effect pregnancy. Thus the breeding value of one bull is greatly increased, conception is more certain, fewer bulls need be kept and only the very best need be used for breeding. In Russia, last year, more than 70,000 horses were artificially bred. In Denmark, artificial breeding was established in 1936, and in the first year, 1,200 cows were impregnated by that method with a forty per cent better record of conceptions than by natural means.

Chalked on the right side of the ledger in cooperative artificial breeding are: More accurate breeding records of the cooperating herds than is usually kept by individual breeders; superior sires available at less cost per service (average natural service cost in New Jersey is $7.03 a cow; fee for artificial service has been set at $5); dairymen who have been milk producers only may now become breeders as well; dairymen who have not been raising calves may now raise their own replacements; owners of small herds save the expense and bother of keeping a bull; space occupied by the bull can be put to other use; and danger of disease spread from cow to cow by the bull will be practically eliminated.

This is only a partial list. To it may be added the opportunity for linebreeding on a large scale; breeding of yearling heifers to a large, heavy sire are eliminated; a better breeding program; better ability to measure the genetic ability of sires. Lengthen the list to suit yourself.

The artificial breeding is managed by a committee of five, elected by the association membership. They are: Clifford Snyder, Pittstown; David W. Amerman, Neshanic; Charles V. N. Davis, Somerville; George Edgar, Belvidere, and William C. Voegtlen, Lebanon. At present the participation on the project will be limited to the 1,050 cows now entered.

Outstanding sire to head the work is N. J. E. S. Sir Mutual Ormsby Jewel Alice, who has been leased from his joint owners, the New Jersey Experiment Station and Peter P. Van Nuys, president of the Holstein-Friesian Association. He is one of the outstanding proved bulls of the United States. His first thirteen daughters averaged 15,470 pounds of 3.85 per cent milk and 596 pounds of fat while their thirteen dams averaged 14,090 pounds of 3.5 per cent milk and 493 pounds of fat. This gives "Alice" a "B" index (three-times-a-day milking) of 16,850 pounds of 4.20 per cent milk and 708 pounds of butterfat. The income from the sale of additional milk produced by the daughters of this bull as compared with their dams has amounted to $36 a year. If you like to count your chickens before they are hatched, you can figure that this bull if used three years will contribute the sizable sum of about $135,000 to the members through artificial breeding to 500 or more cows yearly. He is now only six years of age and his daughters should milk for five years. Another sire to be used is Sensation Aaggie Beets Career, owned by the State Experiment Station.

Artificial breeding is here, thanks to Perry and the able men who saw eye-to-eye with him. The future looks bright. And again New Jersey has blazed a new trail which others are already following. The progress of the work will be recorded each month in New Jersey Farm and Garden, which is the official publication of the Holstein-Friesian Association, so that those interested will be able to be in constant touch with the epoch-making project.

PART VIII

World War II and the Second
Agricultural Revolution

51

Second Agricultural Revolution Begins with World War II

World War II saw an unprecedented increase in agricultural output. The wartime need for food and the doubling of the prices received by farmers for their products motivated increased production, but a combination of favorable physical circumstances amounting to a technological revolution made the large-scale increase possible.

The factors that made up the technological revolution included widespread progress in mechanization, greater use of lime and fertilizer, cover crops and other conservation practices, use of improved varieties, a better balanced feeding of livestock, and more effective control of insects and disease. These technological improvements had been developing for several years before World War II, but their current effects and possibilities were obscured by the drought and depression of the 1930's. The breaking of these restraints and the great wartime demand for farm products led to the adoption of an accumulation of technological improvements that, taken together, revolutionized agricultural production.

Shortly after World War II a number of reports on these technological changes were released by the U.S. Bureau of Agricultural Economics. They were followed by a summary report, *Changes in American Farming*, by Sherman E. Johnson, that discusses both the changes in production and the changes in the technology of production.

Changes in American Farming during World War II

Sherman E. Johnson, *Changes in American Farming*, U.S. Department of Agriculture Miscellaneous Publication No. 707, pp. 1, 3-5, 10, 13, 18, 20, 24, 25, 27, 45, 47, 56 (Washington, U.S. Government Printing Office, December, 1949).

RECORD FARM OUTPUT

Farmers in the United States achieved a remarkable production record in the war years. The increase in total farm output from 1935-39 to 1944 was twice as large as during the entire period from 1919-23 to 1935-39. This was accomplished without significant expansion in the acreage of cropland, and despite scarce supplies of labor, machinery, and farm materials. The high level reached during the war has been maintained in the early postwar years, and the 1948 output was an all-time record.

The output of farm products available for human use for the three full war years 1942-44 averaged 128 percent of the prewar years 1935-39. In 1946 the level was 133 percent of prewar. Despite a short corn crop the output in 1947 averaged 129 percent of prewar. . . . With a bumper corn crop in 1948 farm output reached the record total of 149 percent of 1935-39.

This increase in output constitutes an unprecedented break from previous trends. Usually, changes in farming develop very slowly. They are often unnoticed until the record over a period of years is examined. Even such major innovations as the tractor and complementary machines adapted for mechanical power were introduced so gradually that they escaped special attention until their cumulative effects became unusually pronounced.

Sometimes extremely favorable or unfavorable weather brings large year-to-year changes in production. For example, 1934 was a year of catastrophic drought, and farm production was much lower than in the preceding years. In 1942, growing conditions were unusually favorable. In fact, consistently good weather was experienced in the three war years 1942-44 compared with the average of the years 1935-39. But those prewar years reflect weather conditions that were less favorable to farm production than is the expectancy over a period of years. And although weather factors were more favorable in 1942-44 than longer-time expectancy, other forces were responsible for most of the increase in production.

Considering the average of the years 1942-44, it appears that about one-fourth of the total increase in production can be accounted for by weather conditions that were more favorable than in the prewar years 1935-39. This means that with normal weather farm output in 1942-44 would have averaged about 120 percent of 1935-39.

Obviously then, only a rather small part of the wartime increase in production can be explained by favorable weather. And it follows that average weather alone would not bring a return to prewar production levels. Extremely unfavorable weather would reduce output temporarily. But agriculture experienced a production revolution during the war years, and a large part of the change is irreversible. It will persist under peacetime conditions. To understand what has taken place it is necessary to analyze what happened in the war and early postwar years, to compare this experience with the record in World War I, and to trace the foundation for production increases that was laid in the interwar years.

THE WAR YEARS

COMBINATION OF FORCES BACK OF HIGHER OUTPUT

War and wartime needs for food, and the doubling of the prices received by farmers for their products, furnished the driving force for increased production, but a combination of favorable physical circumstances made the large-scale increase possible. Potential production capacity had been built up over the several years previous to the outbreak of World War II. This increased capacity had its origin in several factors, and each contributed to the higher wartime output. By a fortunate conjuncture of circumstances widespread progress in mechanization, greater use of lime and fertilizer, cover crops, and other conservation practices, use of improved varieties, a better balanced feeding of livestock, and more effective control of insects and disease, had all gathered momentum over the several years preceding World War II. Their current effects were obscured by the drought and depression of the 1930's, but developments had reached a stage where these improvements could be effectively combined and used in an all-out production effort. The result was unprecedented increase in output.

The joint effects of these technological improvements on the volume of production may be illustrated by comparing them with the effects of the flow of water in its several tributaries on the water level of a large river. If water rises to flood stage in one of the tributaries this will, of course, increase the water level in the main stream, but if the tributary is small the effect may be scarcely noticeable when its flood reaches the main channel. Similarly, the effect of single improvements in farm production, that are important by themselves, are scarcely perceptible in their effect on total production. But if all the tributaries of a large river reach flood stage at the same time, the water in the main channel also rises to flood stage, and the change in the water level does not escape notice. In a sense this is the effect that adoption of the accumulation of technological improvements had on farm production in the years of World War II.

But one might make the comparison somewhat differently, and

more correctly, by saying that the production-increasing poten-
tialities of improvements that were made over a decade, and
that normally would have been diverted gradually into the production stream, were held back by the drought and depression
of the 1930's. It was the breaking of these restraints that caused
the flood of production in the war years—in the same way that a
simultaneous breaking of dams on several tributaries will cause a
river to reach flood stage from water that was accumulated from
a normal flow at the source.

ACCUMULATION OF POTENTIAL CAPACITY

As this accumulation of potential production capacity had escaped notice, the increase that was achieved was much larger
than could have been forecast from past trends. It was much
greater than the expansion that took place in World War I,
because there was no similar accumulation of potential improvements at that time. Perhaps none familiar with the South would
have been so rash as to forecast, in the fall of 1941, that the acreage
of peanuts picked and threshed in 1942 would be 177 percent of
1941, and that production for the years 1942-44 would average
175 percent of 1935-39. Likewise, none from the Corn Belt would
have dared to forecast in 1941 that the production of soybeans
harvested for beans in the years 1942-44 would be 338 percent
of the production in 1935-39. . . .

Mechanization was one of the most influential factors back of
the increased output of farm products. The number of tractors
on farms had gradually increased from less than 250,000 in 1920
to nearly 2,500,000 in 1945. Use of mechanical power and complementary equipment usually means more total production, but
its most important effect is that a much larger share of the product goes to market. As mechanical power is substituted for
draft animals, the land formerly used for horse and mule feed
becomes available for producing commodities for human use. The
shift to mechanical power from 1918 to 1945 made available about
55,000,000 crop acres, or about 15 percent of the available cropland, for the production of marketable commodities. In World War
I this large area of cropland and millions of acres of pasture had
to be used for producing feed for horses and mules.

Greater use of fertilizer and lime was another influential factor
in stepping up farm output. Measured in plant nutrients (N, P_2O_5,

K_2 O), the total consumption of commercial fertilizer in 1945 was 95 percent above the quantity used in the prewar years, 1935-39. Application of liming materials was more than three times as large as in the prewar years. Based on estimates of additional output from increased use, it appears that the increased production resulting from the additional use of lime and fertilizer in 1945 accounted for about 15 percent of the total increase in output since 1935-39.

Crop improvements were another notable source of increased output. Use of hybrid seed increases the yield expectancy of corn about 20 percent. New varieties of oats adapted for use in the Corn Belt and Lake States, and rust-resistant improved winter varieties for the Southern States, were widely adopted in the later war years. Continued progress was made in shifting to the higher yielding and more nutritious legume hays.

Total land used for intertilled crops increased by about 6,000,000 acres, or 4 percent, from 1935-39 to 1944. Meanwhile, the total cropland used for crops increased about 9,000,000 acres, or 3 percent. This is a rather small change and is therefore a minor factor in increased output.

The building up of both livestock numbers and feed supplies in the years immediately preceding the war, and in 1942, made possible larger marketings of livestock and livestock products, especially in 1943 and 1944. Livestock production was increased also by the feeding of accumulated supplies of wheat, and of some imported wheat and feed grains. But feeding of both the accumulated supplies and the larger imports accounted for only about 10 percent of the total concentrates fed to livestock in the year ended October 1, 1944. Thus by far the largest proportion of the livestock output came from current production of grain, forage, and pasture; and from an increase of more than one-half in oilseed meals for livestock feed.

Fortunately there were no major outbreaks of either plant or animal diseases or of insect damage in the years of World War II. That no livestock diseases reached epidemic proportions despite record-breaking inventories of livestock was not only good fortune; it was an indication of the effectiveness of modern control methods, and of the vigilance of both farmers and technicians in controlling sporadic outbreaks. Insect damage was held to low levels despite shortages of such important insecticides as rotenone and pyrethrum.

With financial and patriotic incentives as encouragement, and with education and persuasion centered on virtually all-out production of strategic products, farmers and their families worked long hours and often utilized, to the best of their knowledge, every possible means of increasing output. Their efforts bore fruit so well that, even though about one-fourth of the food output went to military and other war-emergency uses, there was food enough in 1944 and 1945 to provide our civilians with a per capita food consumption 12 to 14 percent higher than took place in the prewar years, 1935-39. In somewhat different terms, the output of food in 1944 was enough to feed about 50,000,000 more people than were fed by the average quantity produced in 1935-39, assuming the same dietary levels for both periods.

UNFAVORABLE FACTORS MINIMIZED

That more people could be fed resulted partly from a change in the production pattern—more oil crops, beans, and peas, and less cotton—and from a more complete utilization of the output. But the shifts in production that were necessitated by war needs, made increases in the total volume of production more difficult. Production per acre or per animal is usually lowered when a product is grown on land that is less suited for its production, or by growers who have insufficient experience.

The wartime increases in production were achieved with a constantly shrinking labor supply. The total farm population dropped from 30,000,000 in 1940 to 25,000,000 in 1945. In many small farm areas the decrease in farm population represented a correction of under-employment on farms that existed before the war; but in most of the commercial farming areas the result was a labor shortage. . . .The shift to mechanical power and the increase in production per acre have made it possible also to increase the number of animal units of productive livestock. Thus the total increase in livestock production is derived both from larger numbers of breeding stock and from the higher output per unit of breeding stock. On the other hand, increased crop production is largely the result of higher production per acre because changes in the acreage of cropland have been relatively small.

The higher output per acre and per animal, combined with mechanization, made possible the larger output per worker. The three series—production per acre, per animal, and per worker—

summarize the startling changes that have taken place in farming since the years of World War I.

During the time that progress in technology has increased output per man so greatly in agriculture, the same phenomenon has occurred in industry. . . .

This poses a key question for the postwar years. Will peacetime industry and service occupations expand sufficiently to absorb at satisfactory wage levels (1) the workers currently displaced by technological progress in both agriculture and industry and (2) the net supply of new workers (after allowing replacements for death and retirement) that enter the labor market each year? This is a crucial question. . . .

CHANGES IN THE USE OF FARM MACHINES

EFFECTS OF SHIFTS TO MECHANICAL POWER

The rapid shift from animal power to mechanical power for farm production in the interwar period constituted one of the most important changes that has ever taken place in American agriculture. It was a cornerstone in the foundation for increased production.

One result of this change was a transfer of resources from the production of power on the farm to the production of livestock and crops for sale in the market. This transfer released about 55,000,-000 acres of cropland for the production of marketable farm products. That, of course, is the most startling effect that mechanization has had on American farms.

But other effects are also striking. The shift to mechanical power and complementary equipment brings an increased output per worker both by enabling him to do the job faster and by doing a better job of tillage or other operation, and in that way realizing more benefit from other improved practices. The physical burden of farm work is lessened because the drudgery of hand labor is eliminated. Fewer workers are needed in farm production. Physical strength becomes relatively less necessary, and mechanical skill becomes more necessary, in the performance of farm work. . . .

MECHANICAL-POWER PHASE COMPARED WITH
EARLIER DEVELOPMENTS

The impact of mechanical power and complementary equipment on the transformation of agricultural production in the interwar,

war, and early postwar years, may well be compared with the agricultural revolution that followed the introduction of improved machinery for use with animal power. The steel plow, the mower, the reaper, and later the self binder, were the primary developments in the animal-power phase of mechanization, which began about 1830 and was well stabilized by the beginning of World War I. The mechanical-power phase had then begun, but it did not gain full momentum until the war was over. And the really noteworthy effects have come in recent years.

In fact, the mechanical-power phase of farm mechanization has not yet been stabilized. Wheat production is almost completely mechanized and corn production is well on the way in the main producing areas. Hay harvesting is in a state of flux, with several radically different methods competing for adoption in all the chief hay-producing areas. Mechanization of the cotton harvest is only in its beginning stages, and tobacco is still a hand-labor crop. Considerable progress has been made in labor-saving equipment for the dairy enterprise but relatively less attention has been given to improvements in housing and other equipment for the livestock enterprises than for crop production. Advances in this domain give promise of yielding substantial savings in capital investment as well as in labor.

A look at the new mechanical developments that are already on the horizon leads to the conclusion that the future impacts of mechanization on agricultural production will be just as influential in the decade 1949-58 as were those of the preceding decade. Two of the major developments will be the increase in number of tractors, especially the small sizes fitted with equipment suitable for use on small farms, and the fairly rapid adoption of mechanical cotton pickers and strippers. These developments, along with many others, will have far-reaching repercussions on production and on the number of workers that will be needed in agriculture.

CHANGES IN LAND USE, CONSERVATION AND FERTILIZER PRACTICES

SHIFTS IN LAND USES

Many changes in the use of cropland and permanent pasture took place between the World Wars. In the early part of this

20-year period the rather extensive abandonment of land in the Eastern States was offset by the development of new lands in the Western States. Total cropland acreage in the United States was a little lower in the early 1920's than in 1919, but it rose slowly from 1927 to 1931. From 1932 to 1939 the trend was downward. Total cropland remained at about the low point reached in 1939 until the war year of 1943; then the total increased to within about 1 percent of the 1928-32 peaks.

Acreages of harvested cropland have been more erratic. The effects of the droughts of 1934 and 1936 are especially apparent. The drought's impact was most severe in the Great Plains and Intermountain States, where much of the sod land that had been broken out in the 1920's was abandoned in the 1930's. Some of it was again brought into use during the war, and by 1947 much more of the land formerly in cultivation was back in crop production. There was also new breaking of native sod lands that over a period of years are best suited for permanent pasture. . . .

CHANGES IN THE PRINCIPAL USES OF CROPLAND IN THE UNITED STATES—
1928-32, 1935-39, 1944, AND 1945

Use of cropland	Average, 1928-32 [1,2]	Average, 1935-39 [2]	1944 [2]	1945 [2]	Percentage 1945 is of—	
					1928-32	1935-39
	Million acres	*Million acres*	*Million acres*	*Million acres*	*Percent*	*Percent*
Intertilled crops [3]	176.6	163.0	168.8	157.6	89	97
Close-growing crops [3] .	132.6	133.0	129.8	132.4	100	100
Sod crops [3,4]	77.3	73.5	80.2	82.5	107	112
Total cropland used for crops	386.5	369.5	378.8	372.5	96	101
Summer fallow and idle cropland	41.3	56.9	47.3	54.4	132	96
Total cropland [5]	427.8	426.4	426.1	426.9	100	100

[1] The data on which the 1928-32 estimates are based are less complete than for later periods.

[2] Planted acres so far as available; all others harvested acres.

[3] Adjustments made for multiple use of land by considering first use in the crop year as the primary use.

[4] Including acres in tame hay, hay and cover-crop seeds, and in rotation pasture.

[5] Includes rotation pasture, but does not include wild hay, orchards, vineyards, and farm gardens.

LIMING AND FERTILIZING PRACTICES

Use of lime and commercial fertilizer was greatly accelerated in the immediate prewar and war years, and has continued to increase. A considerable part of the larger farm production can be attributed to the greater use of these materials. But of about equal importance is the potential contribution of lime and fertilizer to the establishment of stable and soil-maintaining systems of farming.

Information on use of liming materials is not available for the years before 1929, when the tonnage of lime used was about 60 percent of the 1935-39 level. The tonnage used annually was nearly doubled from 1935 to 1936, the year when lime was first included in the Agricultural Conservation Program. . . .The use of liming materials in the later war years was more than three times the prewar levels, despite the difficulties in obtaining labor and trucks for crushing and hauling. In 1947 more than four times as much lime was used as was used annually in the years 1935-39. Less lime was used in 1948 mainly because of reduction in the program for conservation materials. . . .

On many soils in the humid regions it is necessary to apply lime in order to get full use of commercial fertilizer, especially the phosphates. And lime and phosphate applications are required for successful stands of the legumes and grasses that are so necessary in a good crop rotation, and for soil maintenance. Some of the increase in use of commercial fertilizer is accounted for by the greater use of phosphates in combination with liming materials for hay and pasture improvement. Nearly all the fertilizer distributed by public agencies has been applied on legumes and on hay and pastureland. But even the relatively large wartime distribution of fertilizer by public agencies accounted for only 10 percent of the total value of the fertilizer that was used.

The increase in consumption of fertilizer is actually an acceleration of a long-time upward trend that was interrupted in the severe depression of the early 1930's. The largest part of the increase has been applied to the cash crops, although a growing proportion of the fertilizer now goes on legumes and grasses. . . .

CHANGES IN CROPS

The greatest contribution of the changes in crops and varieties made to speed up wartime production was the interwar development of improved seeds that greatly increased the yields per acre of our most important crops. Hybrid seed corn is an outstanding example. . . .

CHANGES IN LIVESTOCK PRODUCTION

FACTORS INFLUENCING CHANGES

Three major forces are back of the recent changes in livestock production. They are (1) the shift from animal to mechanical power, (2) the variations in the total feed supply, and (3) the higher production per animal. These forces in turn have been influenced by prices of livestock products and other economic changes.

The decrease in horses and mules of 15,000,000 animal units from 1920 to 1946 released land that could grow feed for an equivalent number of productive livestock (animals and their products that are produced for human use). The saving in grain alone amounted to about 16,000,000 tons in 1946—enough to feed 32,-000,000 hogs to market weight.

Year-to-year changes in the total feed supply have been about as influential as the shift to mechanical power in their effects on livestock production for human use. The severe drought years, 1934 and 1936, reduced total feed consumption (feed grains, hay, and pasture) about one-fifth below the 1928-32 average. On the other hand, total feed consumption in the war years 1942-44 averaged about 28 percent above the 1928-32 levels, and 34 percent higher than those for 1935-39. Feed production in 1942-44 increased more than in proportion to the increase in numbers of livestock, which meant that there was more feed available per animal. Total numbers of livestock fed increased 20 percent above 1935-39 but the increase in livestock production was greater than this. Excluding horses and mules the increase in production was about one-third.

Livestock production was reduced in 1946 and again in 1947. The short corn crop of 1947 placed definite limits on expansion in the early part of 1948, but the favorable livestock-feed price ratios resulting from the large feed-grain crop of 1948 stimulated heavy feeding as well as the breeding of more animals for 1949 production.

In addition to the changes in the supply of feed there have been notable changes in quality, resulting in the feeding of rations that are more balanced with respect to protein and other nutritive elements. The gradual increase in the protein content of the hay supply has been mentioned. The greater supply per animal unit of oilseed meals and other high-protein feeds during the war also helped to balance the feeding rations and to push livestock production upward. . . .

INCENTIVES FOR INCREASED PRODUCTION

That farm production in the 1930's was held in check by drought and depression, despite the technical progress in mechanization and in other lines, has been emphasized. War needs and the incentive of higher incomes broke this dam and released a flood of increased production. But this was not accomplished by one blast at the beginning of the war. It was a fairly gradual process. Both farmers and agricultural workers were too conditioned by the experience with surpluses to believe that the market really would absorb all that the agricultural plant might produce under stimulation. This skepticism was supported by the sag in prices of some products during the year that followed the outbreak of the war in Europe.

But gradually the war demands emerged, and with the passage of the Lend-Lease Act on March 11, 1941, they gathered a momentum that remained unslackened for the duration of the war. Demand was further accelerated in the first two postwar years.

52

World Food Board Proposed

Commercial agriculture in the United States, as in other staple-producing nations, has been periodically plagued by surpluses. The problem has been particularly acute after major wars, since wartime demand has always encouraged the immediate adoption of new technology and the opening up of new agricultural areas.

Many proposals have been suggested for dealing with the surpluses. After World War I, farm leaders urged voluntary reductions in production, greater use of cooperation, and such legislative aids as the McNary-Haugen Plan, cost of production, export debenture, and domestic allotment. After World War II, various ideas for exporting the surpluses and for reducing production were advanced. A number of proposals were adopted and put into operation with varying degrees of success. Governments in other parts of the world, including Cuba, Brazil, Argentina, and Australia, tried various plans for disposing of agricultural surpluses.

The most far-reaching of all proposals for handling agricultural surpluses receiving serious consideration was drawn up in 1946 by Sir John Boyd Orr, then director-general of the Food and Agriculture Organization of the United Nations. He proposed the establishment of a World Food Board which would stabilize prices of agricultural commodities on the world markets; establish a world food reserve adequate for any emergency that might arise through failure of crops in any part of the world; finance the disposal of surplus agricultural products to countries where the need was most urgent; and cooperate with other international organizations to achieve common ends.

The Food and Agriculture Organization appointed a commission to make specific recommendations for a World Food Board or any alternative proposals that would develop and organize production, distribution, and utilization of basic foods to provide diets on a health standard for the people of all countries, and that would stabilize agricultural prices at levels fair to producers and consumers alike.

Both the original objectives and those assigned to the commission were of a controversial nature. The World Food Board, with its implied control of world prices and management of surpluses, was objected to by the United States and other nations and was dropped from consideration. Eventually the commission made a series of proposals calling for aid in expanding agriculture in the poorer nations, emphasis upon better nutrition, and the further development of commodity agreements between the nations most concerned with a particular commodity. Individual countries were to implement the recommendations with the assistance of the Food and Agriculture Organization.

Sir John Boyd Orr Proposes a World Food Board

Food and Agriculture Organization, *Proposals for a World Food Board*, pp. 1-4, 10-12 (Washington, 1946).

There has never been enough food in the world. Before the war there were 1,000 million people consuming less than 2250 calories. By contrast, in the United Kingdom, even with the present acute shortage, the average intake per head is 2750 calories. The calorie intake does not tell the full story. At the lower levels of intake the food consists mainly of cereals, which are the cheapest satisfiers of hunger. A diet sufficient for health must contain a large proportion of animal products and fruits and vegetables. These supply calories at a much higher cost, but they are rich in constituents necessary for health.

Food consumption depends on purchasing power. As family income rises the consumption of the more expensive foods increases. Thus, for example, it is estimated that before the war the diet of about one-third (the poorest third) of the population of the United States of America was not up to the health standard owing to insufficient consumption of animal products and fruits and vegetables. Full employment and high wages during the war have been accompanied by an increase in the consumption of these foods; for example, egg consumption was increased by 30 percent and that of liquid milk by 29 percent. In the United Kingdom, in spite of the national food shortage, the consumption of certain foods of special value for health rose substantially—that of liquid milk by more than 40 percent—and in the poorest families by over 100 percent.

Food consumption is directly correlated with health. As diet deteriorates in quality, health and physical abilities decline and length of life decreases. In communities where the diet is adequate, the average length of life is nearly seventy years compared with thirty to forty years in the worst fed communities. Unfortunately, poverty is associated with other conditions adverse to health, and it is difficult to assess the relative killing power of the different disease-producing factors. But the remarkable improvement in health and physical well-being following an improvement in diet shows that inadequate food is one of the main causes of the preventable diseases, misery, and premature death which afflict the majority of the human race.

Although these facts have been stated at length time and time again in authoritative official and unofficial reports, it is necessary to refer to them here because they are fundamental to the long-term problems of food and agriculture.

AGRICULTURE

The Problem of Increasing Production

It is difficult to estimate accurately how much the production of each of the main foodstuffs would need to be increased to provide adequate food for the whole population of the world, because for some countries statistics are absent or unreliable. It is known, however, that even in the wealthiest countries in prewar days between 20 percent and 30 percent of the population did not have enough of the more expensive foods essential for health. Estimates for the United States of America show that the production of these foods would need to be increased above the prewar level by 15 percent in the case of butter to 75 percent in the case of fruits and vegetables, to provide a fully adequate diet for every citizen. In the United Kingdom it is estimated that the additional amounts of food needed to bring the diet of the whole population up to the health standard represent an increase of 25 percent for meat to 65-70 percent for other animal products and fruits and vegetables.

It is obvious that if production goals be based on full physiological requirements, the world production of these more expensive foods of special value for health will need to be increased by more than 100 percent. The World Food Survey recently completed by FAO indicates that substantial increases will be needed even to meet goals that by no means represent optimum nutrition. There will also need to be an increase in the production of cereals, for direct human consumption in some areas, but even more in the long run to help produce the needed animal products. When cereals were being burned in the 1930's there were hundreds of millions of people in the world hungry. The first problem of production, therefore, is how to get sufficient food not only to feed the expanding population but also to feed people better.

The rapid growth of population in the United Kingdom in the nineteenth century raised fears that world population might outrun world capacity to produce food. Today, similar fears are held by some regarding the Asiatic countries.

The advance of agricultural science has enabled us to produce more and more food with less and less labor. The war showed how rapidly food production can be increased when technical and other resources are available. In the United Kingdom the increase in production estimated in calories amounted to as much as 70 percent over the prewar level. In the United States production increased in six years by 37 percent as measured in dollar values at constant prices, and that with 8 percent less labor. There are large areas in which agricultural methods have changed little for 2,000 years, where there is great potential capacity for increased production, and other areas which could be made productive by irrigation and flood control programs.

The rapid increase in population in certain countries is a serious political problem, and full weight must be given to its bearing on food production. The history of the western world shows that industrialization and rising standards of living are accompanied by a fall in the rate of population growth, and there is no good reason to believe that this will not occur in other regions.

The limiting factor is not the physical capacity to produce enough food but the ability of nations to bring about the complex economic adjustments necessary to make adequate production and distribution possible. The application of science is solving the problem of production but at the same time is creating its own problems. Mechanization reduces the number of the workers needed to produce a given amount of food. Unless profitable employment is found in other industries, agriculture is left with partially employed people. In underdeveloped countries the gradual adoption of such methods as mechanization must go hand in hand with the building up of industry. The net result would be to increase the numbers who are fully employed and to enlarge the world's total wealth.

Major Problems of Producers

The problems of food producers vary with the type of agriculture. In underdeveloped countries food is produced on very small holdings cultivated by obsolete methods. The net return is not sufficient to enable producers to obtain the barest necessities of life. A large proportion of the thousand million people with an intake of less than 2250 calories consists of this class of primary producer. As already noted, the problem here is one of providing profitable employment in other industries and of education in modern methods of cultivation. Underlying this problem is that of providing the needed capital equipment.

In countries where modern agricultural science is applied, the main problem is one of finding a continuous market at a remunerative price. A relatively small excess of supply over economic demand is followed by a big drop in prices, as occurred in the late 1920's. On the other hand, a relatively small excess in economic demand over supply is followed by a big increase in prices; this is dramatically demonstrated in war, when prices have to be controlled to prevent an excessive rise. Besides these cyclical movements, there are week-to-week and month-to-month oscillations in prices. In nine out of ten years in the decade between 1928 and 1938 the price of wheat on the world market fluctuated by 70 percent. These fluctuations are the bane of agricultural producers. . . .

It has been suggested above that a food policy based on human needs is the best starting point for solving the problems discussed in the present report. For this a World Food Board with the necessary authority and funds is needed to set the desired chain of events in motion.

THE SUGGESTED WORLD FOOD BOARD

Structure and Functions

The temporary organizations created to deal with the food scarcity caused by the war foreshadow the kind of permanent organization needed. The recently created International Emergency Food Council, working through commodity committees, encourages stabilization of prices by getting agreement on price schedules and also by promoting a certain amount of unified buying; and it recommends the allocation of export surpluses according to the needs of different countries. A continuation of this international cooperation is needed because even if these temporary organizations bring the world out of the present food emergency, there will still remain the great scarcity of food that existed before the war and at the same time the agricultural problems of fluctuation in prices and the accumulation of unmarketable "surpluses."

The proposed World Food Board, which would act through commodity committees, might be established as a new international agency, or the Constitution of FAO could be altered to enable it to set up the Board. There are drawbacks to having a multiplicity of international agencies acting in the same field. If the latter alternative were thought to be the better means, the Board could be appointed by the Conference of FAO, which it is hoped will ultimately include representatives of all countries. But as the actions of the Board would involve broad problems of world economics and finance, it would be necessary to include in it representatives of other interested international organizations—for example, the International Bank for Reconstruction and Development, the Economic and Social Council, and the proposed International Trade Organization. The working relationship between the Board and ITO would need to be close, since the latter agency, according to present indications, will be concerned with the broad field of commercial and commodity policy.

The functions of the World Food Board would be:

1. To stabilize prices of agricultural commodities on world markets, including provision of the necessary funds for stabilizing operations.

2. To establish a world food reserve adequate for any emergency that might arise through failure of crops in any part of the world.

3. To provide funds for financing the disposal of surplus agricultural products on special terms to countries where the need for them is most urgent.

4. To cooperate with organizations concerned with international credits for industrial and agricultural development, and with trade and commodity policy, in order that their common ends might be more quickly and effectively achieved.

OPERATIONS

For stabilization of prices in agriculture the World Food Board, operating through its commodity committees, should be given power to hold stocks of each of the most important commodities. This proposal, it may be noted, is in line with principles previously put forward by the League of Nations and other bodies. The Board would undertake the investigations necessary to determine what world prices would call forth the quantities that could currently be marketed. It would announce a maximum and minimum price and would undertake to buy into its stock when the world price fell below the declared minimum and sell from its stock when the world price exceeded the maximum. Care would be needed to commence operations at the correct moment and to choose an appropriate world price.

The Board would need a revolving fund to operate such a plan. No precise estimate of the amount required can be made at present. Moreover, the need for funds would grow gradually as first one commodity and then another was brought under the aegis of the plan. For safety, the normal stocks held by the agency should represent six to twelve months' trade, the amounts varying with different commodities. In determining the contributions to be made to the fund, the relative benefits derived from the stabilizing operations by different countries—exporting and importing, developed and underdeveloped—would need to be carefully weighed.

Since the agency would normally be buying at its minimum and selling at its maximum price, it should earn enough to cover the quite considerable costs of storage. It would, of course, have on occasion to hold very much larger stocks than the normal, but these extra holdings should be financed by borrowing on the market against its commodity assets. The need for such operations would be greatest in time of depression when funds are available at advantageous rates.

Producers of livestock products and other perishables not suited to long-term stock holding will find their markets both greatly stabilized by the buffer stock operations on feed grains and other items and greatly enlarged through the nutritional policies concurrently developed. Certain livestock products capable of being stored for long periods might be included directly in the operations.

In the case of a few commodities there may be danger of competitive export subsidization which, if tolerated, would destroy the international stock holding program. In such cases it might be necessary to negotiate schedules of export quotas between governments until new markets could be developed. This contingency has been recognized and provided for in a similar way in the United States proposals for an International Trade Organization.

The objective of the operations of the World Food Board would be to ensure that sufficient food is produced and distributed to bring the consumption of all peoples up to a health standard. The need for additional food is so great that if human requirements could be translated into economic demand, there would be no question of surpluses of the basic foods—surpluses which before the war many people came to regard as inevitable and which if permitted to re-emerge might overwhelm the Board. The basic problem here is the financial one of increasing the purchasing power of the people who are unable to obtain sufficient food for their needs. The Board must be able to divert unmarketable surpluses to these consumers and arrange for financing the cost of selling at prices which the consumers are able to afford.

THE NEED FOR IMMEDIATE ACTION

The suggestion to set up a World Food Board with funds and authority to take measures necessary in solving long-standing problems of nutrition and agriculture is neither a revolutionary nor a new idea. The proposal merely synthesizes many national and international measures and brings them together in one organization which has the machinery and the funds to correlate them and take executive action to carry them out.

It may seem premature to put forward such an ambitious proposal, but we are living in a world which is being driven so fast by the advance of science that bold measures are required if we are to resolve the tremendous social and economic problems that face all countries. In the specific case of food production and international trade in food, an adequate world policy will be needed much sooner than many realize.

There are only two alternatives for the nations today: either cooperation for mutual benefit in a world policy, or a drift back to nationalistic policies leading to economic conflict which may well be the prelude to a third world war that will end our civilization.

A Chronology of American Agricultural History

1493
Christopher Columbus introduced barley, grapes, sugar cane, wheat, and horses into the New World.

c. 1585
Potato taken from South America to Spain.

1609
Settlers at Jamestown learned from Indians how to grow corn.

1614
First tobacco from Virginia to be commercially acceptable exported to England.
Governor of Virginia allotted 3-acre holdings to settlers in Virginia as supplement to communal system.

1619
Head right, that is, fifty acres of land for every colonist transported, introduced in Virginia.
Virginia began compulsory inspection of tobacco with the aim of controlling production.
First Negro slaves brought to Jamestown.

1621
Pilgrims at Plymouth learned to grow corn from the Indian, Squanto.
October 21. King ordered that all tobacco grown in Virginia be shipped to England.

1623
Virginia assembly directed that mulberry trees be planted to encourage silk industry.

1626
First flour mill in colonies built in New Amsterdam.

1629
June 7. Patroon system of large landholdings established in New Netherland.

1640

Connecticut offered land bounties for the cultivation of wheat and ordered every family to plant hemp.

1646

Patents for improved scythe and sawmill granted Joseph Jenks by Massachusetts.

1669-1670

Plant-testing garden established at Ashley River settlement in South Carolina.

1679

April 25. Virginia assembly declared importation or shipment from Virginia ports of North Carolina tobacco illegal.

1682

Virginians attempt to raise tobacco prices by cutting plants.

c. 1695

Cultivation of rice in South Carolina became commercialized, apparently as a result of introduction of superior seed from Madagascar.

1719

Potato, which originated in New World, first cultivated in English colonies by Scotch-Irish settlers of Londonderry, N.H.

1730

Virginia's tobacco inspection law provided for inspection for quality at ports.

1731

John Bartram established a botanical garden near Philadelphia.
Jethro Tull published *The Horse Hoeing Husbandry.*

1733

Public experimental garden established in Savannah, Georgia.

1742

Sugar cane introduced into Louisiana from San Domingo by Jesuit priests.
Eliza Lucas Pinckney established indigo as a commercial crop in South Carolina.

1743

American Philosophical Society, earliest society in the United States to promote scientific agriculture, organized.

1748

May 13. British Parliament provided bounty for all indigo imported from American colonies.

1763

Proclamation by British government closed the trans-Allegheny region to settlement.

1767

Sea Island cotton cultivated in Georgia but not widely grown until after the Revolutionary War.

1780

October 10. Continental Congress urged states to cede western lands to the nation, with the pledge that these lands would be settled and admitted as states.

c. 1784

Commercial exportation of cotton to England began.

1785

Philadelphia Society for Promoting Agriculture and the South Carolina Society for Promoting and Improving Agriculture and Other Rural Concerns organized.

May 20. Ordinance of 1785 established plan for disposing of western land.

1786-1787

Shays' Rebellion in western Massachusetts was armed revolt of farmers protesting economic inequities.

1787

July 13. Ordinance of 1787 established a system for the government of western land.

1790

Total population 3,929,214; over 90 per cent of the persons gainfully employed were engaged in agriculture.

1792

A professorship of natural history, chemistry, and agriculture was established at Columbia College in New York.

1793

Eli Whitney invented the cotton gin.

Thomas Jefferson invented a moldboard for a plow based upon scientific principles.

1796

December 7. President George Washington recommended creation of a national board of agriculture.

1797

Charles Newbold of New Jersey received a patent for the first cast-iron plow.

1798

John Chapman, the "Johnny Appleseed" of legend, planted his first apple seeds in the Ohio Valley.

1800

Total population 5,308,483.

1801

Refrigerator invented in 1801 by Thomas Moore of Maryland.

1802

Colonel David Humphries, U.S. ambassador to Spain, sent 91 Merino sheep to his Connecticut home.

1803

George Washington Parke Custis inaugurated yearly competitions at his Arlington, Virginia, estate in sheepshearing and in sheep and wool exhibitions.

1804

First fair of an agricultural nature held in Washington, D.C.

1805

The first corn-fat herd of cattle driven from the Ohio Valley over the mountains to eastern markets.

1807

Elkanah Watson exhibited Merino sheep at Pittsfield, Massachusetts, and then organized an agricultural fair for working farmers, first held in 1810.

1810

Total population 7,239,881.
The *Agricultural Museum,* first farm periodical, began publication.

1811

Berkshire Agricultural Society, to sponsor fairs for local farmers, organized under leadership of Elkanah Watson.

1813

John Lorain began discussing the value of cross-breeding corn to obtain high yields.

1816

The "year in which there was no summer" in New England.

1817

Henry Clay imported the first Hereford cattle into the United States.

1818

A horticultural society was organized in New York.

Peter Durand, an Englishman, introduced the tin can into America.

Jethro Wood patented an iron plow with interchangeable parts.

1819

The *American Farmer*, first farmer's periodical to attain wide circulation, began publication.

March 26. Secretary of the Treasury William H. Crawford asked United States consuls abroad to introduce valuable new plants.

April 7. New York Board of Agriculture established by the state legislature.

1820

Total population 9,638,453; 72 per cent of persons gainfully employed were engaged in agriculture.

1821

Edmund Ruffin published first version of his "Essay on Calcareous Manures."

1824

First samples of Peruvian guano introduced.

1825

October 26. Erie Canal completed.

1826

First Chinese mulberry tree in United States set out in Baltimore.

1829

First organized flower show held in Boston.

1830

Total population 12,866,020.

1833

John Lane began to manufacture steel plows.

Obed Hussey patented first successful horse-drawn grain reaper.

1834

Cyrus H. McCormick patented his grain reaper.

1836

Grain combine patented by Hiram Moore and J. Hascall.

July 4. Patent Office created as a separate bureau; Henry L. Ellsworth appointed Commissioner of Patents.

1837

John Deere began manufacturing plows with steel share and smooth, wrought iron moldboard.

Patent Office began distribution of foreign seeds and plants at personal expense of Commissioner Henry L. Ellsworth.
A practical threshing machine patented by the Pitts brothers.

1838

July 7. Law approved granting land in Florida to Henry Perrine for a tropical plant introduction garden.

1839

Craze for growing Chinese mulberry trees in order to cultivate silk worms, which began about 1833, came to an end.
Double-row, horse-drawn corn planter invented by D. S. Rockwell.
March 3. Congress appropriated $1,000 from the patent fund for collecting agricultural statistics, conducting agricultural investigations, and distributing seeds.

1840

Total population 17,069,453; farm population 9,012,000 (estimated); 69 per cent of persons gainfully employed were engaged in agriculture.

1841

Improved hoe drill for sowing grain patented by Moses and Samuel Pennock.
New York held first major state agricultural fair.

1842

First grain elevator constructed in Buffalo, N.Y.

1843

First commercial shipment of Peruvian guano to the United States arrived in Baltimore.

1844

Grain header patented by George Esterly.
First of a series of patents granted to William F. Ketchum for mowing machines.

1846

March 27. First free homestead bill introduced in Congress and defeated.
June 26. Great Britain repealed Corn Laws, greatly increasing exports of agricultural products from United States.

1847

Revolving disk harrow patented by G. Page.
Mormons began irrigation in Utah.

1849

Mixed fertilizers first manufactured commercially in Baltimore.
First important poultry show held in Boston.
March 3. Department of Interior created and Patent Office transferred to it.

1850

Total population 23,191,876; farm population 11,680,000 (estimated); 64 per cent of persons gainfully employed were engaged in agriculture.
September 20. First federal land grant for railroad construction.

1851

American Pomological Society organized by consolidation of American Congress of Fruit Growers and North American Pomological Congress, both organized in 1848.
Butter moved successfully in refrigerator cars by railroad from northern New York to Boston.
Patent for mechanical refrigeration issued to John Gorrie.
Cooperative cheese factory organized in Oneida County, New York.

1852

United States Agricultural Society organized.

1853

Patent for a widely used corn planter granted to G. W. Brown.

1854

December 5. Patent granted on a two-wheeled jointed bar mower.

1855

February 12. Michigan Agricultural College established by the state legislature.
February 23. Pennsylvania Farmers' High School, later Pennsylvania State College and now Pennsylvania State University, established by state legislature.

1856

Patent for condensing milk issued to Gail Borden.
Two-horse straddle row cultivator patented.
March 6. Maryland state legislature appropriated funds to aid in the establishment of the Maryland Agricultural College.

1857

Michigan Agricultural College opened to students.
Grimm alfalfa brought from Germany to Minnesota.

1858

Harvester which gathered grain into bundles patented by C. W. and W. W. Marsh.

1859

Charles R. Darwin published *Origin of the Species.*

1860

Total population 31,443,321; farm population 15,141,000 (estimated); 58 per cent of persons gainfully employed were engaged in agriculture.

1861-1865

Demand for food products led to commercialization of northern agriculture and a temporary diversification of southern agriculture, giving impetus to the first American agricultural revolution.

1862

May 15. The Department of Agriculture, headed by a Commissioner of Agriculture, established.
May 20. Homestead Act approved.
July 1. An act granting land to the Union Pacific Railroad Company and the Central Pacific Railroad Company for the construction of a transcontinental railroad approved.
July 1. Isaac Newton became first Commissioner of Agriculture.
July 2. Morrill Land Grant College Act approved.

c. 1864

Durum wheat introduced into the Dakotas by Russian immigrants.

1864

Harpoon for lifting hay patented by E. L. Walker.

1865

December 18. Slavery abolished by thirteenth amendment to the Constitution.
December 25. Union Stockyards opened at Chicago.

1866

Gregor Johann Mendel published *Experiments in Plant Hybridisation.*

1867

Patrons of Husbandry, later known as the National Grange, organized.

1868

A refrigerator car widely used by railroads in the 1870's patented by William Davis.
November 14. First farmers' institute held at Manhattan, Kansas.

1869

February 2. Patent for plow made of chilled iron granted James Oliver.
November. W. O. Atwater published an analysis of corn.

1870

Total population 38,558,371; farm population 18,373,000 (estimated);53 per cent of persons gainfully employed were engaged in agriculture.
First occurrence of foot-and-mouth disease among cattle.

1871

The Bahia or navel orange successfully introduced from Brazil.
April 7. First Granger law regulating railroads and warehouses passed in Illinois.

1873

First silo constructed in the United States.
Economic panic marked beginning of period of depression.
Grasshoppers became a serious pest in the West.

1874

November 24. Glidden patent on barbed wire issued.

1875

First state agricultural experiment station established at Wesleyan University, Middletown, Connecticut.
Bonanza wheat farming with machines began in Red River Valley.

1877

March 3. U.S. Entomological Commission established to study grasshoppers.

1878

A twine-knotter for use in binding grain perfected by John F. Appleby.
American Fat Stock Show held in Chicago each year until 1897.
Sugar beets cultivated successfully in Maine under system of vertical integration.

1879

William Deering's twine grain binder placed on market.

1880

Total population 50,155,783; farm population 22,981,000 (estimated); 49 per cent of persons gainfully employed were engaged in agriculture.
National Farmers' Alliance, or Northern Alliance, organized by Milton George.

1881

Pure-food laws passed by Illinois, Michigan, New Jersey, and New York.

1882

Koch, a German bacteriologist, isolated tubercle bacillus.
Modern cream separator, invented in Sweden, brought to the United States.
Bordeaux mixture, a fungicide, discovered in France.

1884

Smooth bromegrass (*Bromus inermis*) introduced.
May 29. Bureau of Animal Industry established by act of Congress.

1885

Kansas, Nebraska, and Colorado passed quarantine laws aimed at stopping Texas cattle from being driven across their boundaries.

1886-1887

Hard winter marked end of range cattle industry of the Great Plains.

1887

Land Grant College Association established.
March 2. Hatch Experiment Station Act approved.

1888-1889

Vedalia beetle or ladybird introduced from Australia to control fluted scale, which threatened citrus fruit orchards of California.

1889

Southern Alliance formed by merger of several agricultural organizations.
Bureau of Animal Industry found that cattle fever was carried by ticks.
February 9. Department of Agriculture raised to cabinet status.
February 15. Norman J. Colman took oath of office as first Secretary of Agriculture.
March 6. Jeremiah M. Rusk succeeded Norman J. Colman as Secretary of Agriculture.

1890

Total population 62,947,714; farm population 26,379,000 (estimated); 43 per cent of persons gainfully employed were engaged in agriculture.
The Census Bureau reported that the frontier line as such had ceased to exist.
Stephen M. Babcock perfected a test for measuring butterfat content of milk.
August 30. Congress provided for inspection by the Department of Agriculture of pork products to be exported.
October 1. Weather Bureau transferred from War Department to Department of Agriculture by act of Congress.

1891

May 19. People's or Populist party launched as national organization.

1892

Last case of pleuropneumonia in American cattle disposed of.
Successful gasoline tractor built.
Boll weevil began attacking cotton.

1896

Rural free delivery system for handling mail started.

1898

Trap nesting for the selection of better-laying hens began.

1900

Total population 75,994,575; farm population 29,414,000 (estimated); 38 per cent of persons gainfully employed were engaged in agriculture.

Idea of breeding disease-resistant plants developed from research on cotton wilt disease.
International Livestock Exposition began yearly exhibitions.
Special work for farm youth organized in Macoupin County, Illinois, and in other areas shortly thereafter, with name "4-H" being adopted in 1913.

1902

Farmers Union (Farmers Educational and Cooperative Union of America) organized.
American Society of Equity organized.
Hugo DeVries, a Dutch botanist, announced his theory of mutation.
June 17. Reclamation Act signed.

1903

C. W. Hart and C. H. Parr established the first firm devoted to manufacturing gasoline tractors.
A serum for hog cholera developed.

1904

Railroads ran special trains promoting improved farming.

1905

International Institute of Agriculture established.
California Fruit Growers Exchange established as successor to Southern California Fruit Exchange.

1906

June 30. Pure Food and Drug Act approved.
        Meat Inspection Act approved.

1908

May 13-15. White House Conference on Conservation.
August 10. Country Life Commission organized by President Theodore Roosevelt.

1910

Total population 91,972,266; farm population 32,077,000 (estimated); 31 per cent of persons gainfully employed were engaged in agriculture.
Girls' canning and garden clubs originated in Aiken County, South Carolina.

1911

First Farm Bureau formed in Broome County, New York.

1912

Thomas Hunt Morgan announced his gene theory.
Marquis wheat introduced.
August 24. Parcel post system established by act of Congress.

1914

May 8. Smith-Lever Act formalized cooperative agricultural extension work.

August 1. World War I began in Europe.

August 18. Cotton Futures Act, first major attempt to regulate marketing of farm products, approved.

1915

Nonpartisan League organized in North Dakota.

1916

July 17. Federal Farm Loan Act approved.

August 11. United States Warehouse Act approved.

Grain Standards Act approved.

1916-1918

System for growing modern hybrid seed corn developed by Donald F. Jones.

1917

European corn borer discovered near Boston, Massachusetts.

Kansas Red wheat developed.

February 23. Smith-Hughes Vocational Act became law.

August 10. Food and Fuel Control Act approved.

President Wilson established the Food Administration by executive order.

Food Production Act approved.

August 30. President fixed minimum price of $2.20 a bushel for wheat, raised to $2.26 on June 21, 1918.

September 1. Grain Corporation of the Food Administration began operations.

November 13. Food Administration announced supports of hog prices at specified level in relation to corn, but did not maintain this price.

1918

Ceres wheat developed.

January 26. Food Administrator Herbert C. Hoover asked voluntary observance of wheatless Mondays and Wednesdays, meatless Tuesdays, porkless Thursdays and Saturdays, and use of Victory bread.

July 1. Sugar rationing went into effect.

July 1. Sugar Equalization Board incorporated to allocate and distribute supplies of sugar.

December 23. All food regulations suspended by Food Administration.

1919

Japanese beetles found established in New Jersey.

1920

Total population 105,710,620; farm population 31,614,269; 27 per cent of persons gainfully employed were engaged in agriculture.

American Farm Bureau Federation organized.
Farm prices declined sharply in the summer.
May. Government guarantees on wheat prices ended.

1921

Farm bloc organized in Congress.
January 4. War Finance Corporation revived by Congress over President's veto as farm relief measure.
May 31. Senator George Norris introduced bill for export of agricultural commodities by a government corporation.
August 15. Packers' and Stockyards Act approved.

1922

Equality for Agriculture by George N. Peek and Hugh S. Johnson published.
National Agricultural Conference met in Washington.
February 18. Capper-Volstead Act, exempting producer cooperatives from anti-trust laws, approved.
June 3. Federal Reserve Act amended to provide agricultural representation on Federal Reserve Board.
September 21. Grain Futures Act approved.

1923

First annual farm outlook conference held.
March 4. Agricultural Credits Act approved.

1924

A second National Agricultural Conference called by the President.
January 16. First McNary-Haugen farm relief bill introduced into Congress.

1925

American Institute of Cooperation established.
Commercial production and sale of hybrid seed corn got under way.
The Master Farmer movement began.
February 24. Purnell Act authorized funds for economic research in agricultural experiment stations.

1926

Successful light gasoline tractor developed.
Domestic allotment plan proposed.
Export debenture plan proposed.
July 2. Congress created Division of Cooperative Marketing in Department of Agriculture.

1927

Mechanical cotton picker invented by John D. Rust.
February 25. McNary-Haugen bill vetoed by President Calvin Coolidge.

1928

May 23. McNary-Haugen bill vetoed for second time by President Calvin Coolidge.

1929

"Great" depression began.
June 15. Agricultural Marketing Act, establishing Federal Farm Board, approved.

1930

Total population 122,775,046; farm population 30,445,350; 21 per cent of persons gainfully employed were engaged in agriculture.
Severe drought in Midwestern and Southern states.
February 10. Grain Stabilization Corporation chartered under auspices of Federal Farm Board.
June 5. Cotton Stabilization Corporation chartered under auspices of Federal Farm Board.

1931

National Conference on Land Utilization called by Secretary of Agriculture and Executive Committee of Association of Land Grant Colleges and Universities.

1932

Farm Holiday Movement, led by Milo Reno.
Tenmarq wheat distributed.

1933-1934

Drought and dust storms in the West.

1933

March 31. Civilian Conservation Corps created by Unemployment Relief Act.
May 12. Agricultural Adjustment Act approved.
        Federal Emergency Relief Administration established by Federal Emergency Relief Act.
May 18. Tennessee Valley Authority Act approved.
June 16. Farm Credit Act consolidated all rural credit agencies under Farm Credit Administration.

1934

Department of Agriculture and Iowa Agricultural Experiment Station imported Danish hogs for cross-breeding in an attempt to develop meat-type hogs.
Thatcher wheat released to growers.
February 23. Crop Loan Act approved.
April 21. Cotton Control Act approved.
May 9. Jones-Costigan Sugar Act approved.

June 28. Tobacco Control Act approved.
Taylor Grazing Act gave Department of Interior power to regulate grazing on public domain of the West.
Frazier-Lemke Farm Bankruptcy Act approved.

1935

April 27. Soil Conservation Service established by the Soil Erosion Act.
April 30. Resettlement Administration created by executive order of the President.
May 11. Rural Electrification Administration established by order of the President.
May 27. Frazier-Lemke Farm Bankruptcy Act invalidated by Supreme Court.

1936

January 6. Agricultural Adjustment Act invalidated by Supreme Court.
February 29. Soil Conservation and Domestic Allotment Act approved.

1937

June 3. Agricultural Marketing Agreement Act approved.
July 22. Bankhead-Jones Farm Tenant Act approved.

1938

February 16. Second Agricultural Adjustment Act approved.
June 25. Federal Food, Drug, and Cosmetic Act approved.

1939

A food stamp plan became effective in some cities.
June 23. United States and Great Britain agreed to exchange 600,000 bales of American cotton for 85,000 tons of British rubber.
September 1. World War II began in Europe.

1940

Total population 131,820,000; farm population 30,840,000; 18 per cent of persons gainfully employed were engaged in agriculture.

1941-1945

The Second American Agricultural Revolution began during World War II.

1941

January 7. Office of Production Management created by executive order.
March 11. Lend-Lease Act approved.
April 11. Office of Price Administration created by executive order.
July 1. Steagall Amendment provided for price supports for expansion of production of non-basic agricultural commodities.

1942

DDT, the value of which as an insecticide had been demonstrated in Switzerland in 1939, introduced into the United States.

January 16. War Production Board established by executive order.
January 30. Emergency Price Control Act approved.
June 9. Establishment of Combined Food Board announced by President Roosevelt and Prime Minister Churchill.
June 30. Civilian Conservation Corps came to end when no appropriation made.
December 5. Authority over food assigned to Secretary of Agriculture by executive order.

1943

March 26. Food Production and Distribution Administration, later War Food Administration, established within Department of Agriculture by executive order.
May 18-June 3. Conference provided for United Nations Food and Agricultural Organization.

1944

Beltsville Small White turkey developed.

1945

August 21. President Truman announced termination of Lend-Lease.
November 24. Food rationing ended on all products except sugar.

1946

Sir John Boyd Orr of England proposed a World Food Board to handle problems of shortages and surpluses.
June 4. National School Lunch Act approved.
August 14. Research and Marketing Act approved.
October 24. All food products except sugar, sirups, and rice removed from price control.

1947

June 12. Sugar rationing discontinued.

1948-1949

Agricultural acts incorporated principle of flexible price support and provided change in parity formula.

1949

Rural telephone program begun by Rural Electrification Administration.
Usefulness of antibiotics in promoting animal nutrition demonstrated.

1950

Total population 151,132,000; farm population 25,058,000; 11 per cent of persons gainfully employed were engaged in agriculture.

1951

Organic chemicals known as chelates found to be useful in protecting plants against deficiencies in certain metal nutrients.

1954

July 10. Agricultural Trade Development and Assistance Act approved.
August 28. Agricultural Act of 1954 established flexible price supports, authorized commodity set-asides, and provided support for wool through payments.
September 1. Social Security Act amended to extend coverage to farm operators.

1955

Rural Development Program begun by Department of Agriculture.
Department of Agriculture scientists, using radioactive material as a tool, eradicated screwworm fly from island of Curacao.

1956

Gibberellic acid, plant growth regulator first described in Japan, placed on American market.
Rural Electrification Administration made first loan for a nuclear power generator.
May 28. Agricultural Act of 1956 authorized Soil Bank Program and established Commission on Increased Industrial Use of Agricultural Products.

1958

Total population 173,435,000 (estimated); farm population 20,827,000 (estimated); 9 per cent of persons gainfully employed were engaged in agriculture.
Mediterranean fruit fly, which had invaded Florida in 1956, apparently eradicated.
New wilt-resistant tomato, Pink Shipper, became available.

Selected Readings in the
History of American Agriculture

The purpose of this list is to refer the general reader and student to secondary materials on major subjects in agricultural history. The books and articles listed contain footnote references and bibliographies which will guide the student to other literature on a subject. Most of the works cited have been published since World War II. Those of an earlier date are either unique or are regarded as particularly outstanding. Since many worthwhile studies have necessarily been omitted, the serious reader is urged to regard this list only as a preliminary introduction to the literature.

General

Bidwell, Percy W., and John I. Falconer. *History of Agriculture in the Northern United States, 1620-1860.* 512 pp. Washington, Carnegie Institute of Washington. 1925.

Edwards, Everett E. "American Agriculture—The First 300 Years," U.S. Department of Agriculture, *Yearbook of Agriculture,* 1940, pp. 171-276.

Gray, Lewis C. *History of Agriculture in the Southern United States to 1860.* 2 vols. Washington, Carnegie Institution of Washington. 1933.

Shannon, Fred A. *The Farmer's Last Frontier: Agriculture, 1860-1897.* 434 pp. New York, Farrar & Rinehart. 1945.

Shideler, James H. *Farm Crisis, 1919-1923.* 345 pp. Berkeley, University of California Press. 1957.

States and Regions

Cathey, Cornelius Oliver. *Agricultural Developments in North Carolina, 1783-1860.* 229 pp. Chapel Hill, University of North Carolina Press. 1956.

Fletcher, Stevenson W. *Pennsylvania Agriculture and Country Life,* Vol. 1, 1640-1840; Vol. 2, 1840-1940. Harrisburg, Pennsylvania Historical and Museum Commission. 1950, 1955.

Jarchow, Merrill E. *The Earth Brought Forth: A History of Minnesota Agriculture to 1885.* 314 pp. St. Paul, Minnesota Historical Society. 1949.

Jordan, Weymouth T. *Ante-Bellum Alabama: Town and Country.* 172 pp. Tallahassee, Florida State University. 1957.

McNall, Neil A. *An Agricultural History of the Genessee Valley, 1790-1860.* 276 pp. Philadelphia, University of Pennsylvania Press. 1952.

Moore, John H. *Agriculture in Ante-Bellum Mississippi.* 268 pp. New York, Bookman Associates. 1958.

Range, Willard. *A Century of Georgia Agriculture, 1850-1950.* 333 pp. Athens, University of Georgia Press. 1954.

Ross, Earle D. *Iowa Agriculture: An Historical Survey.* 226 pp. Iowa City, State Historical Society of Iowa. 1951.

Saloutos, Theodore. "Southern Agriculture and the Problems of Readjustment: 1865-1877," *Agricultural History,* 30:58-76. April, 1956.

Schmidt, Hubert G. *Rural Hunterdon: An Agricultural History.* 331 pp. New Brunswick, N.J., Rutgers University Press. 1945.

Woodward, Carl R. *Ploughs and Politicks: Charles Read of New Jersey and His Notes on Agriculture, 1715-1774.* 468 pp. New Brunswick, N.J., Rutgers University Press. 1941.

Background

Carrier, Lyman. *The Beginnings of Agriculture in America.* 323 pp. New York, McGraw-Hill Book Co. 1923.

Cutler, Hugh C. "Food Sources in the New World," *Agricultural History,* 28:43-49. April, 1954.

Edwards, Everett E., and Wayne D. Rasmussen. *A Bibliography on the Agriculture of the American Indians,* U.S. Department of Agriculture Miscellaneous Publication No. 447. 107 pp. Washington, 1942.

Fussell, G. E. "Social and Agrarian Background of the Pilgrim Fathers," *Agricultural History,* 7:183-202. October, 1933.

Loehr, Rodney C. "The Influence of English Agriculture on American Agriculture, 1775-1825," *Agricultural History,* 11:3-15. January, 1937.

Whitaker, Arthur P. "The Spanish Contribution to American Agriculture," *Agricultural History,* 3:1-14. January, 1929.

Credit

Anderson, George L. "From Cattle to Wheat: The Impact of Agricultural Developments on Banking in Early Wichita," *Agricultural History,* 33:3-15. January, 1959.

Bogue, Allan G. *Money at Interest; The Farm Mortgage on the Middle Border.* 293 pp. Ithaca, Cornell University Press. 1955.

Crops

Anderson, Edgar, and William L. Brown. "The History of the Common Maize Varieties of the United States Corn Belt," *Agricultural History,* 26:2-8. January, 1952.

Coulter, E. Merton. *Thomas Spalding of Sapelo.* 334 pp. University, La., Louisiana State University Press. 1940.

Davis, Charles S. *The Cotton Kingdom in Alabama.* 233 pp. Montgomery, Alabama State Department of Archives and History. 1939.

Edwards, Everett E., and Horace H. Russell. "Wendelin Grimm and Alfalfa," *Minnesota History,* 19:21-33. March, 1938.

House, Albert V., ed. *Planter Management and Capitalism in Ante-Bellum Georgia: The Journal of Hugh Fraser Grant, Ricegrower*. 329 pp. New York, Columbia University Press. 1954.

Kemmerer, Donald L. "The Pre-Civil War South's Leading Crop, Corn," *Agricultural History*, 23:236-239. October, 1949.

Malin, James C. *Winter Wheat in the Golden Belt of Kansas: A Study in Adaptation to Subhumid Geographical Environment*. 290 pp. Lawrence, Kans., University of Kansas. 1944.

Phillips, Edward H. "The Gulf Coast Rice Industry," *Agricultural History*, 25:91-96. April, 1951.

Pinkett, Harold T. "Maryland as a Source of Food Supplies during the American Revolution," *Maryland Historical Magazine*, 46:157-172. September, 1951.

Robert, Joseph C. *The Story of Tobacco in America*. 296 pp. New York, Alfred A. Knopf. 1949.

Schmidt, Louis B. "The Westward Movement of the Wheat Growing Industry in the United States," *Iowa Journal of History and Politics*, 18:396-412. July, 1920.

Sitterson, J. Carlyle. *Sugar Country: The Sugar Cane Industry of the South, 1753-1950*. 414 pp. Lexington, University of Kentucky Press. 1953.

Street, J. H. *The New Revolution in the Cotton Economy*. 294 pp. Chapel Hill, University of North Carolina Press. 1957.

Tilley, Nannie M. *The Bright Tobacco Industry, 1860-1929*. 754 pp. Chapel Hill, University of North Carolina Press. 1948.

Wallace, Henry A., and William L. Brown. *Corn and Its Early Fathers*. 134 pp. East Lansing, Michigan State University Press. 1956.

Weatherwax, Paul. *Indian Corn in Old America*. 253 pp. New York, Macmillan. 1954.

Education

Bailey, Joseph C. *Seaman A. Knapp; Schoolmaster of American Agriculture*. 307 pp. New York, Columbia University Press. 1945.

Baker, Gladys. *The County Agent*. 226 pp. Chicago, University of Chicago Press. 1939.

Eddy, Edward Danforth, Jr. *Colleges for Our Land and Time; The Land-Grant Idea in American Education*. 328 pp. New York, Harper & Brothers. 1957.

Ellsworth, Clayton S. "The Coming of Rural Consolidated Schools to the Ohio Valley, 1892-1912," *Agricultural History*, 30:119-128. July, 1956.

Glover, Wilbur H. *Farm and College; The College of Agriculture of the University of Wisconsin*. 462 pp. Madison, University of Wisconsin Press. 1952.

Neely, Wayne C. *The Agricultural Fair*. 313 pp. New York, Columbia University Press. 1935.

Ross, Earle D. *The Land-Grant Idea at Iowa State College; A Centennial Trial Balance, 1858-1958*. 310 pp. Ames, Iowa State College Press. 1958.

Scott, Roy V. "Farmers' Institutes in Louisiana, 1897-1906," *Journal of Southern History*, 25:73-90. February, 1959.

True, Alfred C. *A History of Agricultural Education in the United States, 1785-1925*, U.S. Department of Agriculture Miscellaneous Publication No. 36. 436 pp. Washington, U.S. Government Printing Office. 1929.

True, Alfred C. *A History of Agricultural Extension Work in the United States, 1785-1923*, U.S. Department of Agriculture Miscellaneous Publication No. 15. 220 pp. Washington, U.S. Government Printing Office. 1928.

Farm Organizations and Movements

Barns, William D. "The Influence of the West Virginia Grange upon Public Agricultural Education of Less than College Grade, 1873-1914," *West Virginia History*, 10:5-24. October, 1948.

Buck, Solon J. *The Granger Movement*. 384 pp. Cambridge, Harvard University Press. 1913.

Chambers, Clarke A. *California Farm Organizations: A Historical Study of the Grange, the Farm Bureau, and the Associated Farmers, 1929-1941*. 277 pp. Berkeley, University of California Press. 1952.

Fletcher, Stevenson W. *The Philadelphia Society for Promoting Agriculture, 1785-1955*. 105 pp. Philadelphia, Philadelphia Society for Promoting Agriculture. 1959.

Hicks, John D. *The Populist Revolt: A History of the Farmers' Alliance and the People's Party*. 473 pp. Minneapolis, University of Minnesota Press. 1931.

Kile, Orville M. *The Farm Bureau Through Three Decades*. 416 pp. Baltimore, The Waverly Press. 1948.

Merk, Frederick. "Eastern Antecedents of the Grangers," *Agricultural History*, 23:1-8. January, 1949.

Saloutos, Theodore, and John D. Hicks. *Agricultural Discontent in the Middle West, 1900-1939*. 581 pp. Madison, University of Wisconsin Press. 1951.

Schmidt, Louis B. "The Role and Techniques of Agrarian Pressure Groups," *Agricultural History*, 30:49-58. April, 1956.

Taylor, Carl C. *The Farmer's Movement, 1620-1920*. 519 pp. New York, American Book Co. 1953.

Tucker, William P. "Populism Up-to-Date: The Story of the Farmers' Union," *Agricultural History*, 21:198-208. October, 1947.

Governmental Policies and Programs

Benedict, Murray R. *Farm Policies of the United States, 1790-1950*. 548 pp. New York, Twentieth Century Fund. 1953.

Davis, Chester C. "The Development of Agricultural Policy Since the End of the World War," U.S. Department of Agriculture, *Yearbook of Agriculture*, 1940, pp. 297-326.

Edwards, Everett E., ed. *Washington, Jefferson, Lincoln and Agriculture*. 102 pp. Washington, U.S. Department of Agriculture. November, 1937.

Fite, Gilbert C. *George N. Peek and the Fight for Farm Parity*. 314 pp. Norman, University of Oklahoma Press. 1954.

Gaus, John M., and Leon O. Wolcott. *Public Administration and the United States Department of Agriculture*. 534 pp. Chicago, Public Administration Service. 1940.

Harding, T. Swann. *Some Landmarks in the History of the Department of Agriculture*, U.S. Bureau of Agricultural Economics Agricultural History Series No. 2. 112 pp. Washington, U.S. Department of Agriculture. 1951.

Harding, T. Swann. *Two Blades of Grass: A History of Scientific Development in the U.S. Department of Agriculture*. 367 pp. Norman, University of Oklahoma Press. 1947.

Klose, Nelson. *America's Crop Heritage: The History of Foreign Plant Introduction by the Federal Government*. 156 pp. Ames, Iowa State College Press. 1950.

Nourse, Edwin G., Joseph S. Davis, and John D. Black. *Three Years of the Agricultural Adjustment Administration*. 600 pp. Washington, Brookings Institution. 1937.

Person, H. S. "The Rural Electrification Administration in Perspective," *Agricultural History*, 24:70-89. April, 1950.

Ross, Earle D. "The Civil War Agricultural New Deal," *Social Forces*, 15:97-104. October, 1936.

Tontz, Robert L. "Origin of the Base Period Concept of Parity—A Significant Value Judgment in Agricultural Policy," *Agricultural History*, 32:3-13. January, 1958.

True, Alfred C. *A History of Agricultural Experimentation and Research in the United States, 1607-1925; Including a History of the United States Department of Agriculture*, U.S. Department of Agriculture Miscellaneous Publication No. 251. 321 pp. Washington, U.S. Government Printing Office. 1937.

Labor

Cox, LaWanda F. "The American Agricultural Wage Earner, 1865-1900," *Agricultural History*, 22:95-114. April, 1948.

Phillips, Ulrich B. *Life and Labor in the Old South*. 375 pp. Boston, Little, Brown & Co. 1929.

Rasmussen, Wayne D. *A History of the Emergency Farm Labor Supply Program, 1943-47*, U.S. Department of Agriculture Monograph No. 13. 298 pp. Washington, U.S. Government Printing Office. 1951.

Stampp, Kenneth M. *The Peculiar Institution; Slavery in the Ante-Bellum South*. 436 pp. New York, Alfred A. Knopf. 1956.

Stephenson, Wendell H. *Isaac Franklin, Slave Trader and Planter of the Old South*. 368 pp. University, Louisiana State University Press. 1938.

Taylor, Paul S. "Plantation Laborer Before the Civil War," *Agricultural History*, 28:1-21. January, 1954.

Zeichner, Oscar. "The Transition from Slave to Free Agricultural Labor in the Southern United States," *Agricultural History*, 13:22-32. January, 1939.

Land Policies

Carstensen, Vernon. *Farms or Forests; Evolution of A State Land Policy for Northern Wisconsin, 1850-1932.* 130 pp. Madison, Wisconsin, College of Agriculture. 1958.

Ellis, David M. *Landlords and Farmers in the Hudson-Mohawk Region, 1790-1850.* 347 pp. Ithaca, N.Y., Cornell University Press. 1946.

Gates, Paul W. *Fifty Million Acres: Conflicts over Kansas Land Policy, 1854-1890.* 311 pp. Ithaca, N.Y., Cornell University Press. 1954.

Gates, Paul W. "The Homestead Law in an Incongruous Land System," *American Historical Review,* 41:652-681. July, 1936.

Gates, Paul W. *The Illinois Central Railroad and Its Colonization Work.* 374 pp. Cambridge, Harvard University Press. 1934.

Harris, Marshall. *Origin of the Land Tenure System in the United States.* 445 pp. Ames, Iowa State College Press. 1953.

LeDuc, Thomas. "State Disposal of the Agricultural College Land Scrip," *Agricultural History,* 28:99-107. July, 1954.

Peffer, E. Louise. *The Closing of the Public Domain: Disposal and Reservation Policies, 1900-1950.* 372 pp. Stanford, Stanford University Press. 1951.

Robbins, Roy M. *Our Landed Heritage: The Public Domain, 1776-1936.* 450 pp. Princeton, Princeton University Press. 1942.

Livestock

Brown, Harry J., ed. *Letters from a Texas Sheep Ranch.* 156 pp. Urbana, University of Illinois Press. 1959.

Dale, Edward E. *The Range Cattle Industry.* 216 pp. Norman, University of Oklahoma Press. 1930.

Frink, Maurice, W. T. Jackson, and A. W. Spring. *When Grass Was King.* 464 pp. Boulder, University of Colorado Press. 1956.

Henlein, Paul C. *Cattle Kingdom in the Ohio Valley, 1783-1860.* 198 pp. Lexington, University of Kentucky Press. 1959.

Lemmer, George F. "The Spread of Improved Cattle Through the Eastern United States to 1850," *Agricultural History,* 21:79-93. April, 1947.

Oliphant, J. Orin. "The Eastward Movement of Cattle from the Oregon Country," *Agricultural History,* 20:19-43. January, 1946.

Oliphant, J. Orin. "History of the Livestock Industry in the Pacific Northwest," *Oregon Historical Quarterly,* 49:3-29. March, 1948.

Thompson, James W. *A History of Livestock Raising in the United States, 1607-1860,* U.S. Department of Agriculture Agricultural History Series No. 5. 182 pp. Washington, U.S. Department of Agriculture. 1942.

Towne, Charles W., and Edward N. Wentworth. *Cattle and Men.* 384 pp. Norman, University of Oklahoma Press. 1955.

Towne, Charles W., and Edward N. Wentworth. *Pigs: From Cave to Corn Belt.* 305 pp. Norman, University of Oklahoma Press. 1950.

Towne, Charles W., and Edward N. Wentworth. *Shepherd's Empire.* 364 pp. Norman, University of Oklahoma Press. 1945.

Wentworth, Edward N. *America's Sheep Trails.* 667 pp. Ames, Iowa State College Press. 1948.

Machinery

Danhof, Clarence H. "Gathering the Grass," *Agricultural History*, 30: 169-173. October 1956.

Gray, R. B. *Development of the Agricultural Tractor in the United States*, Part 1. 46 pp. Washington, U.S. Department of Agriculture. 1954.

Green, C. M. *Eli Whitney and the Birth of American Technology*. 215 pp. Boston, Little, Brown and Company. 1956.

Higgins, F. Hal. "John M. Horner and the Development of the Combined Harvester," *Agricultural History*, 32:14-24. January, 1958.

Hutchinson, William T. *Cyrus Hall McCormick:* Vol. I, *Seed Time, 1809-1856*. 439 pp. New York, Century Co. 1930; Vol. II, *Harvest, 1856-1884*. 793 pp. New York, D. Appleton-Century Co. 1935.

Jones, Robert L. "The Introduction of Farm Machinery into Ohio Prior to 1865," *Ohio State Archaeological and Historical Quarterly*, 58: 1-20. January, 1949.

Wik, Reynold M. *Steam Power on the American Farm*. 288 pp. Philadelphia, University of Pennsylvania Press. 1953.

Marketing

Atherton, Lewis E. *Main Street on the Middle Border*. 368 pp. Bloomington, Indiana University Press. 1954.

Atherton, Lewis E. *The Pioneer Merchant in Mid-America*, University of Missouri Studies, Vol. 14, No. 2. 135 pp. Columbia, 1939.

Atherton, Lewis E. *The Southern Country Store, 1800-1860*. 227 pp. Baton Rouge, Louisiana State University Press. 1949.

Brunger, Eric. "Dairying and Urban Development in New York State, 1850-1900," *Agricultural History*, 29:169-174. October, 1955.

Cummings, Richard O. *The American and His Food: A History of Food Habits in the United States*. 267 pp. Chicago, University of Chicago Press. 1940.

Haskins, Ralph W. "Planter and Cotton Factor in the Old South: Some Areas of Friction," *Agricultural History*, 29:1-14. January, 1955.

Knapp, Joseph G. *E. A. Stokdyk—Architect of Cooperation*. 229 pp. Washington, American Institute of Cooperation. 1953.

Lee, Guy A. "The Historical Significance of the Chicago Grain Elevator System," *Agricultural History*, 11:16-32. January, 1937.

Loehr, Rodney C. "Self-Sufficiency on the Farm," *Agricultural History*, 26:37-41. April, 1952.

Wall, Bennett H. "Ebenezer Pettigrew's Efforts to Control the Marketing of His Crops," *Agricultural History*, 27:123-132. October, 1953.

Weiss, Harry B. *The History of Applejack or Apple Brandy in New Jersey from Colonial Times to the Present*. 265 pp. Trenton, N.J., New Jersey Agricultural Society. 1954.

Periodicals

Bardolph, Richard. *Agricultural Literature and the Early Illinois Farmer*. 200 pp. Urbana, University of Illinois Press. 1948.

Carman, Harry J. *Jesse Buel, Agricultural Reformer*. 609 pp. New York, Columbia University Press. 1947.

Demaree, Albert L. *The American Agricultural Press, 1819-1860.* 430 pp. New York, Columbia University Press. 1941.

Lemmer, George F. *Norman J. Colman and Colman's Rural World: A Study in Agricultural Leadership,* University of Missouri Studies, Vol. 25, No. 3. 168 pp. Columbia, 1953.

Murphy, Donald R. "The Centennial of a Farm Paper," *Palimpsest,* 37:449-480. September, 1956.

Osborn, George C. "The Southern Agricultural Press and Some Significant Rural Problems, 1900-1940," *Agricultural History,* 29:115-122. July, 1955.

Schlebecker, John T., and Andrew W. Hopkins. *A History of Dairy Journalism in the United States, 1810-1950.* 423 pp. Madison, University of Wisconsin Press. 1957.

Socolofsky, Homer E. "Development of the Capper Farm Press," *Agricultural History,* 31:34-43. October, 1957.

Soil Utilization

Bogue, Margaret B. "The Swamp Land Act and Wet Land Utilization in Illinois, 1850-1890," *Agricultural History,* 25:169-180. October, 1951.

Craven, Avery O. *Soil Exhaustion as a Factor in the Agricultural History of Virginia and Maryland, 1606-1860.* 179 pp. Urbana, University of Illinois. 1926.

Dunbar, Robert G. "The Search for a Stable Water Right in Montana," *Agricultural History,* 28:138-149. October, 1954.

Hall, Arthur R. "Terracing in the Southern Piedmont," *Agricultural History,* 23:96-109. April, 1949.

Hargreaves, Mary W. M. *Dry Farming in the Northern Great Plains, 1900-1925.* 587 pp. Cambridge, Harvard University Press. 1957.

Technology

Anderson, Oscar E., Jr. *Refrigeration in America; A History of a New Technology and Its Impact.* 344 pp. Princeton, Princeton University Press. 1953.

Bonner, James C. "Advancing Trends in Southern Agriculture, 1840-1860," *Agricultural History,* 22:248-259. October, 1948.

Cavert, William L. "The Technological Revolution in Agriculture," *Agricultural History,* 30:18-27. January, 1956.

Craven, Avery O. *Edmund Ruffin: A Study in Secession.* 283 pp. New York, D. Appleton and Company. 1932.

Destler, Chester McA. "David Dickson's 'System of Farming' and the Agricultural Revolution in the Deep South, 1850-1885," *Agricultural History,* 31:30-39. January, 1957.

Hayter, Earl W. "Barbed Wire Fencing—A Prairie Invention," *Agricultural History,* 13:189-207. October, 1939.

Johnson, Sherman E. *Changes in American Farming,* U.S. Department of Agriculture Miscellaneous Publication No. 707. 75 pp. 1949.

Jordan, Weymouth T. *Hugh Davis and His Alabama Plantation.* 177 pp. University, Ala., University of Alabama Press. 1948.

Jordan, Weymouth T. "The Peruvian Guano Gospel in the Old South," *Agricultural History*, 24:211-221. October, 1950.

Ross, Earle D. "Retardation in Farm Technology before the Power Age," *Agricultural History*, 30:11-18. January, 1956.

Schlebecker, John T. "Grasshoppers in American Agricultural History," *Agricultural History*, 27:85-93. July, 1953.

Taylor, Rosser H. "The Sale and Application of Commercial Fertilizers in the South Atlantic States to 1900," *Agricultural History*, 21:46-52. January, 1947.

Throne, Mildred. "Southern Iowa Agriculture, 1833-1890; The Progress from Subsistence to Commercial Corn-Belt Farming," *Agricultural History*, 23:124-130. April, 1949.

Transportation

Benson, Lee. *Merchants, Farmers and Railroads: Railroad Regulation and New York Politics, 1850-1887*. 310 pp. Cambridge, Harvard University Press. 1955.

Fuller, Wayne E. "Good Roads and Rural Free Delivery of Mail," *Mississippi Valley Historical Review*, 42:67-83. June, 1955.

Greever, William S. "A Comparison of Railroad Land-Grant Policies," *Agricultural History*, 25:83-90. April, 1951.

Jones, C. Clyde. "The Burlington Railroad and Agricultural Policy in the 1920's," *Agricultural History*, 31:67-74. October, 1957.

Murray, Stanley N. "Railroads and Agricultural Development of the Red River Valley of the North, 1870-1890," *Agricultural History*, 31:57-66. October, 1957.

Taylor, George R. *The Transportation Revolution, 1815-1860*. 490 pp. New York, Rinehart & Company. 1951.

Turner, Charles W. "Railroad Service to Virginia Farmers, 1828-1860," *Agricultural History*, 22:239-248. October, 1948.

Index

Acorns, 21-22
Adams, John Quincy, 105
Agricultural Act of 1948, 310
Agricultural Act of 1949, 310
Agricultural Act of 1954, 311
Agricultural Act of 1956, 311
Agricultural Adjustment Act of 1933, 248, 259, 308
Agricultural Adjustment Act of 1938, 309
Agricultural chemistry, 143
Agricultural colleges: established, 109-110, 301, 302; petition for land grants to aid, 110-111; development of, 143; and county agent system, 179; demonstration work of, 181; improvement in country life by, 190-191, 194; association of established, 304; participated in land use conference, 308
Agricultural credit. *See* Credit
Agricultural Credits Act of 1923, 307
Agricultural education. *See* Agricultural colleges *and* Education, agricultural
Agricultural exhibitions: inaugurated, 55, 298; poultry show, 300; fat stock, 303; International Livestock Exposition, 305
Agricultural experimentation: by members of agricultural societies, 41; by U.S. Patent Office, 105; Department of Agriculture authorized to conduct, 106; es-

tablishment of state stations to conduct, 143-145
Agricultural experiment stations. *See* State agricultural experiment stations
Agricultural extension work: development of, 178-188; boys' and girls' clubs, 179, 185-186, 305; Smith-Lever law established, 179, 306; need for, 191, 195-196; Four-H clubs, 305
Agricultural fairs: mentioned, 51, 72; at Pittsfield, 58-60, 298; first major state, 300
Agricultural journals: first, 51-54, 298; mentioned, 72, 298, 299. *See also* names of specific journals
Agricultural Marketing Act of 1929, 253, 308
Agricultural Marketing Agreement Act of 1937, 259, 309
Agricultural Museum (Georgetown, D.C.), 52-54, 298
Agricultural population. *See* Population, agricultural
Agricultural reform: types of, 72
Agricultural revolution: in England, 25-32, 63; second, 275-286, 309; change to animal power marks, 282; first, 302
Agricultural societies: first established, 41, 297; membership of early, 41-42; mentioned, 51, 53, 72; local, 54-60, 298; United States, 105, 110, 301; advocated Department of Agriculture, 105;